The Second
MAURETANIA
1939-65

Maiden Voyage Arrival of the "Mauretania" in New York, 24th June, 1939.

The Second
MAURETANIA
1939~65

Authentically reproduced from a rare 1939 commemorative
edition of 'The Shipbuilder and Marine Engine-builder'
'The Cunard White Star North Atlantic Twin-Screw
Geared-Turbine Passenger Steamship *Mauretania*'
with additional new material by Mark D. Warren

Patrick Stephens Limited

First published by
The Shipbuilder and Marine Engine-builder in June 1939
PSL edition first published in 1989

British Library Cataloguing in Publication Data

Warren, Mark D.
The second Mauretania 1939-65.
1. Steam liners: Mauretania, (Ship)
I. Title
623.8'2432

ISBN 1-85260-233-3

Patrick Stephens Limited is part of the Thorsons Publishing
Group, Wellingborough, Northamptonshire NN8 2RQ, England.

Printed in Great Britain by Butler & Tanner Limited,
Frome, Somerset

2 4 6 8 10 9 7 5 3 1

INTRODUCTION

THIS book is primarily a facsimile reprint of a special volume published in June, 1939, by *The Shipbuilder and Marine Engine-builder* to celebrate the triumphant maiden voyage of The R.M.S. *Mauretania* (II), the newest addition to the fleet of the Cunard Steamship Company. Until now, this scarce original publication has been universally acknowledged as containing the most comprehensive published text detailing the construction, outfitting and launch of the "new" *Mauretania*.

To commemorate the 50th anniversary of the R.M.S. *Mauretania's* maiden voyage on 17th June, 1939, this definitive work is now republished with 51 additional photographs, and one blueprint plan (Plate D). The newly added photographs include 32 found in Plates VII–XXXIII and three found in Plates A, B and C. Other new photographs include: the *Mauretania* facing the new title page and on page xviii, the Cabin Class Lounge on page xxii, the eight photographs of various Cunard and White Star vessels on page 2, the two photos of the *Mauretania* on pages 44 and 77, the North Atlantic Wall Map on page 103, the Ladies' Hairdressing Saloon on page 108 and the *Mauretania* on page 111. Minor alterations to the 1939 format include the reproduction of Plates I–VI as double page spreads instead of "gatefolds", and the inclusion of two pages of advertisements selected from the 56 found in the original publication.

Incorporating the most modern innovations, the *Mauretania* (II) was not only an exceptionally beautiful vessel both inside and out, but also a fine, seaworthy ship that distinguished herself throughout the Second World War by safely carrying a total of 380,481 troops a distance of 568,748 miles on 55 voyages. Unfortunately, until now, the great accomplishments of the *Mauretania*, for both her company and her country, have not been fully appreciated. From the outset, the "new" *Mauretania* was deprived of her own identity when, for marketing purposes, she was named after her illustrious predecessor whose legend was already unsurpassable. Compounding this, the *Mauretania* was constructed during the same decade as two other extraordinary vessels, the *Queen Mary* and the *Queen Elizabeth* which, in size alone, exceeded all others. Nevertheless, the record clearly illustrates that the *Mauretania* (II) was indeed a very successful and significant vessel in the history of the twentieth century North Atlantic steamship.

With the launching of the *Mauretania* in 1938, the shipbuilders, Cammell Laird and Company Ltd., of Birkenhead, also celebrated the centennial anniversary of the first successful demonstration of the screw propeller in their iron-hulled steamboat, the *Robert F. Stockton.** With the maiden voyage of the *Mauretania* in 1939, Cammell Laird again celebrated another important centennial anniversary — that of the maiden voyage of the *British Queen*, which had been built under the direction of John Laird for the British & American Steam Navigation Company.†

The first vessel Laird Brothers constructed for the Cunard Steamship Company was the iron-hulled *Cephalonia* in 1882. With dimensions of 430ft. 6ins. b.p.** (440ft. o.l.††), 46ft. 6ins. breadth of beam, and 5,517 gross registered tons (G.R.T.), this single-screw, 14-knot vessel was at the time the largest ship to have been constructed on the Mersey. In 1903, Laird Brothers amalgamated with Cammells of Sheffield, which had been founded in 1837, to form Cammell Laird & Company. The second vessel the Company built for Cunard was the steel-hulled *Samaria* (II) of 1921. With

dimensions of 601ft. 6ins. b.p. (624ft. o.l.), 73ft. 6ins. breadth of beam and 19,602 G.R.T., the twin-screw, steam-turbine *Samaria* at the time of her launching was also the largest vessel to be built on the Mersey. With the launching of the second *Mauretania*, the Company's third ship for Cunard, this tradition was continued, as she too was the largest vessel constructed on the Mersey up to that time.

The events that persuaded the Directors of Cunard to build the second *Mauretania* date from about 1930, when it was decided that the time had come to restore the Company's declining image which had resulted from the rapidly growing competition with such Continental lines as Norddeutscher Lloyd, Compagnie Générale Transatlantique, Navigazione Generale Italiana and Lloyd Sabaudo. A decision was therefore made to build two new super-liners of unparalleled size and speed. With only these two ships, for the first time a weekly transatlantic service between Southampton, Cherbourg and New York, including "turn around" time in port, could be maintained.

As the carriage of mails accounted for only a small part of the Company's revenues, the smallest size needed relative to passenger capacity and profitability on such a schedule was about 80,000 G.R.T., with an overall length of about 1,000ft. and a speed of at least 28.5 knots. While plans were being finalized, an order for the first ship was placed with John Brown & Company of Clydebank on 1st December, 1930. At first, construction of "Number 534", as the *Queen Mary* was then called, proceeded on schedule with a launch date set for May, 1932. Unfortunately, after £1.5 million was spent, work was unexpectedly suspended on 10th December, 1931, because of a disastrous drop in passenger revenues that had resulted from the ever-growing Depression.* All North Atlantic passenger lines had been adversely affected, as overall traffic had plummeted from 1,002,353 in 1930, to only 685,456 in 1931.

For 27 months, the gigantic empty hull towered above the shipyard unfinished and rusting, until, after much debate, the House of Commons passed the North Atlantic Shipping Act of 1934. Under that Act, the Government consented to lend Cunard the sum of £3 million for the completion of "No. 534", with an additional £1.5 million for "working capital" and £5 million advanced towards the construction of her proposed sister. However, the Government stipulated that they would only finance this new building if Cunard agreed to merge their assets with those of the failing White Star Line. With no alternative, Cunard agreed, and a new company, Cunard White Star Limited, was officially registered on 1st January, 1934. Cunard's portion of the new Company's assets comprised roughly 62 per cent, with 15 vessels totalling 328,073 G.R.T.; those of White Star accounted for the remaining 38 per cent, with 10 vessels totalling 280,741 G.R.T. Cunard's fleet was not only larger, but also newer, with an average age of less than 13½ years, while the average age of a White Star liner was 19 years.

Even with the immediate future of Cunard and White Star guaranteed, both companies still continue to dispose of old tonnage, a policy which had been adopted at the beginning of the Depression. Between 1931 and the formation of Cunard White Star Ltd., White Star had sold to the shipbreakers six vessels totalling 105,104 G.R.T. Within two years following the merger, another five vessels totalling 176,602 G.R.T., including the *Majestic, Olympic* and *Homeric*, were also sold for demolition†, with three more, totalling 53,905 G.R.T., sold to other lines. In comparison, Cunard had sold only the *Caronia* (19,782 G.R.T.) and the *Carmania* (19,566 G.R.T.) to the shipbreakers prior to the merger. The sale of the first *Mauretania* (30,696 G.R.T.) immediately followed the merger.

With the resumption of the *Queen Mary's* construction in April, 1934, and plans for her sister under way, the Directors of the Company were convinced that Cunard should also have a "second line" of intermediate vessels similar to White Star's twin motorships, *Britannic* (26,840 G.R.T.) and *Georgic* (27,759 G.R.T.). The support for this idea by Sir Percy Bates, the Chairman of Cunard White

---

* The *Robert F. Stockton* was built by the firm of Laird Brothers, which had been founded in 1824 by William Laird. By 1829, he, along with John and Macgregor Laird, had constructed one of the earliest iron-hulled vessels. In 1838, the *Robert F. Stockton*, with its revolutionary means of propulsion, had achieved trial speeds of 13 knots on both the Thames and the Mersey. This surprising performance greatly impressed not only the Admiralty, but also the public, for "The Times" had commented on these trials, saying that "the evidence was quite conclusive as to the success of this important improvement in steam navigation".

† As the largest and most luxurious ship in the world, the *British Queen* had been constructed at a cost of £60,000, with the intention of making her the first vessel to cross the Atlantic using steam power exclusively. However, because the *British Queen* was still unfinished at the time that her chief rival, the *Great Western*, was completed, the distinction was won by her substitute, the *Sirius*.

** Between perpendiculars
†† Overall length

* In 1931, the Cunard Steamship Company reported a loss of £533,204 ($2,418,074.80). The pound conversions within this text may vary, as they are based upon the official exchange rate for each particular year or period discussed.

† The *Doric* was sold to the shipbreakers as a result of a collision, and the *Majestic* was sold after it had been damaged by fire.

Star Ltd., was clearly demonstrated when he stated in April, 1936: "There will always be room in the Atlantic for passenger ships of what might be called 'the second line'. And indeed the needs of Liverpool and London, and other ports, make it necessary that the interests of the Company in that type of tonnage should not be neglected . . . I regard the first, and second, lines of ships not as alternatives but as complementary to each other."*

On 13th May, 1936, the Board of Directors resolved: "That the question of second line ships to be built on the Company's own credit as mentioned by the Chairman to the Chancellor of the Exchequer† . . . be investigated towards the end of June."** Exactly two months later, at the next meeting, the question took on a more concrete form: ". . . the General Manager submitted a Memorandum on this question, emphasising the vital necessity of laying down two new ships of the intermediate type. The Board agreed that this should be done as early as possible and it was decided that the Company's requirements as to accommodation, speed, etc., be sent to the under-noted Builders: Messrs. Harland & Wolff Ltd., Messrs. Vickers-Armstrong Ltd., Messrs. Swan, Hunter & Wigham Richardson Ltd., and Messrs. Cammell Laird & Co. Ltd. It was also decided to make a Press announcement forthwith to the effect that the Board have decided to enter into negotiations with various Shipbuilders for the construction of tonnage to meet the requirements of the Company's intermediate services . . ."††

The issue was again brought up at a subsequent meeting on 16th September 1936: "The whole position with regard to Second Line tonnage was then discussed by the Board, and it was agreed to work provisionally on the hypothesis of building two ships at this time, to be paid for as to half their cost in cash, and the remaining half by the discounting of Bills."**

While all tenders received were generally similar, it is worth noting some specific differences. In their tender dated 30th October, 1936, Harland & Wolff actually submitted two proposals of which the primary difference between the two related to the use of either "Yarrow" or "Babcock Johnson" boilers. The dimensions listed by the Belfast shipbuilder were 735ft. b.p. (778ft. o.l.), 91ft. breadth of beam and about 30,750 G.R.T.*** The vessel would have nine decks as well as a navigating and docking bridge, and according to the "general description", the "proposed passenger and cargo vessel" would "have a rounded stem raked well forward, cruiser stern, one funnel††† and two masts".*** Designed for a service speed of 22 knots, the twin-screw vessel was to have been powered by "Parsons' triple-expansion, condensing, single-reduction geared turbines, in accordance with Parsons' latest and best practice".*** Passenger accommodation throughout was to be generally like that of the *Georgic*, and would have consisted of 522 in Cabin, 572 in Tourist and 500 in Third Class, with a small number of interchangeable Cabin and Tourist Class staterooms. Located on Decks "A" and "B", the public rooms in Cabin Class were to include a Palm Court, Lounge, Long Gallery, Card Room, Children's Playroom, Smoke Room and Verandah Café, as well as a Dining Saloon with accommodation for 300. The recent innovation of air-conditioning was also to have been provided for the Dining Saloon and Lounge of both the Cabin and Tourist Classes.

The proposal Vickers-Armstrong of Barrow-in-Furness presented on 31st October, 1936, represented the shortest vessel of all the tenders offered. Their vessel would have had overall dimensions of 680ft. b.p. (715ft. o.l.), 91ft. breadth of beam and approximately 33,000 G.R.T., with two funnels, one working and one dummy. The propelling machinery would have comprised two sets of Parsons' single-reduction, geared turbines, capable of developing 40,000 shaft horsepower (S.H.P.), which were designed to produce a speed of 22 knots on the "measured mile". Passenger accommodation consisted of 505 in Cabin, 427 in Tourist, and 492

in Third, including 82 berths in Tourist Class that could be interchangeable with Third Class. The Cabin and Tourist Class Dining Saloons and Lounges were also to have been air-conditioned. Vickers-Armstrong's plan, in addition, included a 30 by 18ft. pool for the Cabin Class, "with access also arranged for Tourist Class".*

The Tyneside firm of Swan, Hunter & Wigham Richardson Ltd. presented three proposals on 31st October, 1936, with the difference between them again being the type of boilers selected. With dimensions slightly shorter and narrower than the plans submitted by Harland & Wolff, Swan Hunter's vessel was to have had a length of 725ft. b.p. (764ft. o.l.), 88ft. breadth of beam) and a gross tonnage of about 32,300. Designed with only one funnel and ten decks, this ship was to have been propelled by twin screws, each activated by a set of single-reduction geared turbines of Parsons' type, measuring 40,000 S.H.P. at the service speed of 22 knots. Passenger accommodation provided 502 berths in Cabin, 546 in Tourist and 470 in Third Class. These figures included 45 interchangeable Tourist Class berths that could be used for Third Class, as well as 159 Cabin berths that could be used alternatively for Tourist Class.

Cabin Class public rooms included a Palm Court, Card Room, Drawing Room, Long Gallery, Writing Room, Studio, Entrance Hall, Lounge and Ballroom, Smoking Room with a cocktail bar, Verandah, Children's Room, Hairdressing Rooms, a Dining Saloon with seating for 300, as well as a Swimming Bath and Gymnasium. Tourist Class public rooms included a Writing Room and Library, Children's Room, Entrance Hall, Smoking Room, Lounge, Hairdressing Rooms, and a Dining Saloon with seating for 300. In Third Class there would have been a Lounge, Smoking Room, Ladies' Room, Children's Room, and a Dining Saloon with seating for 300. Each room was to have been decorated in a fashion similar to those found on the *Georgic*, with the Dining Saloon and Lounge in both Cabin and Tourist Classes air-conditioned. The Chairman of Swan Hunter, J. Denham Christie, wrote to Sir Percy Bates on 31st October, 1936, explaining that the cost of "the decorations and furnishings of cabin class and tourist class public rooms including main entrances and stairways, shops and swimming pool is £100,000 [and] . . . we could give delivery of the ship in 27 months from receipt of order and approval of plans".*

Cammell Laird & Company Ltd. duly submitted their first tender to Cunard on 31st October, 1936. The vessel would have ten decks and two funnels, with a length of 740ft. b.p.†, 90ft. breadth of beam and 39ft. depth to "D" Deck. Designed for a service speed of 22 knots (with 23.5 knots expected on her trials), the twin-screw, single-geared turbine liner would have a capacity for 509 Cabin Class passengers in 258 rooms, 553 Tourist Class passengers in 211 rooms and 504 Third Class passengers in 164 rooms, as well as berths for about 500 crew members. Cabin Class accommodation was also to consist of a Winter Garden, Observation Lounge and Cocktail Bar, Entrance Hall, Main Lounge (also referred to as the Palm Court), Nursery, Reading and Writing Room, Tea Lounge, Gallery, Smoking Room, Foyer, Dining Saloon, Private Dining Saloon, Children's Dining Saloon, Swimming Pool, Gymnasium and Lido, as well as four suites comprising eight rooms on "A" Deck. Tourist Class public rooms including a Smoking Room, Reading and Writing Room, Nursery, Entrance Hall, Lounge, Foyer and Dining Saloon.**

After receiving a letter from Sir Percy Bates dated 24th November, 1936, stating that the dimensions of the proposed vessel had to suit the King George V Wet Dock in London, Cammell Laird made the necessary slight alterations to their original proposal and re-submitted it on 15th December, 1936. The revised dimensions would now be 732ft. b.p. (769ft. 6ins. o.l.), 89ft. breadth of beam, 38ft. 6ins. depth to "D" Deck and about 33,000 G.R.T. Additionally, the original "first cost" estimate of £1,803,000 ($8,816,670) was now reduced by £28,000 to the new figure of £1,775,000 ($8,679, 750), "partly made up by the altered dimensions and partly by a reduction in the cost of the decorations".††

The following day, 16th December, the Cunard White Star Directors met and "decided that it is desirable to proceed with the building of one ship as early as possible in order that delivery may be obtained in 1939".*** Five days later, Johnson met with Bates

---

* "MAURETANIA" Launch Booklet; 28th July, 1938.
† Neville Chamberlain
** "Extracts from Minutes of Board Meetings of Cunard White Star Limited"; University Archives, The University of Liverpool.
†† "Extracts from Minutes of Board Meetings of Cunard White Star Limited"; University Archives, The University of Liverpool. Apparently Cunard White Star did not extend the offer to John Brown & Co., as they were about to commence construction of "No. 552" — the *Queen Elizabeth*.
*** "Unaccepted Tenders"; University Archives, The University of Liverpool.
††† It is interesting to note that a profile sketch of the single funnel shows a low, squat structure similar to those found on the *Georgic* and the *Britannic* which, measuring approximately 28ft. in height by about 38ft. 6ins. in length, was secured by six guy wires.

* "Unaccepted Tenders"; University Archives, The University of Liverpool.
† The overall length measurement is not available.
** A listing of Third Class public rooms is not available.
†† From a letter to Bates dated 15th December, 1936, from Robert S. Johnson, Managing Director of Cammell Laird; University Archives, The University of Liverpool.
*** "Minutes of Board Meetings of Cunard white Star Limited"; University Archives, The University of Liverpool.

to discuss Cammell Laird's proposal, and on 28th December, Johnson wrote to Bates stating: "I am now writing to confirm the assurance which I verbally gave on Monday last, that if we are favoured with your order it is our intention to give you a vessel of the Intermediate Class, superior in all respects to the 'Georgic' and we are prepared to comply with any reasonable requests that you may make to us in connection with any of the points that are not specified in detail."*

Another Executive Committee Meeting was held on 29th December in which a memorandum submitted by Bates declared: "All the Builders who have tendered are anxious to have a reply before the end of the year. The need for an early decision is further emphasised by the Company's requirement of delivery by the Spring of 1939. The three Tenders under consideration are those of Swan, Hunter & Company, Cammell Laird & Company, and Harland & Wolff Ltd.:† the Tender price in each case being practically the same — £1,770,000. Careful examination of the three Tenders submitted shows that the Builders' proposals differ in various respects, but it is felt that any of the three ships should be satisfactory and no doubt with alterations here and there could be made to fit the Company's requirements. Of the three Tenders submitted, that of Cammell Laird has been most favourably reported on by the Company's Technical and Passenger Departments."**

However, in the end it was the opinion of the Company's Treasury that decisively swung the pendulum in Cammell Laird's favour. Swan Hunter had proposed monthly instalments of one half in cash and one half in Bills. Harland & Wolff wanted instalments of one-fifth of the contract price paid at the time the keel was laid, when framing was completed, when plating was completed, at launch, and at time of delivery. Based on the initial contract price of £1,775,000, Cammell Laird's terms were: 5 per cent when the keel is completely laid (about the beginning of 1937); 10 per cent when the vessel is framed (about the end of September, 1937); 10 per cent when the vessel is half-plated (about the middle of January, 1938); 10 per cent when the vessel is fully plated (about the middle of March, 1938); 10 per cent when the vessel is launched (about the middle of June, 1938); 10 per cent when the boilers are in place (about the middle of August, 1938); 10 per cent when decorative work has commenced (about the middle of September, 1938); 15 per cent when decorative work is 50 per cent completed (by middle of November, 1938); 15 per cent when vessel is delivered (around the end of March, 1939); 5 per cent balance due three months after delivery.

This payment schedule would allow the Company Treasury to draw upon "such proportion of the cash payments as is derived from the Depreciation money for the *Queen Mary*", and as "the time factor has an important bearing on the matter and in view of all circumstances and the fact that Cammell Laird's ship was the most favourably reported on . . . we have to-day decided to inform him [Johnson] that the order will be placed with his Company and the Contract completed in due course; and we are advising Swan, Hunter, and Harland & Wolff that on this occasion their Tender is not the one that we are able to accept".** In a letter from H.J Flewitt, Secretary of Cunard White Star, to Johnson, dated 30th December, 1936, informing him of the Directors' decision, Flewitt wrote: "I am asked to emphasise that delivery of the vessel by 31st March 1939 is of great importance, and we are relying on your expressed ability to complete the ship by that date."†† That evening, an announcement regarding the tentative contract was issued to the Press for publication on 31st December, 1936. Very pleased with the news, Johnson responded to Flewitt on 31st December, stating that "we are confident that we shall be able to complete the ship by 31st March 1939".***

Work on this monumental project commenced immediately with the New Year, beginning with the preliminary draft contracts for "No. 1029" (as the *Mauretania* was then called) simultaneously drawn up by both Cammell Laird and Cunard White Star. Although minor adjustments would be made, by 14th January both contracts had been informally exchanged for comparison. One of the major points for discussion was insurance cover with regard to war risks during the construction phase. Cunard maintained a position that while the ship

was in the possession of the Builders, the burden of cover was the Builders' responsibility. Cammell Laird contended in their initial contract that they would insure the vessel "except in the case of loss or damage directly or indirectly occasioned by happening through or in consequence of war, invasion, hostilities, acts of foreign enemy . . ."* However, since Johnson had already agreed in his preliminary conversations with Bates around Christmas time that the Builders would accept all risks (although neither party actually mentioned "war risks"), by 29th January, the question would be settled in Cunard's favour.

Beginning with rounds of discussions between the Owners and the Builders, key Cunard White Star and Cammell Laird Officers formed the "1029 Building Committee" which, meeting every two to three weeks, discussed and voted upon hundreds of changes proposed by the Owners' and Builders' architects, engineers and designers. On 15th February, the base contract price of £1,775,000 was agreed upon by both parties. Three days later Cammell Laird approved the contract, although the formal contract for "No. 1029" was not signed until 17th June, 1937. On 23rd March, 1937, Cunard approved Cammell Laird's proposal to increase "No. 1029's" beam by 6ins. to 89ft. 6ins., and on 7th April, it was decided to raise the height on the Dining Saloon Deck 6ins. in order to improve the appearance of the ship. For this to be accomplished, the decision was made on 29th April to give the ship an additional 6ins. in depth. Then, in an effort to modernize the vessel's profile as well as to "re-establish the original margin of stability as much as possible",† on 5th May it was also agreed to eliminate Fore and Aft Deck Houses that had been planned originally, as well as the Promenade Deck overhang. To recover the loss of about 50 berths by the elimination of the deck houses, the Builders planned to reduce the size of many rooms on "C" Deck, with a number of private cabin bathrooms to be replaced by showers.

The keel for "No. 1029" was laid on 24th May, 1937, although it would not be until early September of that year that the general plans for the ship were finalized. The first of many "extras" and rebates were incorporated into the contract price, so that by 10th September, 1937, the revised cost approved for constructing "No. 1029" amounted to £1,811,820.10s ($8,957,640.50), with an additional £34,517 ($170,652.04) in other "extras" pending.

In general appearance that would serve as a prototype for the *Queen Elizabeth*, whose keel had been laid at John Brown's Shipyard on 4th December, 1936, the *Mauretania's* design included a "soft-nose" rounded-plate stem, rounded Bridge front, twin masts and cruiser stern. Like the *Queen Elizabeth*, the *Mauretania's* raked funnels** would not need guy wires as they were already well strengthened internally.†† The dimensions that were to be finally agreed upon were 732ft. b.p. (772ft. o.l.), 89ft. 1in. breadth of beam (89ft. 3ins. extreme breadth), 73ft. 6ins. depth to the Promenade Deck and 35,738 G.R.T. (20,170 tons net).*** The height from the keel to the top of the foremast would be 211ft., with the height from keel to fore-funnel top measuring 155ft., or 56ft. from the Sports Deck Promenade.††† In total, the ship's ten decks, designated the Sports, Sun, Promenade, Main, A, B, C, D, E and F, would have a capacity for 1,291 passengers with 588 officers and crew. As originally designed, the number of passengers in each class would be divided as follows: 486 in Cabin, 393 in Tourist and 412 in Third Class. With 12 watertight transverse bulkheads dividing her hull to the height of "C" Deck, the space allotted for general cargo would amount to 389,000 cubic ft., with refrigerated cargo area comprising another 73,290 cubic ft. In addition, there would be garage space for 70 automobiles.

The size of "No. 1029's" immense castings are also worth noting, as the rudder and stock weighed some 90 tons, each shaft bracket 45 tons with corresponding tail-shafts at 25 tons apiece, as well as another 40 tons for the stern frame. Connected to 330 fathoms of cable with 3⅜ inch diameter links weighing a total of 96

* University Archives, The University of Liverpool.
† By 16th November, Vickers-Armstrong had dropped out of the running.
** "Executive Committee Meeting Minutes", dated 30th December, 1936; University Archives, The University of Liverpool.
†† Cammell Laird Archives, Birkenhead.
*** "Proposals"; University Archives, The University of Liverpool.

* "Proposals"; University Archives, The University of Liverpool.
† "S.S. No. 1029 Memoranda"; University Archives, The University of Liverpool.
** Elliptical in shape and measuring 24 by 34ft. in diameter, the rake of both funnels would be 2⅛ins. per foot.
†† Guy wires are shown on Cammell Laird blueprints dated 14th June, 1937. However, extra funnel stiffening and supports at a cost of £2,600 ($12,854.40) eliminated the need for guy wires.
*** According to specifications obtained from Cammell Laird.
††† The aft funnel was 2ft. shorter.

tons, the three anchors each weighed an additional 9¼ tons.*

Fitted with two 25-ton, 19ft. 3ins. diameter[†], high tensile, four-bladed Parsons' manganese bronze propellers of the "Scimitar" type, the *Mauretania* was designed for a service speed of 22 knots. Her engines would consist of two sets of Parsons' single-reduction geared turbines, with each set comprising one high, one intermediate and one low pressure turbine, indicating a total of approximately 42,000 S.H.P. Steam pressure of 425 lbs. per sq. in. would be raised within the six high-pressure, oil-fired, water tube Yarrow boilers** under the closed stokehold system, that, fitted with superheaters and air heaters, produced a final steam temperature of 725 degrees Fahrenheit. As the largest ever constructed, her two 14ft. 6ins. diameter main gear wheels would each weigh 85 tons and have a circumference of 46ft. On each wheel, 500 teeth were precision cut to one hundred thousandth of an inch.[††]

In addition to the propelling machinery, electrical power for the 15,000 lights***, heaters, 870 fans, 11 lifts, 14 winches, 10 derricks, steering, anchor and warping gear, water and fuel oil pumps and 300 various other motors and machines, as well as for the air-conditioning and refrigerating plants, would be supplied by four 800-kW, 225-volt, direct-current turbo-generators. Generating enough power to light a town of 100,000 inhabitants, these generators were controlled from a main switchboard 54ft. in length, and in total some 300 miles of cable would be needed for the electrical system throughout the ship. Three air-conditioning plants with a combined cooling capacity of 3,500,000 cubic ft. per hour would provide cool air with controlled humidity to the Cabin-Class Restaurant and Grand Hall as well as the Tourist-Class Dining Saloon, Cinema and Lounge. One innovative feature for communication on board would be a system consisting of approximately 50 loudspeakers scattered throughout the major public rooms which would enable messages, radio programmes or music to be broadcast to passengers. Another innovation would be the fitting of all three cinemas with motion picture sound systems.

With the goal of producing the most modern, yet practical, vessel possible, the Building Committee continued to make many changes as work progressed at an ever accelerating pace. On 21st September, 1937, it was jointly decided by the Builders and Owners to rename the "Palm Court" the "Lounge", as the former name was outdated. The "Lounge", in turn, was renamed the "Grand Hall". Realizing that "No. 1029" would occasionally make tropical cruises, provision for a deck swimming pool "with a flush steel interior" that would include "decking over the tank during North Atlantic voyages"[†††] was approved on 12th October, subject to agreement by Cammel Laird's engineers. However, on 3rd November, the engineers decided that the proposed deck pool would be too heavy, and that "consideration [would need] to be given to the possibility of producing some lighter type".[†††] The solution would be in the form of a raised canvas swimming pool, costing an additional £4,080 ($20,171.52) and located abaft the Cabin Smoke Room on the Promenade Deck.

With work on "No. 1029" well under way, a name for this new liner had to be selected. While there were several possibilities, the re-use of the name "*Mauretania*", after the legendary Cunard liner sent to the shipbreakers in July, 1935, seemed to be the first choice. Following the decommissioning of the first *Mauretania*, the Board of Trade had reserved that name for Cunard White Star by transferring it to the Red Funnel paddle-steamer, *Queen*. The Directors of Cunard White Star had to select a name not only for "No. 1029", but also for "No. 552" (as the *Queen Elizabeth* was then called).

On 7th September, 1937, Bates sent a coded telegram marked

"Confidential" to Sir Ashley T. Sparks*, Cunard's Resident Director in New York, stating: "Ships names Approval from special quarter has already been given for s.s. 552. Stop. Under consideration call s.s. 1029 Mauretania which has for some time been reserved by Board of Trade for our re-use. Stop. Shall be glad of your views in time discuss next week's Board Meeting."[†] Bates also wrote to one of the Directors of Cunard White Star, Sir Thomas Royden, Bart., C.H., that same day, stating: ". . . I hope very much it will be possible for you to be at the Board Meeting in London on Wednesday of next week, as I specially wish to have a talk with you on the question of the name for 'No. 1029'."[†]

Royden's acknowledgement of Bates's letter on 9th September, in which he explained that he would ". . . not be able to get away for the Board Meeting next Wednesday"[†], prompted Bates to write to him again on the 13th, stating: "We rather badly want to choose a name for No. 1029 in order to give that ship a run of publicity as far in advance of No. 552 as possible. Lister** and the Management here wish to revive the name 'Mauretania', and I have consulted Tom Sparks by cable on this with a view to ascertaining how he regards the name as a business-getter in the United States. I cannot say that I am very keen on the use of this name for this ship myself, as I have a sort of feeling that it ought to be used in the same circumstances as when it was first used, namely, for one of our top-class ships, but I have no very strong feeling about it. It has been suggested to me by Fred[††] that perhaps the use of the name on a Liverpool ship might cause resentment on the Tyne, but whether we ought to take this into account I am uncertain. If Tom Sparks comes down emphatically with approval of the name 'Mauretania', I should support it at the Board."[†] That same day, Sparks sent a coded telegram to Bates from New York stating: "Referring to your telegram 7th instant agree think name 'Mauretania' would be of great value."[†]

In Royden's response to the Chairman's letter on 15th September, he expressed his feelings about the proposed name, stating: "With regard to the name of No. 1029, my first thought was that it would be better to find some other name than 'Mauretania', and I still feel some hesitation in using this name. I am not sure, however, whether this hesitation is not due, at all events in some measure, to sentiment. The first 'Mauretania' and I joined the Cunard the same year, and I can well remember how excited we all were and how frightened we were that in building ships like her and the 'Lusitania' we had gone too far and they would never pay their way. Events proved that we were quite unnecessarily frightened. I made many journeys in the ship before and during the War, and in many ways she has held a very warm corner in my heart. Nevertheless, if New York falls in line with the views of Lister and the Management in Liverpool, and if, in addition, you are in favour of it, I am content that No. 1029 should be called 'Mauretania'."[†]

A Board of Directors Meeting was held on 20th October, 1937, after which a memorandum was sent the following day to Lister, stating: "The Board decided that this ship be named 'Mauretania', which name has already been reserved for the Company. The General Manager was instructed to arrange the launching date after consultation with Messrs. Cammell Laird & Co. Ltd., and to arrange also for the necessary publicity."[†] Lister indeed spoke with Robert Johnson of Cammell Laird that day, who, in turn wrote to Cunard on 22nd October ". . . to confirm that all being well we will launch No. 1029 at 12.15 p.m. on the 28th July next".[†] That same day, Cunard White Star submitted their application for the name *Mauretania* to the Registrar-General of Shipping and Seamen. On 28th January, 1938, the name was officially approved and the Red Funnel paddle-steamer (ex-*Queen*) that had held the name *Mauretania* took the new name *Corfe Castle*.

With an estimated 3,000 men working on the *Mauretania* day and night, preparations were begun in anticipation of her forthcoming launch. In a memorandum written on 8th March, 1938, Lister wrote of his conversation with Johnson who had confirmed that Cammell Laird would "send out all the invitations to the launch", noting Cunard's preference for those who would "be invited to the launching platform and the lunch, the launching platform alone, or just tickets to witness the launch from the Shipyard".[†] Lister went on to say: ". . . the stand behind the dais will accommodate about 2,000, but Mr. Johnson wants to keep the numbers for the luncheon itself down

---

* In an attempt to perfect their design prior to casting, a scale-model wooden anchor attached to a wooden cable was repeatedly raised and lowered from a full-scale wooden model of one side of the bow complete with anchor-recess and hawse-pipe.

[†] On 28th January, 1938, it was decided to increase the diameter of the propellers from 19ft. to 19ft. 3ins. in order to slightly reduce the number of estimated revolutions.

** The *Mauretania* originally was to have had four water tube boilers and three cylindrical boilers. However, this arrangement was changed on 3rd February, 1937, in favour of six water tube boilers of equal size, which would cost an extra £11,250 ($55,620).

[††] These gear wheels were so delicate that they were guarded around the clock prior to installation.

*** The lighting system included powerful spotlights which illuminated the bridge and funnels.

[†††] "No. 1029 Building Committee Minutes"; University Archives, The University of Liverpool.

---

* In his letters, Bates refers to Sir Ashley T. Sparks as "Tom Sparks".

[†] "Name and Launch"; University Archives, The University of Liverpool.

** Sidney J. Lister, General Manager of Cunard White Star Ltd.

[††] Frederick A. Bates, one of the Directors of Cunard White Star Ltd.

to not more than 1,000 . . . all expenses in connection with the launching are to be borne by the Builders and the invitations will be sent out in the Builders' name and not in the joint names of the two Companies."*

However, by April, 1938, it became apparent that the launching date might not be met because of a number of unforeseen minor problems including "trouble between the plumbers and the coppersmiths as to who should do certain work".* On 4th May, Lister again conferred with Johnson, and reminded him that, although progress on the ship had improved, they were still almost a month behind schedule. Lister then explained that the *Mauretania* "will probably be required for some time to run in our Express service, in addition to the other services in which we may place her, and with this view we have to plan our programme twelve months ahead; we were therefore proposing to schedule the 'Mauretania' to sail in either the first or second week of May next year".* Johnson agreed that they, too, were "equally . . . desirous of getting the ship finished"* and promised to find out whether that deadline could be met.

Lister received his answer on 10th May: "Mr. Johnson of Cammell Lairds rang up to say that after making careful enquiries he was afraid there was no chance of delivering the 'Mauretania' to sail in the first or second week of May, but he quite expects to deliver her by the end of May. I told him that we were rather disappointed at this, but that of course we must have a finished ship. We were anxious to get a sailing in May, because naturally we wished to have the ship coming out in a good season of the year, both from a weather and traffic point of view.† Probably her first sailing would be direct from Liverpool to New York, returning to Southampton, where she would be fitted in with the 'Queen Mary' and the 'Aquitana'."*

In an attempt to maintain the revised maiden voyage sailing date, Johnson wrote to Cunard White Star on 11th May, proposing the following: "With reference to the telephone conversation I had with Mr. Lister I confirm that we hope to deliver the 'Mauretania' so that she can sail from Liverpool on the 27th May, 1939, but this delivery can only be attained on the understanding that the Trials of the Gearing in the shop will be dispensed with, or greatly reduced, as the time taken up in this operation might be quite considerable. Up to now we have had practically no trouble with our Gearing as we take extreme care in the cutting and we would suggest that the Admiralty procedure, which we also carry out for other Shipowners, should be sufficient."**

Cunard White Star tentatively agreed to this proposal in their response on 24th May, provided that this plan was acceptable to both Cunard's Superintendent Engineer, Mr. Austin, and Cammell Laird's Engineering Department. Subsequent discussions on 7th June between Austin and Cammell Laird's Engineering Manager, Mr. McMenemey, resulted in an agreement outlined in a memorandum from Austin dated 11th June. It stated: ". . . the requirements of the specifications regarding the running in of the gears in the shop under load would be carried out as far as time permits. When the time arrives at which it is indicated that delay will be caused if this method is proceeded with, the running in of the gears by this method will be discontinued in the shops and arrangements will be made, if necessary, to complete the bedding of the gear wheel and pinion teeth in the ship during the trials, before acceptance of the ship."**

By forgoing full trials of the gearing, Johnson was able to keep his word, as the launching indeed took place on Thursday, 28th July, 1938. The fact that the hull was completed and delivered on the date promised by Johnson is a remarkable tribute to his competence and technical mastery of the shipbuilding business. The construction of the *Mauretania*, along with her mates, the "*Queens*", had become a symbol of Britain's economic resurrection following the Depression, and her launching was a momentous event not only for Cunard White Star and Cammell Laird, but also for the entire United Kingdom.

Dominating the shipyard, the freshly painted hull of the *Mauretania* stood majestically on the ways gleaming from stem to stern. In the record time of only 14 months following the laying of the keel, some 16,300 tons of steel, including thousands of plates averaging 7ft. wide by 33ft. in length, had been assembled with some 2½ million rivets into the shape of her graceful hull. With all ten decks completely plated, the equivalent of 60 miles of scaffolding that had surrounded the *Mauretania* had finally been removed. After

an evening of rain and gale-force winds, the sun came out to set the scene for what would be a perfect launching. Over 50,000 people packed Cammell Laird's shipyard, to witness with many thousands of others along the shoreline* "the Mersey's biggest splash", as the launch was described by the Press.

Lady Bates, wife of the Chairman of Cunard White Star and a granddaughter of Charles MacIver, one of the founders of the Cunard Line†, had consented to perform the ceremony. The following account by the "Liverpool Daily Post"** best described the event: "The few moments of waiting time after Lady Bates, led by Mr. R.S. Johnson, managing director of the yard, and accompanied by a small party which included Sir Percy Bates and Mr. W.L. Hichens, chairman of Cammell Laird's, mounted the platform, were occupied while Lady Bates posed for the cameramen, who, for an hour or more had been flirting with death as they clambered about the girders of the nearest crane. Watched by thousands of eager eyes, Lady Bates firmly gripped the bottle and flung it at the bows. It shattered in a widening splash of white foam and its spray flew back over the platform. The parting of the flags that hid the famous name allowed something of the customary tension to relax, for the mechanism proved recalcitrant and it took a minute or two before Lady Bates, stepping forward to the microphones, said: 'I count myself extremely lucky to have the opportunity of launching this great ship. It is a proud day not only for me, but for the yard and the Cunard White Star Line. This ship is the largest that has ever been built in England. I hope that, like her namesake, she may make her appeal on both sides of the Atlantic. To the men in the yard who made her I say that at every visit to the yard I have been thrilled by their work, and I offer both my congratulations on their skill and all my good wishes for their happiness and for the happiness of those who are near to them. To the ship and all who serve or sail in her I wish all good fortune.' Proudly and clearly she said, 'I name you . . . Mauretania'; she pressed the button, and with barely five seconds hiatus the colossal stem had begun to drop away from the rail of the platform. Mauretania had taken life.''

It took only 50 seconds for the *Mauretania* to slide 777ft. down No. 6 slipway, which previously had launched such vessels as the Cunarder *Samaria* (II), the battleship H.M.S. *Rodney* and, most recently, Britain's first vessel designed and built as an aircraft carrier, H.M.S. *Ark Royal*. Without requiring drag-chains to slow her momentum in the mile-wide Mersey, the newest vessel of the Cunard fleet came to a slow stop, sitting high on the water, with a draft of only 14ft. 8⅛ins. forward, 15ft. 9¹¹⁄₁₆ins. amidships and 17ft. 4⅝ins. aft, before she began to swing downstream. With 12 aeroplanes circling overhead, the *Mauretania* was under tow to her fitting-out berth within 10 minutes, while workmen in small rowing-boats collected the tons of grease and the splintered wooden cradle and forepoppets that by now littered the water.

Over 1,200 guests were invited to celebrate the occasion at a special gala luncheon presided over by W.L. Hichens. After speaking of Cammell Laird's long-held ambition to build for Cunard White Star one of the great Atlantic ocean liners that both Cunard and White Star had been famous for, Hichens congratulated Lady Bates on her first launch, saying that he had "never seen so perfect an exhibition of craftmanship launching". He then presented her with a diamond bracelet watch and read a telegram from Lord Derby congratulating her on "a most brilliant successful ceremony".*** Telegrams from the Southern Railway staff at Southampton and the Southampton Harbour Board followed.

Other telegrams at the luncheon included one to Sir Percy Bates from the Ship Lore Society in Liverpool: "Congratulations and best wishes for success new ship. May she prove worthy of great name she bears."††; from Red Funnel Steamers Ltd. of Southampton (owners of the ex-*Queen*), addressed to the Chairman and Directors of Cunard White Star and Cammell Laird: "Greetings to the new Mauretania With best wishes for an even more successful career than her illustrious namesake."††; from the ex-*Queen* to the new *Mauretania*: "On the day of your baptism, your diminutive step-sister sends greetings and cordial wishes for a long and famous career."***

While admitting that she was one of the world's worst sailors,

---

* "Name and Launch"; University Archives, The University of Liverpool.
† Passenger traffic between England and the U.S. was expected to be especially heavy in the summer of 1939, largely due to the opening of the New York World's Fair.
** "Delivery"; University Archives, The University of Liverpool.

* "Cammell Laird Magazine", April, 1964, states that a total of over 100,000 people witnessed the launch.
† Several other grandchildren of Charles MacIver were also present at the post-launch luncheon.
** July 19, 1938; University Archives, The University of Liverpool.
†† "Name and Launch; University Archives, The University of Liverpool.
*** "Liverpool Daily Post", 29th July, 1939; University Archives, The University of Liverpool.

Lady Bates said that she intended to travel in the *Mauretania* on her maiden voyage. She went on to say: "Shipbuilding does not stand still, and immense strides have been made since her namesake was built. I feel confident that this beautiful child of the Mersey will be a popular ship. Child as she is, the 'Mauretania' has not yet developed a voice for herself, and, therefore, on her behalf, I thank you for your kind expressions for her future career."*

Without wasting any time, the pre-launch work-force of 3,000 men that had constructed the great hull once again descended into the ship to begin the installation of machinery, boilers and passenger accommodation. However, before the job could be completed, the number of workers on the *Mauretania* would increase to about 5,000. It has been estimated that, in addition to the yard workers, approximately 150,000 people in over 100 cities and towns throughout the United Kingdom took some part in manufacturing or supplying various components needed for the completion of the ship.

As work on the machinery and boilers began, the Building Committee continued to meet and discuss details pertaining to passenger accommodation and proposed structural modifications. At a typical meeting on 18th July, 1938, the Committee approved a long list of items totalling £13,980 ($68,362.20) in additional costs. They ranged from the mundane to the most consequential: "Deletion of the breakwater on the forecastle forward of No. 1 Hatch — Rebate £110.0.0"; "Fitting a dome over Cabin Lounge & deleting one 2-berth Cabin stateroom and one shower room — Extra £142.0.0"; "Fitting up a Laundry & making provision for staff (Plant provided by Company). Deleting nine 2-berth rooms, one 4-berth room, 1 Stewardess's room, 1 Gents. & 1 Ladies' Lavatory, and adding one 3-berth room with toilet — Rebate £640.0.0"; "Fitting 68 additional sidelights on Main and 'A' Decks — Extra £883.0.0"; and "Increasing the number of Private Baths, Shower baths and Toilets in the Cabin Class, and introducing a number of Shower baths in the Tourist Class — Extra £10,280.0.0."†

In addition, the Committee approved the contracts for the decoration of the Public Rooms and Cabin Suites on that date, with Waring & Gillow (1932) Ltd. receiving 12 Cabin Class and eight Tourist Class assignments, while G. Parnall & Co. Ltd. received contracts for an additional seven Cabin Class public rooms. With regard to one group of Cabin Class staterooms: "The sum of £7,640.0.0 was quoted by the Builders for the fitting of 54 Cabin Staterooms in veneered hardwood. This matter was again considered, and the Builders were asked to submit a revised quotation for fitting 24 staterooms in veneered hardwood and the balance of 30 rooms in fabric with a hardwood dado. 'Approved'. This suggestion has reduced the cost to £4,483.0.0 and the Builders have been instructed to proceed with the work on this basis. 'Approved'."†

Even though in this case the Committee reduced a number of Cabin Class staterooms that would be panelled in hardwood veneers, overall the *Mauretania's* public and private rooms would be enriched with finely figured exotic and rare veneers. In early August, 1938, the Decorative Architect in charge of the *Mauretania*, Mr J. Patrick McBride of the firm of A. McInnes Gardner & Partners of Glasgow, met with a representative from Messrs. George Parnall & Co. to select the following Cabin Class public room veneers to be used by that firm, as dictated in a memorandum dated 8th August, 1938**: "*Cabin Class Grand Hall* — Figured Peroba, Striped Peroba [and] Two figurines of finely figured Ash Burr. *Cabin Class Library* — Maple Butt and Straight Grained Maple [and] Blistered Sapeli. *Cabin Lounge* — Primavera, Paldao [and] Elm Burr. *Cabin Class Gymnasium* — Straight Grained Ash [and] Weathered Sycamore. *Cabin Class Entrance, Amidships* — Betula."††

McBride then made a similar visit to the studios of Messrs. Waring and Gillow Ltd. on 11th August to select veneers to be used. A memorandum dated 16th August, 1938**, includes: "*Cabin Dining Saloon* — Panelling in mahogany with additional veneers of Pomelli, Nigerian Cherry, Plane Tree Burr. *Observation Lounge* — Panelling in Bleached Olive Ash with relieving veneers of Bird's Eye Maple, Elm Burr and Australian Walnut. *Smoke Room* — Panelling generally in Cherry Burr with relieving veneers in Australian Maple and Queensland Walnut, with featuring panels in

Masur Birch. *Entrances, Forward and Aft* — Panelling generally in Figured Betula with doors and other relieving features in fine Elm Burr, Palado, and or Queensland Walnut. *Forward Staircase* — Panelling in Weathered Sycamore with relieving bandings of Queensland Walnut. *Tourist Dining Saloon* — Panelling generally in Weathered Sycamore with relieving veneers of Zebrano, White Sycamore and Elm Burr. *Lounge* — Panelling generally in Peroba with relieving veneers of Straight White Ash and Fine White Ash Burr. *Smoke Room* — Panelling generally in Open Grain Chestnut with relieving veneers in Queensland Walnut, and featuring panels in Chestnut Burr. *Cinema* — Panelling in Indian Silver Grey Wood with bandings of Macassar Ebony. *Children's Room* — Panelling in Silky Oak with bandings of Zabrano. *Gymnasium* — Panelling of Slavonian Oak with bandings of Brown Oak. *All Entrances* — Panelling in Nigerian Cherry with relieving veneers of Sapeli, Mahogany and Cherry Burr."

Rare woods were found not only in the Cabin and Tourist Class public rooms, but also in the Third Class public rooms — as indicated by a memo dated 6th September, 1938*, which suggested that the following woods be incorporated into those rooms: light toned birch, slightly bleached Nigeria cherry, sycamore, light mahogany, Australian walnut, light oak, Macassar ebony and Indian silver greywood. The number of Joiners working with these woods numbered only 180 on 17th September, 1938. However, by 4th February, 1939, that number increased to 745, with Cammell Laird employing 520 on the ship and 104 in the shops; Messrs. Waring and Gillow, 98 on the ship; Messrs. George Parnall & Co., 18; and Messrs. Purdy & Millards of Belfast, five.

On 14th October, 1938, the Committee again discussed the topic of the Cabin staterooms that had been brought up on 18th July, determining that: ". . . the following selections made of Veneers for the 24 Cabin Staterooms which are to be finished in polished hardwood: [include] Six staterooms to be panelled in White Sycamore (Furniture in Bubinga†); Four Staterooms to be panelled in Weathered Sycamore (Furniture in Quilted Maple); Two Staterooms to be panelled in Weathered Sycamore (Furniture in Nigerian Cherry); [and] Twelve Staterooms to be panelled in Figured White Ash (Furniture in Betula). 'Approved'."**

Also at that meeting: "It was reported that the question of installing Turkish Baths in the space where the Massage Room was to be fitted had been raised . . . [and] in view of the deck height being only 8ft. and the thickness of insulation required both on floor and ceiling . . . the finished deck height would be such as to render the scheme impracticable. As the New York Office considered the fitting of Electric Baths satisfactory . . . it was decided not to proceed any further with this matter . . . 'Approved'."**

At another meeting on 30th December, 1938, the Committee discussed 22 items, including one pertaining to the use of linen and table-settings: "As the 'Mauretania' will be acting on occasions as the relief ship to the 'Queen Mary' and the 'Queen Elizabeth' in the Southampton-New York Service, it was reported, for the purposes of record, that the type and quality of the Electro-plate, Cutlery, Crockery and Linen will be the same on all three ships."**

It is interesting to note that one proposed feature that was published in a 1938 newspaper account, stated: "Decorative schemes for public rooms on the 'Mauretania', it is revealed, will include a large illuminated fountain to be banked with masses of flowers in the main entrance . . ." While this may have been planned, it is not mentioned in any records extant on the ship. Although the *Bremen* of 1929 had a fountain in the centre of the First Class Ball Room, this feature would have been highly unusual, and was probably altered on the *Mauretania* to the semi-circular *jardinière* that enclosed an ebony pylon within a semi-elliptical recess in the First Class Foyer on "B" Deck.

As work on the passenger accommodation continued to progress, decorative work in the public rooms commenced on 28th January, 1939. Even at this late date, many details regarding the general scheme of the public rooms were being planned. In a memorandum dated 25th February, 1939**, the following decorative features were discussed: "*Cabin Entrance 'A' Deck Forward* — Painted map by W. McDowell approved subject to minor alterations suggested by Mr. Crail. These chiefly concerned the elimination of the large tracts of

* "Liverpool Daily Post", 29th July, 1939; University Archives, The University of Liverpool.
† "Minutes of Board Meetings — Cunard White Star Limited"; University Archives, The University of Liverpool.
** "Decorative Work"; University Archives, University of Liverpool.
†† "The heart of Canadian Birch."

* "Decorative Work"; University Archives, The University of Liverpool.
† African rosewood.
** "Minutes of Board Meetings — Cunard White Star Limited"; University Archives, The University of Liverpool.

Canada and Europe, and Lindbergh's aeroplane, and the giving of more emphasis to the U.S.A. and the British Isles."; "*Cabin Entrance Promenade Deck* — The scheme by Charles Pears shewing the old 'Mauretania' leaving the Tyne on first commission was not very enthusiastically received, and as an alternative to a new scheme altogether it was thought that Mersey riverside might be introduced, and this could be done with little trouble. However, Mr. Johnson of Cammell Laird's has taken the attitude that the old ship should be entirely deleted and a new design submitted to replace it."; "*Grand Hall* — The idea of the lac and gesso screen to the aft end was approved. The three carved panels to the raised roof sides and over the proscenium were thought to be much too grotesque, and it was agreed that we should ask the artist — Barney Seale — to prepare revisions to the infilling of these panels."; "*Cabin Lounge* — The incised frieze shewing the signs of the Zodiac was approved. The model to the niche at the forward end over the fireplace approved provided the various recommendations made are carried out and that Mr. Crail or Sir Thomas Brocklebank could visit the Studio before the work is cast."*

On 24th April, 1939, only 54 days before the *Mauretania* sailed on her maiden voyage, S.V. Bilham of Cunard White Star's Furnishing Department wrote to H.J. Flewitt to ". . . confirm that we are obtaining from the decorative Contractors samples of the coverings which are to be used in the Cabin Lounge, Cabin Grand Hall and Cabin Dining Saloon, and these will be forwarded to you in the course of a few days. In the meantime I would inform you briefly of the colour schemes proposed for these particular places. *Main Lounge* — the colour scheme of this room is carried out in light shades of blue, the curtains being blue and tan with a similar combination of colours in other fabrics to the furniture whilst the carpet is of a light fawn shade embodying tan and brown motifs. *Cabin Grand Hall* — The predominating colour in this room will be green, the window curtains being of crushed velvet, whilst the contrasting coverings of rich fawn corded velvets, the same colour also being introduced in the tapestry designs. *Cabin Dining Saloon* — The predominating note of colour in this room, apart from the warm mahogany of the panelling, will be a rich blue, as the Dining Room chairs are upholstered in hide of this colour, the dress cloths for tables are of a cream linen with blue trellis design woven in it."*

Meanwhile, final plans for the trials and maiden voyage had been revised as early as 1st November, 1938, when Lister had written to Johnson: "With the date of the 'Mauretania's' delivery now getting nearer, we are preparing the necessary plans and sailing arrangements for the vessel next year. This is just to advise you that we are now advertising the vessel to make her maiden voyage from Liverpool on Saturday, May 27, which is the date we have been working on for some time . . ."† Johnson replied on 4th November, stating: ". . . so far as I can see at present it will not be possible for us to have the 'Mauretania' ready to run her trials until 31st May next and I believe this can only be attained by working a considerable amount of overtime. I am sorry we are not able to do better than this but actually we were detained two months by the alterations that were made and we are only asking two months extra time."† Lister, in turn, telephoned Johnson that day, after which he dictated a memorandum, stating in part: "He [Johnson] said to get her finished by the end of May next to undertake her trials is the very best that they could promise; that he had had difficulties with the plumbers and coppersmiths. I told him that was not our concern, that he must work overtime to compensate for this. He replied that he was working overtime and that he may have to come back on us for help. I intimated that we were already paying far more for the ship than we had contemplated, to which he remarked, 'And you are getting a very different ship from what you set out first to build'. I have not told him yet that we accept the 31st May. If nothing unforeseen occurs, if trials commenced May 31 I assume ship can sail June 17."†

On 7th November, Lister wrote to Johnson: "If we cannot have a 27th May sailing it is essential that it be not later than the 17th June, and it is furthermore of importance to us that we promptly advertise this date. As to the delay, is it not a fact that this ship has been held back because of the long stay of the 'Ark Royal' in your Yard?"† Johnson's reply to Lister on 9th November clarified Cammell Laird's position: "What we propose doing is to put the 'Mauretania' into the Gladstone Graving Dock on the 16th May

next. We will keep her there until the 31st May when we will take her on her trials. It is our intention if possible to put the top part of the Rudder, that is the Stock portion, into the ship and partially fit the Steering Gear before the vessel leaves here. It will then only be a question of putting the lower portion into the ship in the dry dock. With regard to the last clause of your letter the facts are quite contrary to what you suggest. As a matter of fact we have been blamed on several occasions both by the Admiralty and Ellerman Lines for holding up work on their vessels in favour of the 'Mauretania'. I can assure you that the 'Mauretania' has had the closest attention of everybody from the date we got the order. If we complete her as we intend by the end of May next we will have done something pretty wonderful in shipbuilding."*

And "pretty wonderful" it certainly was, as against overwhelming odds Johnson and his men delivered the *Mauretania* as promised. Basin trials of "the [vessel's] main machinery were successfully carried out on the 2nd and 4th instant"*, prior to berthing in the Gladstone Dock on 16th May, 1939, where two coats of anti-corrosive paint and one coat of anti-fouling was applied. On schedule, the *Mauretania* left Gladstone Dock on Wednesday, 31st May, 1939 at 9.30 a.m., and proceeded to the Liverpool Bar. After preliminary steering trials, the machinery was worked up to full power over the course of 12 hours, before arriving off the Tail of the Bank at 3.30 a.m. on Thursday, 1st June. At 9.47 that morning, the *Mauretania* then proceeded to Arran, where five progressive "measured mile" speed trials were carried out. Even on the last of these double runs, where the mean speed of 25.14 knots was achieved at 147.8 r.p.m., indicating 47,800 horsepower, "there was a remarkable absence of vibration even at overload power. In the after part of the accommodation on the lower deck there was a little propeller noise, but no vibration".* Everyone on board was delighted, including Sir Percy Bates, who later wrote to Sir Stephen J. Pigott of Messrs. John Brown & Co. Ltd. of Clydebank: "I am glad to say that the trials were in every respect satisfactory, and the speed and power developed fully up to our expectations. I might say that in all parts the ship was exceedingly quiet."† The following day, the Wireless Direction Finder was calibrated and the 24-hour consumption and endurance trial began. When this last test was completed at 10 a.m. on 3rd June, 1939, the "Maury", as she was already affectionately known, proceeded to the Liverpool Bar and docked in the Gladstone Dock at 12.30 p.m.

Before taking on provisions for her maiden voyage, the Port H.P., Starboard I.P. and Starboard L.P. Turbines, the Turbo Generator Turbine Casing as well as the Port and Starboard Gearing were opened and inspected. All boilers were also opened at this time and cleaned internally and externally. At 12 o'clock noon on 10th June, 1939, the Builders officially handed the ship over to the Owners, and on Saturday, 17th June, at 7.40 p.m., the *Mauretania* left Liverpool on her maiden transatlantic voyage. According to the "New York Herald Tribune": "Her progress downstream was a three-hour ceremonial. Garlanded from bow to stern with wind-whipped flags, the new 'Mauretania' glided past the yard of Cammell Laird Ltd., where she was built, convoyed by 100 tugs, 100 seaplanes and three army bombers. Fifty thousand inhabitants of Liverpool and Birkenhead lined the shores to cheer her . . ."**

In charge of the new £1,928,812 ($8,602,501.50) *Mauretania*†† was Captain A.T. Brown, who after three years as Staff Captain of the first *Mauretania*, had the honour of commanding that vessel on her historic last voyage to the shipbreakers. Also on board the *Mauretania* (II) was veteran pilot, Mr. J.E. McCarthy, who had not only piloted the first *Mauretania* up Ambrose Channel in New York on her maiden voyage on 22nd November, 1907, but had also piloted the ship down that channel on her last voyage from New York on 26th September, 1934. Amongst the new *Mauretania's* 829 passengers were Mr. and Mrs. Robert Middlemass of Glasgow, who had also been passengers on the old *Mauretania's* maiden voyage. And like the old *Mauretania*, which had carried some £2,750,000 ($13,384,250) worth of gold bullion on that first voyage, the new *Mauretania* carried a similar shipment valued at £3,200,000

---

* "Decorative Work"; University Archives, The University of Liverpool.
† "Delivery"; University Archives, The University of Liverpool.

* "Delivery"; University Archives, The University of Liverpool.
† 12th June, 1939. "Delivery"; University Archives, The University of Liverpool.
** 17th June, 1939. The Steamship Historical Society of America, Inc., The University of Baltimore Library, Baltimore, Maryland.
†† Following the maiden voyage, this amount would be increased to the "final first cost" figure of £1,991,673.17s ($8,882,864.70), as a result of additional expenses which had yet to be included.

($14,272,000) on her maiden voyage.

After making a three-hour stop in Cobh, the *Mauretania* (II) arrived in New York at 9.30 a.m. on Saturday, 24th June, having traversed 2,912 miles in 141 hours and 20 minutes, at an average speed of 20.6 knots. Greeted by the whistles of numerous tugs and harbour craft, the new *Mauretania* was escorted to Pier 90, at the foot of West 50th Street, with a small fleet of aeroplanes and a blimp. In addition to the many hundreds who lined the shore along Lower Manhattan, over 1,000 people crowded at the dockside to witness the berthing of this great new ship. After what had been described as an "uneventful" voyage, Captain Brown remarked to reporters that the *Mauretania* was "an extraordinarily fine ship from a seaman's point of view". The Captain went on to say: "We had only one forenoon of rough weather, but the ship certainly didn't even bat an eyelash at that. And I am happy to say that there appears to be a complete absence of vibration, even at full speed. You gentlemen may remember that the old 'Mauretania' always had a friendly feeling about her — an atmosphere of friendship and personality. This ship actually seems to have inherited those qualities."* Sir Percy Bates also commented on the voyage, saying: "This is a quiet ship — the quietest I have ever travelled in. I suppose she has been helped by her name — that certainly helped to pull the crew together into a good organization very speedily. They know the ship and already are beginning to be proud of her. I think in the end they may be as proud of her as they were of the old 'Mauretania'." Bates then stated: "It is my own opinion that the truly remarkable features on this ship are not to be found in the cabin or tourist classes, fine as they are, but in the third class and the crew's quarters. I am sure the crew accommodations are the best in any British ship. This is a good year for the 'Mauretania' to come out, so that she can become known to the travelling public before the 'Queen Elizabeth' comes out. It is difficult to say now whether we will retire any of our older ships, especially the 'Aquitania'. She is a good ship and a popular ship and we should be sorry to retire her. But it must depend on the passenger traffic. There is no doubt that disturbed conditions in Europe have hurt Atlantic travel. Traffic on the ocean is a very delicate barometer of events and conditions, and the result is that trade has not had a reasonable chance in these last two years. Still, I am inclined to be optimistic about the European situation now."*

Among the few minor problems that had been encountered was a little trouble "with the refrigerating machinery which in turn affected the supply of chilled water for cooling and dehumidifying the air".[†] Nevertheless, even in the uncomfortable heat, "with the air-conditioning plant in action there was a noticeable difference in the temperature and humidity in the air-conditioned spaces".[†]

On Friday, 30th June, at 11 p.m., the *Mauretania* (II) left New York on her return maiden voyage, and arrived in Southampton via Cherbourg on Friday, 7th July, at 1.30 p.m. The voyage took 142 hours 22 minutes, in which the distance of 3,130 miles was traversed at the average speed of 22 knots. A memorandum sent to the General Manager from the Naval Architect's Department** further detailed the event: "More severe weather was encountered on the return voyage. Confused seas were met and for a time the sea was on the quarter. This caused the ship to pitch, and roll mostly to the port side. The rolling was not excessive or uncomfortable. Under conditions the rolling was not regular, the inclinations being about 5 degrees to one side and 2 degrees to the other. During part of the return voyage some propeller vibration was observed but not more than was natural under the conditions and apparently caused little or no comment. It is probable that the condition of loading may have considerable effect as it may be noted that on the return voyage there was only 208 tons of cargo while on the outward journey there was 1,737 tons of cargo."

With the completion of her maiden voyage, the *Mauretania* was ready to assume her position alongside the *Britannic* and the *Georgic* on the London-Le Havre-Southampton-Cobh-New York run. With the *Queen Mary* and the *Aquitania* on the Cherbourg-Southampton route, and the *Franconia, Laconia, Samaria Scythia* alternating between Galway, Belfast, Dublin, Liverpool and Cobh, Cunard White Star had reached its zenith. But history was about to repeat itself. Just as Cunard had finally reached its long-held dream of a

three-ship weekly express service in the summer of 1914, the outbreak of the First World War in August had shattered its justifiable expectations. After completing only three voyages, the new *Aquitania* was stripped of her beautiful fittings and refitted for war. Now, after 25 years of rebuilding its respective fleets, Cunard White Star would again experience the front-line impact of another war which, this time, would claim nine of its vessels totalling 144,682 G.R.T. and obliterate all normal passenger services for the next six years.

Scheduled to arrive in London on Sunday, 3rd September, 1939, the *Mauretania* left New York to complete her third voyage on Saturday, 26th August. As the international situation worsened by the hour, it was decided on 31st August, in mid-ocean, to terminate the voyage a day early at Southampton. This was a timely decision, as the following day, Friday, 1st September, 1939, Germany ruthlessly invaded Poland. On 3rd September, Britain and France declared war on Germany, and the Allies' first casualty, the Donaldson liner *Athenia*, was torpedoed and sunk without warning 200 miles west of the Hebrides, with a loss of 112 lives.

Understandably, the *Mauretania* did not keep her next scheduled sailing date of Thursday, 7th September. Instead, she left for New York on the 14th, painted a dull wartime grey with blacked-out ports that cloaked the view of the sea from her 698 passengers. Mounted on her aft decks near piles of protective sandbags, two 3-inch anti-aircraft guns and one 6-inch gun were covered with canvas tarpaulins. Returning to Liverpool on 7th October, the *Mauretania* was berthed in the Gladstone Dock where, if left for any period of time, she would most assuredly attract the Luftwaffe's attention as an easy target. Eventually the madness of this tactical blunder was realized, and on 2nd November, the Mersey Docks and Harbour Board petitioned Cunard to move the ship. Expressing no objection, the Admiralty wisely granted permission on 30th November for the ship to be moved to New York. On 10th December, 1939, the *Mauretania* left Liverpool and arrived in New York six days later. Meanwhile, the *Queen Mary* had been *en route* to New York when war was declared. After disembarking a record 2,332 passengers, the pride of the Cunard fleet was berthed alongside the *Normandie*, which had already sought safety in New York from the ominous Atlantic. Together with the *Mauretania*, they formed an impressive trio which would not be surpassed until 7th March, 1940, when the new *Queen Elizabeth* steamed up the Hudson River after making her historic, 26-knot, top-secret "maiden voyage" dash from Glasgow.* The *Mauretania* was quickly moved to Pier 86 to accommodate the new "Queen", and for the first time, the *Queen Elizabeth*, the *Queen Mary* and the *Normandie*, the three largest ships in the world, with a combined G.R.T. of 247,709, lay side by side, along with the *Mauretania*, to await their orders.

On 30th January, 1940, Cyril Hurcomb, Director-General of the Ministry of Shipping, had written to Cunard White Star to inform them of the Ministry's new "Liner Requisition Scheme" which stated: ". . . in the interest of the efficient prosecution of the war, it has become necessary to requisition under Regulation 53 of the Defence (General) Regulations, 1939, all ships (other than the excepted ships mentioned below) owned by the Company . . ." Besides "ships registered in a Dominion, India or Burma", or those "which on the 1st February 1940 were already requisitioned by or chartered to His Majesty's Government in the United Kingdom", the "excepted ships" to the scheme were the *Aquitania*, the *Mauretania*, the *Queen Mary* and the nearly completed *Queen Elizabeth*.[†]

With regard to the "excepted ships", the following terms for monetary reimbursement by the Government were formally outlined in the "Memorandum on Arrangements between the Minister of Shipping and Cunard White Star Limited"**: ". . . the Minister shall pay to the Company an allowance at the rate of 5% per annum on the first cost of the 'Queen Mary', 'Queen Elizabeth' and 'Mauretania' and on the war risks insurance valuation for total loss on the

---

* "New York Herald Tribune", 25th June, 1939. The Steamship Historical Society of America, Inc., University of Baltimore Library, Baltimore, Maryland.
[†] "Delivery"; University Archives, The University of Liverpool.
** 10th July, 1939. University Archives, The University of Liverpool.

* The *Queen Elizabeth* had originally been scheduled to sail on her maiden voyage from Southampton to New York on 24th April, 1940. However, with the declaration of war she instead sailed for New York on 2nd March so that she, too, would be safe from German bombers. When completed as the largest ship in the world, the final "first cost" of the *Queen Elizabeth* would be £5,509,508.3s.7d ($22,258,381).
[†] University Archives, The University of Liverpool.
** "Agreement with Government". No date, but believed to be 10th February, 1941. University Archives, The University of Liverpool.

3rd September 1939 of the 'Aquitania'."* Other important terms included: "While any of the excepted ships shall . . . be laid up or out of commission for any reason whatever the Company shall be responsible for her care and maintenance, including the costs of moving the vessel to a laying up port."† With regard to the reconditioning of these vessels, ". . . the Minister will, on application by the Company, make such contribution towards that cost as he may consider reasonable having regard to the period during which the ship was operating . . . and to the nature and extent of the work of restoration, reconditioning and repair paid for by him hereunder."†

On 6th March, 1940, Cunard White Star was informed by the Ministry of Shipping that the *Mauretania* was "required for urgent Government service [and] is hereby requisitioned."† Actually, the *Mauretania* was under Admiralty orders when she was moved from her berth to make way for the *Queen Elizabeth*. Now it was official, and much work had to be done to prepare her for trooping duties. Cunard White Star immediately sent one of their officials from the Furnishing Department to New York on the *Antonia* to supervise the removal of as much furniture as possible while in New York**, as well as plan the dismantlement of the public and private rooms in order to accommodate troops. A complement of new crew members for the *Mauretania*, as well as 500 new men for the *Queen Mary*, also made the trip to New York on board the *Antonia*.

The *Mauretania* was the first of the four liners to leave New York, on 20th March, 1940, followed by the *Queen Mary* on 21st March. Looking quite sombre in her grey, yet retaining her fine, distinctive lines, the *Mauretania* cut loose from her moorings under the strictest security at 8 p.m., and within 5 minutes was freed by her tugs and on her way to war. Although her destination was top secret, local newspapers were fairly accurate when they reported that she would probably make for Halifax or Bermuda before heading to Australia. The *Mauretania's* destination was indeed Australia, with stops in Bermuda, Colon, Balboa and Honolulu before arriving in Sydney on 14th April.

After arriving in Sydney, work immediately commenced on refitting the ship for troop-carrying duties. On the Monkey Island atop the Bridge, four rocket containers and four ammunition boxes were placed near a newly constructed Gunnery Control Tower and new "RADAR" Tower. Nearby, on the Captain's Deck and Sports Deck, 12 guns, 4 rocket stands and 36 ammunition boxes were installed. The Navigating Bridge was fitted with a "Plastic Armour" and "Steel Bulletproof Screen" around the wheelhouse, along with a "Plastic Armour" bulkhead inside the wheelhouse itself. The Engine Room Casing Top and the Aft Funnel Casing were both fitted with two guns, gun pits and ammunition boxes, with another gun positioned on the Raised Promenade Deck Aft, and a 12-pound gun near the Steering Engine Skylight. The Main Deck Forward (Forecastle Deck) was reserved for two 12-pound guns, gun pits and ammunition boxes that were protected by an armour plate shield, as well as two Oerliken guns, gun pits and corresponding shell magazines. Two additional Oerliken guns were also mounted on the Main Deck Aft, complete with gun pits and ammunition boxes. Finally, two P.A.C. rocket stands and one 12-pound gun were installed on the After Docking Bridge, along with a 6-inch gun, ammunition boxes and two magazines on "A" Deck Aft.

Interior changes made to passenger accommodation on the Sun Deck consisted of entirely gutting starboard Cabin-Class Staterooms S17 to S33 and removing all bulkheads in order to use that space, along with the Verandah Café, as a Troop Hospital. The Verandah Café was also fitted with lavatories for hospital use. Staterooms S2 to S24 retained their bulkheads but were stripped of all furnishings, including showers and toilets, so that Simmons cots, loudspeakers and other troop fittings could be installed.

* As for all other vessels, they would be paid the following basic rates: prior to 1st March, 1940, 11s 3d per G.R.T. per calendar month, increasing to 12s 6d per G.R.T. per calendar month on 1st March, 1940. That basic rate of hire would gradually increase every 8 to 9 months, so that by 1st January, 1945, the Government would be paying Cunard the rate of 18s per G.R.T. per calendar month.
† "Agreement with Government"; University Archives, The University of Liverpool.
** According to a memorandum in the University Archives, The University of Liverpool, dated 14th April, 1947, the cost of "packing, loading and storage of [the *Mauretania's*] furniture at New York" amounted to £2,087.3s.1d ($8,432.27). In comparison, between the time the *Queen Elizabeth* arrived and the date she left New York on 13th November, 1940, there had been enough time to remove almost all of her fittings and furniture, the storage of which would cost the Admiralty £52,907.8s.8d ($213,745.99).

On the Promenade Deck, the Observation Lounge was originally fitted with Standee berths, with additional toilet facilities now located in the adjoining pantries. Later, the Lounge would be converted into a Recreation Space, equipped with Sea Transport furniture. The Writing Room was converted into a Guard and Orderly Room, while the Port Side Kiosk (shop) was used as an Officers' Canteen. Although Sea Transport furniture had replaced the original fittings, the Grand Hall would still be used as a Public Room, with the Library now used as the Conference Room. The Cabin-Class Smoke Room was entirely rebuilt as another Troop Hospital, with the Gymnasium serving as a Medical Inspection Room. The Cabin-Class Children's Room became an Orderly Room, while the Dark Room was converted into a troop latrine. Outside, on the aft deck, the canvas swimming pool was altered to accommodate troop showers.

On the Main Deck, all staterooms, with the exception of the Suite Rooms, were stripped of their furnishings and fitted with Simmons cots. Standee berths were installed in both the Tourist Cinema and Lounge. However, the Lounge would later be converted into another Recreation Room. An additional Gyro Compass with batteries was installed in the Tourist Cinema Projection Room, the Tourist Children's Room was transformed into an Orderly Room, and the Tourist Shop became a Regimental Office.

On "A" Deck, the Third-Class Cinema Forward, at first fitted with Standee berths, was later changed to a Recreation Space. The Third-Class Lounge had shelves, counters and lockers installed as the Canteen, while Staterooms A2 to A70, and A1 to A73, had their furniture removed to accommodate troops and staff in cots. Staterooms A76 to A100, and A77 to A101, were entirely gutted along with all bathrooms, so the space could now be used as a Troop Deck, complete with hammock fittings and latrines. Nearby, the Tourist Smoke Room was converted into the Troop's Dry Canteen, and the Tourist Gymnasium into a Troop Galley.

On "B" Deck, the Cabin Dining Saloon became the Officers' Dining Saloon, the Tourist Dining Saloon was used as a Troop Mess Hall and the Third-Class Smoke Room was converted into the Troop's Wet Canteen. Third-Class Staterooms B2 to B54, and B1 to B85, were altered to Troop Mess Decks with hammock fittings, while Tourist Staterooms B56 to B112, and B87 to B145, were totally gutted of all bulkheads and used as a Troop Deck, also with hammock fittings.

The Third-Class Dining Saloon on "C" Deck was used as a Troop Mess Hall, while Third-Class Cabins C1 to C81, and C2 to C76, were used for crew accommodation. Tourist-Class Staterooms C78 to C138, and C83 to C145, were totally dismantled for use as a Troop Mess Deck, as were interchangeable Tourist/Third-Class Cabins D42 to D80, and D41 to D83. Below, on "E" Deck, the swimming pool was drained and fitted with shelves for use as a storeroom, while another storeroom, along with an armoury and rifle-racks, was installed in Lower Hold No. 4. On every deck throughout the ship, numerous loudspeakers, water fountains, latrines and other essential troop fittings were also installed.

Tragically, after requiring a full year of working around the clock to construct the *Mauretania's* interior accommodation in record time, more than 50 per cent of her staterooms were essentially destroyed in less than three weeks. In Sydney, a fire broke out in the starboard No. 5 hold on "E" Deck, where furniture, carpeting and bedding had been stored. This was apparently the result of the careless handling of an acetylene torch, but the damage was quickly repaired.*

Once conversion was completed, H.M.T. *Mauretania* began her First Period of war service by sailing from Sydney to Fremantle with 2,184 Australian troops on 5th May, 1940. In Fremantle, an additional 162 men joined the ship before leaving for Cape Town, where a number of nursing sisters also embarked. After making one stop in Freetown, and another in Greenock on 16th June, the *Mauretania* arrived in Liverpool on 22nd June.

While in Scotland, the Captain commented that, since leaving Sydney, the *Mauretania* had maintained a speed of only 19 knots, so as not to outpace the slower vessels in the convoy. He went on to state: "It might be worthwhile considering the formation of a 22 or 23 knot convoy in order to get the benefit of the faster type of ship. Such a convoy would cut down the long journey from Australia

* Less than two years later, the U.S.S. *Lafayette* (ex-*Normandie*) would be destroyed at her berth in New York by a fire that is said to have been accidentally started by an acetylene torch. However, since her conversion to a troopship was almost complete, and her entry into the war would most certainly have brought earlier victory to the Allies, many believe that the superliner was actually a victim of sabotage.

by almost 100 miles per day and in so doing would decrease the risk of damage from submarine attack."* Apparently his advice was well taken, as the following spring the *Mauretania* found herself taking part in one of the greatest convoys of all time, when she accompanied the *Queen Elizabeth*, the *Queen Mary*, the *Aquitania* and the *Nieuw Amsterdam* around Australia from Sydney to Fremantle. This was the ninth trooping voyage for the *Mauretania*, and began in Wellington on 7th April, 1941, when she had embarked 4,400 New Zealand troops before sailing to Sydney with the *Nieuw Amsterdam*. There they joined the *Queen Elizabeth* and the *Aquitania*. At Jervis Bay, the *Queen Mary* completed the convoy, which was now escorted by one heavy cruiser and several light cruisers. Carrying 22,000 servicemen, the most valuable fleet of merchant ships ever to sail together strictly maintained their columns 1,000 yards apart, with 800 yards separating those vessels in columns. The destination of the two "*Queens*" was Trincomalee, Ceylon, while the *Mauretania* would stop at Colombo before continuing on to Port Tewfik, to disembark her troops. From there, the *Mauretania* sailed on to Durban, arriving there on 1st June, 1941. Using Durban as her home port, the *Mauretania* would shuttle troops on her next 11 voyages between 10th June, 1941, and 16th June, 1942, from Durban to the ports of Suez, Port Tewfik, Aden and Bombay. Voyage No. 22 was the only exception, as Bombay was the final destination of that voyage.

On 28th June, 1942, the *Mauretania* left Durban with 3,000 German P.O.W.s, heading for Newport News via Port Elizabeth, Rio de Janeiro and Bermuda. At around 9 o'clock on the evening that the *Mauretania* anchored in Rio, it was discovered that about 30 P.O.W.s had managed to escape by breaking a sidelight which had been secured by an iron deadlight and welded bars. Obscured from view by the shadow of an overhead lifeboat, the men had slid down a rope of blankets, and were in the process of swimming ashore when they were spotted by patrol launches, who quickly returned them to the ship.

On previous voyages across the expansive Indian Ocean in the early part of the war, the *Mauretania* had been relatively safe from German submarines. With the entry of the Japanese into the war following their attack on Pearl Harbor, 7th December 1941, that margin of safety was greatly reduced. In comparison, Rio was never safe, as German submarines always seemed to be in the vicinity of that neutral port, hoping, perhaps, to claim the £50,000 reward Hitler was reported to have offered to the U-boat Captain who could sink the *Queen Mary*.

It was for this reason, as well as the problem of locating a safe refuelling port beyond the submarine-infested West Indies, that the *Mauretania's* stay in Rio was prolonged. However, around noon on 2nd September, only moments before the ship planned to leave, a message was received from United States Naval Authorities, advising: "Remain at anchor until further orders". At 3.15 p.m., British and American Routeing Officers boarded the ship and told the Captain that the Brazilian Air Force had spotted a German submarine outside the harbour at 10.30 that morning. As no escort for the *Mauretania* was available, it was decided after a quick conference to make a full-speed run for the open Atlantic through a narrow but deep channel between a number of small islands south of the harbour. In an exciting display of adept manoeuvring, the *Mauretania* then made a 24 knot dash, zigzagging hard-a-port then hard-a-starboard past the coastal islands, much to the astonishment of sunbathers, who least expected the ship, or the resulting great wash upon the shore.

Following her safe arrival in Newport News on 15th September, 1942, the *Mauretania* then left for Wellington on 7th October, making stops in Rio, Durban, Suez, Colombo, Fremantle and Sydney, before anchoring off New Zealand on 15th December. Yet, as lengthy as this voyage was, her longest was still to come.

On Christmas Eve, 1942, the *Mauretania* again left Wellington, this time destined for England by way of Honolulu, San Francisco, Honolulu again, Wellington, Fremantle, Bombay, Diego Suarez, Cape Town and Freetown, before arriving in Liverpool on 8th April, 1943. In total, 20,104 tons of oil and 28,194 tons of water would be consumed on this 36,454-mile voyage. In addition, 2,744,536 lbs. of troop supplies valued at £63,209 ($254,732.27) were to be consumed on board, including: 310,200 lbs. of flour and cereal; 108,449 lbs. of coffee, tea and sugar; 70,468 lbs. of bacon and ham; 129,124 lbs. of butter, eggs and milk powder; 184,507 lbs. of fresh

vegetables; 342,800 lbs. of potatoes; 525,916 lbs. of meats and 392,000 lbs. of soap and disinfectants. In addition to these "catering" supplies, the following items were handled by the Canteen: 368,325 bottles of cordials and minerals; 10,000 cigars; 35,302 ozs. of tobacco; 13,425,700 cigarettes and 849,579 miscellaneous items.

The preparation of food on all voyages, and especially this one, was an enormous undertaking. Each serviceman was fed on the "British Scale" of three times a day, with four sittings each for Breakfast (0700-1100 hrs), Lunch (1130-1530 hrs), and Dinner (1730-2130 hrs). Officers had their choice of three sittings daily for Breakfast (0730-1030 hrs), Lunch (1200-1500 hrs), and Dinner (1800-2100 hrs). Troop menus typically consisted of the following: Breakfast — Stewed fruit, fried egg and bacon, bread and butter, preserves and tea; Dinner — Roast pork with savoury sauce, purée of turnips, boiled potatoes, plum pudding with sweet sauce and coffee; Tea — Canned crayfish, potato, beetroot and onion salad, bread and butter, fresh fruit, jam and tea.

On 24th April, 1943, the *Mauretania* again departed from Liverpool and arrived in New York on 7th May. After three days of replenishing supplies, she was once again on her way to Colombo via Trinidad, Rio, Cape Town and Diego Suarez, arriving in Ceylon on 18th June. Eight days later, the *Mauretania* headed back to Liverpool on her 32nd trooping voyage, via Port Tewfik, Diego Suarez, Cape Town and Freetown. This was to be the last voyage in the First Period of her wartime career, having safely carried 127,938 servicemen 331,459 miles on 26 voyages.

The Second Period would consist of 20 North Atlantic round-trip voyages between 27th August, 1943, and 17th March, 1945, in which another 173,991 troops would be safely carried a total of 139,157 miles. Because of the very large numbers of American servicemen travelling in both directions, the 575 crew members and the permanent Service Staff of about 80 were under great strain, as many had worked on the ship continuously since the beginning of the war. In an attempt to provide some relief, "liberty" for a portion of the crew was staggered each trip, so that those on shore leave would rejoin the ship on the next voyage.

Statistics for one such voyage, No. 34, leaving Liverpool for Boston on 22nd September, and returning on 17th October, 1943, show that average speeds of 21.02 knots westbound and 21.53 knots eastbound were maintained over a distance of 7,253 miles. In peacetime, this speed would have been judged as quite good, but considering that approximately 16,000 servicemen were carried, along with 541,514 lbs. of food and 4,193 tons of water, not to mention the 4,380 tons of fuel oil, her performance was nothing short of remarkable.

With over 8,000 men on board at one time, the number of meals per person would be limited to the "American Scale" of only two per day. Breakfast for the troops would be served at six sittings (0630-1130 hrs), while Officers had four sittings (0700-1100 hrs). A typical breakfast would consist of compote of peaches, rolled oats with milk, grilled sausages with onion gravy, fresh bread, butter, marmalade and coffee. Supper for the troops was also served in six sittings (1530-2130 hrs), and in four sittings for Officers (1600-2000 hrs). A not unusual dinner would consist of roast beef with brown gravy, green peas, boiled potatoes, assorted cold meats, mixed pickles and cheese, fruit salad, fresh bread and butter, jam and coffee.

Following the completion of voyage No. 53, the *Mauretania* began the Third Period of her war service, which consisted of only nine voyages from Liverpool — three long round-trips through various zones*, and six North Atlantic round-trips. These nine voyages were nevertheless significant, as a total of 78,552 people were carried a distance of 98,132 miles. The first voyage of this period began on 4th April, 1945, when the *Mauretania* left Liverpool for Port Said, Suez, Bombay, Durban, Cape Town and Freetown, before returning to Liverpool on 30th May. During this voyage, the events that led to the end of the war in Europe had followed in quick succession. Hitler had committed suicide on 30th April; Berlin surrendered to the Soviets on 2nd May, followed by Germany's capitulation on 7th May. With "VE-Day" declared on 8th May, only the final stages

---

* University Archives, The University of Liverpool.

* According to an article in "Sea Breezes" (November, 1986), by J.H. Isherwood, the *Mauretania* also made a voyage to Singapore in August, 1946. Isherwood states that the return trip to Liverpool was made in 16 days 15 hours, with the average speed for the entire trip being 23.1 knots. Since more specific information regarding this voyage is not available, it has not been included in the above figures.

of the war with Japan remained.

The *Mauretania's* next trooping voyage, No. 55, was to take her around the world. Departing from Liverpool on 3rd July, 1945, she stopped in Cristobal, Pearl Harbor, Wellington, Sydney, Fremantle, Durban, Cape Town and Freetown before returning to Liverpool on 22nd September. In total, 28,662 miles were traversed in 81 days, with her actual ocean steaming time amounting to 56 days 6 hours and 30 minutes, which gave her an average of 509.28 miles covered for every day at sea. By the time she returned, the war was over. Japan had unconditionally surrendered on 16th August, after the United States had dropped atomic bombs on Hiroshima, on 6th August, and Nagasaki, on 9th August, 1945.

Although the war had ended, the *Mauretania* would remain in Government service to repatriate thousands of soldiers who had fought in Europe and North Africa. Following one more round-trip voyage from Liverpool to Bombay via Port Said and Suez, six more round-trip voyages were made across the Atlantic to bring American and Canadian servicemen home. The *Mauretania* even played an important part in conveying new British brides to both the States and the Dominion. On 19th August, 1946, the *Mauretania* left Liverpool for Halifax on her final Government voyage with Field Marshal Montgomery among her passengers. Upon the ship's return to Liverpool on 2nd September, 1946, she was handed back to the Builders for reconditioning. Without having rested throughout the entire war, the *Mauretania* had clearly demonstrated that under the most difficult conditions and in all kinds of weather, she had performed with outstanding reliability, much to the credit of Cammell Laird & Co. Ltd.

The task of reconditioning the *Mauretania* was a major one. Beginning on 9th September, 1946, an average of 1,500 men every day would be employed in restoring the great Cunarder to her pre-war magnificence. To those involved, the term "reconstructing" perhaps would have been more accurate than the term "reconditioning".

The first priority was to remove the guns, rockets, magazines, armour plating, and all other defensive equipment from the ship. All troop fittings, including plumbing and wiring, had then to be removed, before the difficult assignment of completely rebuilding over 300 staterooms, and restoring some 260 others, could begin. In addition, a total of 31,103 linear feet of damaged teak deck planking had to be replaced before all exterior decks could be recaulked.

In late September, a huge crane named "Mammoth" was used to lift the 76-ton aft funnel off the ship, so that new air pre-heaters for the four after boiler uptakes could be installed. The casing tops of four of the ship's six main turbines were also opened and rotors lifted for inspection. Both main gear wheels and pinions for the port and starboard engines were also inspected at this time. Both main condensers were cleaned and tested, as were the six boilers, the furnaces of which required the replacement of almost 15,000 firebricks. The entire electrical system was completely checked and tested, as were the air-conditioning systems. In Lower Hold No. 4, 500 tons of sand ballast and 340 tons of pig iron that had been added for war service were also removed, while an additional 360 tons of pig iron were removed from Lower Hold No. 3.

Meanwhile, work began on refinishing the thousands of sq. ft. of exotic wood veneers in the public rooms, along with the reinstallation of their original decorative fittings. More than 75 per cent of the original furnishings, involving over 10,000 pieces of furniture that had been stored in the United States and Australia, were located and shipped back to Liverpool. From there they would be sent to firms in London, Birmingham, Nottingham and Liverpool for reconditioning. Over 20,000 sq. yds. of ruboleum was relaid throughout the ship. The swimming pool, also, was entirely relined with 10,000 new titles. At this time, the opportunity was taken to implement interior alterations, including the following: the moving of the Barber Shop to the Main Deck so that a Gyro Compass could be installed in that space; the installation of a Midland Bank branch in the Main Entrance on the Promenade Deck; a cocktail bar in the Cabin Veranda Café; and totally redesigned and enlarged quarters for the 600 crew. In addition to a revised tonnage of 35,677, passenger accommodation would now comprise 475 in First, 390 in Cabin and 300 in Tourist Class.

On 22nd February, 1947, the *Mauretania* was moved into the Gladstone Graving Dock so that her propellers and rudder could be inspected, and the hull bottom cleared, repaired and repainted. The rust-streaked grey hull and superstructure, as well as deckhouses, funnels and masts were also scaled and wire-broomed down to the steel, before Cunard's colours could be restored with ten tons of

paint which was applied in four coats.*

With reconditioning completed, at 2.15 p.m. on 15th April, 1947, Cammell Laird officially handed the *Mauretania* over to the Cunard White Star Line. Given the extent of the reconditioning, it is not surprising that the total cost for the work amounted to £1,643,809.13s.8d ($6,624,552.60), or 82.53 per cent of the ship's original cost in pounds sterling.†

To celebrate the reinstatement of the "new" *Mauretania* into North Atlantic service, a two-and-a-half-day "shakedown" cruise through the Irish Sea was planned by the Company. On the evening of 18th April, 1947, approximately 400 guests boarded the ship at Princes Landing Stage in Liverpool, and at 10.30 the following morning an immaculate *Mauretania* cleared the Liverpool Bar. However, the weather would not be favourable for this voyage, for after passing north of Skye, threatening conditions forced her to retreat home. Gale-force winds prohibited refuge in the River Mersey when she arrived off the Bar on 21st April, so the *Mauretania* sought shelter, first off Anglesey, then off Bardsey Island. Still unsafe, as her anchors were being dragged, no alternative remained but to ride out the storm on the open sea. When the weather cleared, the *Mauretania* arrived back in Liverpool on 24th April, having been at sea for five days. As she was scheduled to leave on her post-war maiden transatlantic voyage in only two days, much work needed to be done in order to ready her on time.

In keeping with Cunard's tradition of punctuality, the *Mauretania* kept her sailing date, and arrived in New York on 2nd May. When she returned to Liverpool on 10th June, she had set a new record for herself of 5 days, 12 hours and 30 minutes, having made the eastward crossing at an average speed of 24.33 knots. On her second voyage, the *Mauretania* returned to Southampton, where she was paired with the *Queen Elizabeth* on the Southampton-Cherbourg-New York run until the *Queen Mary* was ready to resume her role on 31st July, 1947.**

Once the *Queen Mary* was in service, the new route of the *Mauretania* was altered to Southampton-Le Havre-Cobh-New York. Minimum fares to or from British ports were: First Class — £80.13s ($325); Cabin Class — £52.2s ($210); Tourist Class — £39.14s ($160); and servants accompanying their employers in First Class — £64.11s ($260). These rates were slightly higher for the French port of Le Havre.

On 20th August, 1947, the first transatlantic liner of post-war design for any company, Cunard's *Media*, left Liverpool for New York on her maiden voyage. With dimensions of 518ft. b.p. (531ft. o.l.), 70ft. breadth of beam and 13,345 G.R.T., the *Media* would be joined on that run by her new mate, the *Parthia*, on 10th April, 1948. Only 17 G.R.T. greater than the *Media*, the *Parthia* was the first ship built for Cunard by Harland & Wolff of Belfast, and both ships would have capacity for 250 First-Class passengers. In May, 1948, the newly reconditioned *Britannic* would join these two ships following her post-war refit.††

Beginning with the winter of 1947, the *Mauretania* assumed her pre-war schedule of two-week Caribbean "Sunshine Cruises",

---

* During the war, the *Mauretania* was involved in numerous minor collisions which required repairs to the hull plating. These included damage caused by: docking in Fremantle, 8th September, 1940; contact with the tanker *Alfred Olsen* in Bombay, March, 1941; docking in Norfolk, 1st October, 1942; in Wellington, February, 1943; in Le Havre, August, 1943; contact with the tug *J.W. Martin* in Halifax, 15th December, 1943; contact with the tanker *Hat Creek* near New York, 8th January, 1944; and docking in Liverpool, May, 1944.

† The breakdown of responsibility for paying the bulk of this amount to Cammell Laird was as follows: Ministry — £1,532,762.8s.10d ($6,177,032.40); Underwriters — £52,396.9s.4d ($211,157.69); Cunard White Star — £56,491.15s.3d ($227,661.75).

** Throughout the war, both "*Queens*" had carried a remarkable total of 1,622,054 passengers, logging 1,150,406 miles in the process. Following Government service, the cost of reconditioning the *Queen Elizabeth* alone amounted to £2,049,774.11s 11d ($10,248,872). It is sadly ironic that Sir Percy Bates died unexpectedly on the very morning the *Queen Elizabeth* departed on her post-war maiden voyage, 16th October, 1946.

†† Converted into a troop transport in March, 1940, the *Georgic* was gutted by fire following a German air raid off Port Tewfik on 14th July, 1941. Salvaged, she re-entered trooping service in December, 1944. Now owned by the Ministry of Transport, the *Georgic* was converted into a one-class emigrant ship in 1948, for use on the Australian run. Chartered for North Atlantic voyages by Cunard between 1950 and 1954, the *Georgic* was sold to shipbreakers in 1955.

making five from New York to Nassau, La Guaira (Caracas), Curacao, Colon and Havana. With rates starting from £98.00 ($395.00), passengers could expect a full day ashore at each port, with an extended stay of two days in Havana.

On 4th January, 1949, the new *Caronia* (II), which had been ordered as mate to the *Mauretania*, commenced commercial service from Southampton to New York. Christened by Princess Elizabeth on 30th October, 1947, the 24-knot *Caronia* had dimensions of 687ft. b.p. (715ft. o.l.), 91ft. breadth of beam and 34,183 G.R.T. Slightly smaller than the *Mauretania*, the newest Cunarder had accommodation for 580 First-Class and 350 Cabin-Class passengers. Known immediately to the public as "The Green Goddess", because her hull and superstructure were painted three shades of green, the *Caronia* was also distinctive in that her single, massive funnel was the largest of any ship afloat.

In December, 1949, the Cunard Steamship Company Ltd. announced that they would be taking over the entire North Atlantic operations of Cunard White Star, having purchased all outstanding White Star shares in 1947, at a price of £2 for every £1 share. Company profits had been phenomenal following the war, largely due to the enormous capacity of the "*Queens*". In the first year of commercial service, the *Queen Elizabeth* alone carried 102,292 passengers on 23 round-trip voyages.

With the "*Queens*" again working for the Company, it was also announced in December, 1949, that the *grande dame* of the Atlantic, the *Aquitania*, would now be finally withdrawn after serving faithfully for 35½ years. Her retirement had been planned to coincide with the introduction of the *Queen Elizabeth* into commercial service, but the outbreak of the Second World War had given her an extra ten years of life.

Cunard continued their post-war building programme with the maiden voyages of the 21,637 G.R.T. *Saxonia* (II) on 2nd September, 1954, and her sister, the 21,717 G.R.T. *Ivernia* (II) on 1st July, 1955. Built for the Liverpool/London-Quebec-Montreal run, these vessels would be joined by the 21,947 G.R.T. *Carinthia* (V) on 27th June, 1956, and by the 21,989 G.R.T. *Sylvania* (V) on 5th June, 1957.

Although windfall profits reached historic levels in the mid-1950s, the tide was beginning to turn for Cunard. With every year following the end of the Second World War, the number of people who chose to fly across the Atlantic grew. Eventually, this inevitable trend would be accelerated by the introduction of commercial jet aircraft* which attracted still greater numbers by further reducing travel time. Slow to accept this fact, the Directors of Cunard at least realized that cruising was becoming more popular, so the *Mauretania* returned to the Gladstone Dock on 3rd October, 1957, for another major overhaul which, this time, would include the extension of the air-conditioning system to all parts of the ship. By the time work was completed in December, at a cost of about £291,666 ($1,400,000), Company Officials were beginning to realize that above the high cost of annual overhauls, regular maintenance and operating costs, coupled with declining profits, consideration still had to be given to depreciation. Specifically, the annual depreciation of the *Mauretania* was calculated to be £99,584, or £272.16s per day. On 31st December, 1956, the "book value" of the ship was listed as £242,815 ($678,910.74). By 31st December, 1957, that amount was reduced to only £143,231 ($400,187.41), and by following the usual practice, that amount would be further reduced by £43,231 ($121,479.11) to remain at the base level of £100,000 ($279,400) by the end of 1958. In comparison, the scrap value of the ship was estimated at that time to be about £200,000 ($558,800).

Freshly refurbished, the *Mauretania* sailed from Southampton to New York on 17th January, 1958, so that she could commence her seasonal West Indies itinerary. Beginning on 11th February, her first totally air-conditioned cruise involved the visiting of 10 ports in 18 days. Prices for this 6,185-mile trip began at £186.17s ($525) for an inside cabin on "C" Deck with bed and upper berth, to £498.5s ($1,400) for an outside stateroom on the Main Deck with two beds. Other cruises that season were as short as five ports in 12 days, with prices ranging from £112.2s ($315), to £275.16s ($775).

In an effort to tap the booming airline business, Cunard acquired Eagle Airways Ltd. in 1959, renaming the company Cunard Eagle. At first glance, this decision appeared to be a wise one, for during the peak North Atlantic travel season that year, 55 per cent, or 1,193,000 people, chose to fly in comparison with 957,000 who

chose to sail. By June, 1962, negotiations were finalized for the acquisition of 30 per cent of British Overseas Airways Corporation at a cost of £8.5 million. The new company would now be B.O.A.C.-Cunard Ltd., but after only moderate success it was sold in 1966 at a £3 million profit to offset the losses incurred following the strike that year by the National Union of Seamen.

Seemingly unaffected by air travel, the *Mauretania* continued to maintain her high standard of excellent, reliable service. Although now 21 years old, she still made consistently fast passages relative to her designed speed. A not untypical example was one voyage from Southampton to New York via Le Havre and Cobh, departing on Friday, 5th August, 1960. The passage to New York was made in only 5 days 1 hour and 18 minutes, at an average speed of 22.94 knots. With 578, 580 and 585 nautical miles logged on three separate days, her performance was anything but average.

While undergoing her annual overhaul at Southampton in the late autumn of 1962, the *Mauretania* was repainted the same three shades of "cruising green" as her mate, the *Caronia*. With the new look came a new itinerary. The Directors had decided that in 1963, the *Mauretania* would cruise the Mediterranean, planning ten voyages from New York to Naples with stops at Gibraltar, Cannes and Genoa. On the first of these voyages, the "Maury" left New York on 28th March, 1963, with 676 passengers. Unfortunately, this route proved to be a poor choice for Cunard, due to the popularity of the "Italia" ships. After arriving in New York on 3rd October, having completed her eighth nine-day voyage from Naples, it was decided to cancel the remaining two voyages.

Early that same year, the *Saxonia* and *Ivernia* were completely reconditioned for cruising, and renamed the *Carmania* (II) and the *Franconia* (VI). Like the *Caronia* and the *Mauretania*, the "new" *Carmania* and the *Franconia* were also painted in "cruising green".

After a short overhaul in Liverpool, the *Mauretania* returned to the Southampton-Le Havre-Cobh-New York run in 1964, interspersed with voyages to the Caribbean, the Mediterranean and the North Cape of Norway, as well as one private charter from Southampton to Milford Haven for the opening of an oil terminal. The *Mauretania* would continue her eclectic itinerary in 1965 which, between the Southampton to New York runs, included a "European Cruise" on 5th July, and a special six-day charter trip to Lisbon beginning on 6th September. On 15th September, the *Mauretania* left New York on a 56-day cruise through the Mediterranean and the Black Sea. This was to be her last, as it was announced during the voyage that the ship would be retired upon arrival at Southampton on 10th November.

Actually, the ship had already been sold to the Sheffield firm of Thomas W. Ward Ltd. for demolition at Inverkeithing. Newspapers had reported only months earlier that Cunard planned to dispose of the ship before the 1966 season began, as no sailings had been scheduled for that year. However, it had been anticipated that the 26-year-old ship would be sold, not scrapped, as she had only recently passed her four-year inspection survey. Often criticized for being considerably slower than the 30-knot "*Queens*", the *Mauretania* was still some 4 knots faster than the new *Saxonia*-Class quartet. The *Mauretania* had also earned the reputation amongst her passengers and crew as being not only a "happy ship", but also a steady ship — the steadiest ever built for the Company. But times had changed, for the concept of cruising in the late 1930s was very different from cruising in the 1960s, and Cunard now regarded her as a "misfit" and a "loner", as well as hopelessly outdated. Like her namesake, time had passed her by — she was a victim of circumstances; so the Directors decided that, instead of continually spending money in an effort to modernize the ship, it would be less expensive in the long run to simply build another.

As early as the late 1950s, plans had been discussed for a replacement for the "*Queens*", which by then were rapidly ageing. Tentatively dubbed the "Q3", the proposed 75,000 G.R.T. vessel would have been only a newer version of the "*Queens*", designed exclusively for the North Atlantic run. However, this plan was soon to be abandoned for a more versatile vessel of smaller dimensions, which could just as easily alternate between cruising or transatlantic sailings. Plans then proceeded for the "Q4" (later *Queen Elizabeth 2*), and by the summer of 1963, negotiations had been completed for partial financing of the £25,427,000 ($71,195,600) project by the Government, in the amount of £17,600,000 ($49,280,000) at 4.5 per cent interest, payable upon delivery of the ship.*

---

* Pan American Airways inaugurated a jet service between New York and London on 26th October, 1958. This would also mark the last year that the number of people flying across the Atlantic would be less than those travelling by sea.

* According to Messrs. Warwick and Flayhart in their book *QE2*, the Government increased the amount of the loan to £24,000,000 in order to help meet the final first cost figure of £29,091,000 ($69,527,490).

On 30th December, 1964, the contract to build the *Queen Elizabeth 2* was signed by John Brown & Company, and on 5th July, 1965, the keel was laid. However, as building capital was needed immediately, Cunard mortgaged five liners and six cargo vessels to a consortium of British banks. This was still not enough, as before tax refunds the Company would be facing a loss of £14,100,000 between the years 1960 and 1965, with a net loss of £1,800,000 in 1965 alone. Regretfully, the *Mauretania* would be among the first to go.

On 20th November, 1965, the *Mauretania* made her final voyage. Arriving three days later at Inverkeithing, she submitted to the solemn process of her demolition, which began almost immediately.

Born a victim of her namesake, the *Mauretania* completed her career in the green cruising livery of her mate, the *Caronia*. In addition, as is so often the case, the *Mauretania* had unfortunately become a casualty of the changing times. But she was a distinctive vessel with her own kind of charm which had made her a perennial favourite among her many devoted passengers.

MARK D. WARREN
NEW YORK

ACKNOWLEDGEMENTS

I would like to acknowledge the assistance of those people who helped me in compiling the photographs and data in the new section, as well as in the production of the book. They include: in New York, Mr. Tim Castle of the Cunard Steamship Company; in Chatham, New Jersey, Mr. Frank Bujjoni (Ret'd) of the Cunard Steamship Company; in Washington, D.C., Mr. John Morton of the Federal Reserve Board; in Newport News, Virginia, Mr. R. Thomas Crew, Jr. and Mrs. Tammy Priddy at the Mariners' Museum; in Lisbon, Portugal, Mr. Guy Plamondon; in Cambridge, Massachusetts, Mr. Kenneth Gaulin; in Woodstock, Ontario, Canada, Mr. Jon Hiscox; and in London, England, Messrs. Martin Taylor and Terry Charman of the Imperial War Museum.

Special thanks for most generous assistance go to: Mr. Jan Loeff of Coral Gables, Florida; Mr. Everett Viez of Boynton Beach, Florida; Laura F. Brown of the Steamship Historical Society of America, Inc., University of Baltimore Library, Baltimore, Maryland; Mrs. Alma Topen of the Archives, University of Glasgow, Glasgow, Scotland; Messrs. Andrew Bowcock and Frank Lindstrom of Cammell Laird Shipbuilders Ltd., of Birkenhead, England; Mr. Thomas W. Coffey of New York City; Mr. Frank A. Trumbour of Ridgewood, New Jersey, for the loan of his original *Shipbuilder* book used in the publication of this reprint; Mrs. Andrea D. Owens of the University Archives, The University of Liverpool, Liverpool, England; Mrs. Catherine Stecchini of Princeton, New Jersey; Mr. William Adams, Senior Editor, and Mr. Darryl Reach, Editorial Director of Patrick Stephens Ltd., Wellingborough, England.

PHOTOGRAPHIC SOURCES

The Cunard Archives at The University of Liverpool supplied the photographs on pages xxii, 108, Plates A, B and VIII–XXXI, with the following exceptions which were supplied by The Steamship Historical Society of America, Inc. (Everett E. Viez Collection), University of Baltimore Library, Baltimore, Maryland: Plates X, XII, XIII, XXI and XXIX. In addition, The Steamship Historical Society of America, Inc. (Everett E. Viez Collection), also supplied the following photographs: the new Frontispiece, pages xviii, 111, Plate C and page 2, with the exception of Fig. 4, which was supplied by The Mariners' Museum, Newport News, Virginia. The photograph on page 77, and the photographs found in Plates VII, XXXII and XXXIII are from the Private Collection of Everett E. Viez in Boynton Beach, Florida. Cammell Laird Archives, Cammell Laird Shipbuilders Ltd., Birkenhead, England, supplied the photograph on page 44, as well as the blueprint plan (Plate D), and the photograph on page 103 is from the booklet "R.M.S. Mauretania", n.p., n.d. (circa 1939). Front cover: Glasgow University Archives, Glasgow, Scotland. Back cover: the Private Collection of Frank A. Trumbour, Ridgewood, New Jersey, U.S.A.

BIBLIOGRAPHY

"Mauretania" Launch Booklet, Cunard White Star Ltd., n.p., 1938. The "New York Herald Tribune", New York, 1939. "Liverpool Daily Post", Liverpool, 1939. Winchester, Clarence and Bird, P.R., *The Queen Elizabeth*: Winchester Publications Ltd., London, 1947. *The Cunard White Star Quadruple-Screw Liner Queen Mary*: first published by the Shipbuilder Press, June, 1936, and reprinted by Patrick Stephens Ltd., London, 1972. "The British Economy Key Statistics 1900-1970": published for the London & Cambridge Economic Service by Times Newspapers Ltd., n.p., n.d. Hughes, Tom, *The Blue Riband of the Atlantic*: Patrick Stephens Ltd., Cambridge, 1973. Konings, Chris, *"Queen Elizabeth" at War*: Patrick Stephens Ltd., Wellingborough, 1985. Warwick, Ronald and Flayhart, William III, *QE2*: W.W. Norton & Co., New York and London, 1985. Johnson, Howard, *The Cunard Story*: Whittet Books Ltd., London, 1987. Warren, Mark, *The Cunard Turbine-Driven Quadruple-Screw Atlantic Liner "Mauretania"*: first published by "Engineering" in 1907 and reprinted by Patrick Stephens Ltd., Wellingborough, 1987. De Kerbrech, Richard P. and Williams, David L., *Cunard White Star Liners of the 1930s*: Conway Maritime Press Ltd., London, 1988. Warren, Mark, *The Quadruple-Screw Turbine-Driven Cunard Liner "Aquitania"*: first published by "Engineering" in 1914 and reprinted by Patrick Stephens Ltd., Wellingborough, 1988.

In addition to the above reference books, the following Collections provided invaluable information in the form of blueprints, brochures, photographs and shipbuilding records: Glasgow University Archives, Glasgow, Scotland; Cammell Laird Archives, Cammell Laird Shipbuilders Ltd., Birkenhead, England; the Private Collection of Everett E. Viez, Boynton Beach, Florida; The Steamship Historical Society of America, Inc., University of Baltimore Library, Baltimore, Maryland; the Private Collection of Frank A. Trumbour, Ridgewood, New Jersey; and — most especially — the Cunard Archives, The University of Liverpool, Liverpool, England.

LIST OF ADDITIONAL ILLUSTRATIONS

"Mauretania" Ready for Launching.

MAURETANIA
SOUVENIR NUMBER
THE SHIPBUILDER AND MARINE ENGINE-BUILDER
Extreme reliability, highest degree of separating efficiency and lowest maintenance costs are good reasons why
CUNARD WHITE STAR LINE
have again fitted
DE LAVAL OIL PURIFIERS
MAURETANIA
T.S.S. Mauretania
DE LAVAL
OIL PURIFIERS
WORLD-WIDE ORGANISATION
BRITISH ISLES: ALFA-LAVAL CO., LTD. GREAT WEST ROAD, BRENTFORD, MIDDX.
FRANCE: Societe Alfa-Laval, 10, Rue Charles V, Paris (IV).
GERMANY: Bergedorfer Eisenwerk A.-G., Bergedorf-Hamburg.
ITALY: Societa Alfa - Laval, Via Farneti 5, Milan.
SWEDEN: Aktiebolaget Separator, Stockholm I.

New York World's Fair

The New "Mauretania"

This magnificent new 34,000-ton liner is an outstanding achievement of 1939 . . . she has no fewer than ten decks and in all classes—cabin, tourist and third—the latest refinements in modern ship luxury have been introduced.

Next Sailing
WEDNESDAY, JULY 19
Southampton—Cherbourg—New York

Later Sailings from Southampton
AUG. 12, SEPT. 9, OCT. 7

SEE AMERICA THIS YEAR

This is the ideal year for a holiday trip to the United States and Canada . . . New York is more inviting than ever with its spectacular World's Fair . . . and Canada in gala mood after the historic Royal Visit . . . excursion sailings from 28th June to 22nd July, and Sept. 25th to Oct. 28th . . . "QUEEN MARY," "AQUITANIA," new "MAURETANIA" and fleet of famous ocean liners.

ATLANTIC EXCURSION FARE
from **£27.5s.** return
(*Third Class*)

WRITE FOR ILLUSTRATED FOLDERS to your local agent or Cunard White Star Ltd., Pier Head, Liverpool, or 26/27, Cockspur Street, S.W.1, and 88, Leadenhall Street, London, E.C.3

Cunard White Star

THE NEW CUNARD WHITE STAR LINER "MAURETANIA."

"The Shipbuilder and Marine Engine-builder."

June, 1939.

Cabin-class Lounge.

MAURETANIA SOUVENIR NUMBER MAURETANIA SOUVENIR NUMBER MAURETANIA SOUVENIR NU... ...RETANIA SOUVENIR NUMBER
SOUVENIR NUMBER MAURETANIA SOUVENIR NUMBER MAURETANIA SOUVENIR NUMBER ...VENIR NUMBER MAURETANIA
NUMBER MAURETANIA SOUVENIR NUMBER MAURETANIA SOUVENIR NUMBER ...BER MAURETANIA SOUVENIR
MAURETANIA SOUVENIR NUMBER MAURETANIA SOUVENIR NUMBER ...ETANIA SOUVENIR NUMBER
SOUVENIR NUMBER MAURETANIA SOUVENIR NUMBER MA... ...NIR NUMBER MAURETANIA
NUMBER MAURETANIA SOUVENIR NUMBER MA... ...ER MAURETANIA SOUVENIR

THE CUNARD WHITE STAR NORTH ATLANTIC

TWIN - SCREW GEARED - TURBINE PASSENGER STEAMSHIP

"MAURETANIA"

(35,739 TONS GROSS)

The largest merchant vessel ever constructed in England

THE SHIPBUILDER AND MARINE ENGINE-BUILDER

Proprietor & Editor—A. G. HOOD, A.Inst.N.A.

SOUVENIR
NUMBER
JUNE
1939

THE SHIPBUILDER AND MARINE E... ...ER THE SHIPBUILDER AND MARINE ENGINE-BUILDER THE SH GINE-BUILDER
JUNE 1939 JUNE 1939 JUNE 1939 J... ...E 1939 JUNE 1939 JUNE 1939 JUNE 1939 JUNE 1939 JUNE 1939 JUNE 1939 1939 JUNE 1939
THE SHIPBUILDER AND MARINE ENGINE-BUILDER THE SHIPBUILDER AND MARINE ENGINE-BUILDER THE SH GINE-BUILDER
JUNE 1939 JUNE 1939 JUNE 1939 JUNE 1939 JUNE 1939 JUNE 1939 JUNE 1939 JUNE 1939 JUNE 1939 1939 JUNE 1939
THE SHIPBUILDER AND MARINE ENGINE-BUILDER THE SHIPBUILDER AND MARINE ENGINE-BUILDER THE SH GINE-BUILDER
JUNE 1939 JUNE 1939 JUNE 1939 JUNE 1939 JUNE 1939 JUNE 1939 JUNE 1939 JUNE 1939 JUNE 1939 1939 JUNE 1939

Published by THE SHIPBUILDER PRESS at 47, VICTORIA STREET, LONDON, S.W.1, and TOWNSVILLE
HOUSE, NEWCASTLE-ON-TYNE, 6, ENGLAND. Made and printed in England by CHARLES BIRCHALL
AND SONS, LTD., 17, JAMES STREET, LIVERPOOL, 2, and 9/11, FENCHURCH AVE., LONDON, E.C.3.

FOUNDED IN JULY, 1906.

EDITED BY A. G HOOD.

THE CUNARD WHITE STAR TWIN-SCREW NORTH ATLANTIC LINER "MAURETANIA."

Lady Bates,

who launched the "Mauretania" on the 28th July, 1938.

Fig. 1.—"Mauretania" (1907).

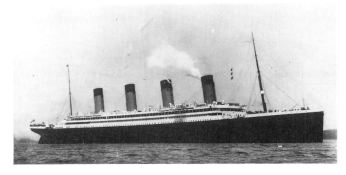

Fig. 2.—"Olympic".

Fig. 3.—"Berengaria".

Fig. 4.—"Aquitania".

Fig. 5.—"Majestic".

Fig. 6.—"Homeric".

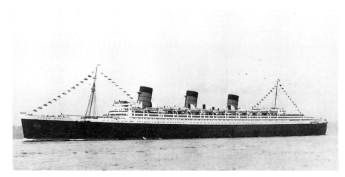

Fig. 7.—"Queen Mary".

Fig. 8.—"Queen Elizabeth".

Notable Cunard & White Star Vessels.

THE OWNERS OF THE "MAURETANIA."

THE CUNARD WHITE STAR, LIMITED—the owners of the great new North Atlantic steamship to which this special number of *The Shipbuilder and Marine Engine-builder* is dedicated—is an amalgamation of the organisations long known as the Cunard Line and the White Star Line, and the company thus formed on the 10th May, 1934, became the owners of the combined North Atlantic fleets of both the original concerns. The *Queen Mary* (at present the largest completed unit of the fleet) was then on the stocks at Clydebank, and the still larger *Queen Elizabeth* (now being completed afloat at Clydebank) and the *Mauretania* (recently delivered from Birkenhead) had not then been ordered.

THE FOUNDING OF THE CUNARD AND WHITE STAR LINES.

In 1837, when Queen Victoria ascended the throne, regular steamship communication between the European and American Continents was a dream of the future rather than an actual reality. Samuel Cunard, however, was convinced that the "vision splendid" was no mere chimera, but a practical proposition whose difficulties would be overcome by suitable vessels having adequate engine power, which would enable them successfully to combat the trying conditions of Atlantic voyaging. Cunard, who came from Halifax, Nova Scotia, was a judge of men as well as of ships, and hence his partners in laying the foundations of the Cunard Line were George Burns and David McIver, the former a shrewd Scot engaged in the coasting trade between England, Scotland and Ireland, and the latter a well-known shipowner residing in Liverpool. The new Atlantic steamship service was inaugurated on the 4th July, 1840, or almost exactly 99 years before the new *Mauretania* began her maiden voyage to New York—on the 17th June, 1939.

The White Star flag was first flown by a line of sailing ships founded about 1850, and mainly engaged in the Australian trade. In 1867 the owner of this line retired and the fleet passed into the hands of the late Thomas Henry Ismay. In 1869 he formed the Oceanic Steam Navigation Company to establish a service of steamships for the Atlantic passenger service. The following year Mr. Ismay was joined in the management of the company by Mr. William Imrie, the title of the managing firm being altered to Ismay, Imrie & Co.

FAMOUS SHIPS OF THE CUNARD LINE.

The ships owned and operated on the North Atlantic for well-nigh a century by the Cunard and White Star Lines may rightly be regarded as marking the stepping stones in the progress of naval architecture and marine engineering.

The pioneer vessel of the Cunard Line was the wooden paddle steamship *Britannia*, of 1,139 tons, launched at Greenock in February, 1840. She was 207ft. long, 34ft. 2in. broad, and 22ft. 4in. deep ; her indicated horse-power was 740, her cargo capacity 225 tons, and she was registered to carry 115 cabin passengers. Her sea speed was 8·4 knots, and the coal consumption was calculated at 38 tons per day. The three sister ships composing the remainder of the first fleet were the *Arcadia*, *Caledonia* and *Columbia*, and the run from Liverpool to Boston used to occupy between 14 and 15 days.

Some seven years later, following the making of a new contract with the British Government, the construction of the wooden steamships *America*, *Niagara*, *Canada* and *Europa* was begun, these vessels being each 251ft. long, with a gross register of 1,825 tons. Their speed was about a knot faster than the pioneer ships of the Line, but the designers adhered to the paddle-wheel. Indeed it was not until 1852 that the Cunard Company decided to introduce the screw propeller in the auxiliary service to the Mediterranean which had then been commenced.

The next important development in the Cunard fleet was the substitution of iron for wood as the material used in the construction of the hull, their first iron steamship being the *Persia*, built in 1855, and then the largest merchant ship afloat. This steamship was 376ft. long, of 3,300 tons gross, and with a speed of 12·9 knots.

In 1867 the screw propeller succeeded the paddle-wheel in the Cunard Atlantic service, the first two screw-propelled

steamships for this traffic being the *China* and *Russia*. The *Russia* was 358ft. long, and in actual service made 13 knots on a coal consumption of 90 tons per day.

In 1879 the adoption of compound steam engines as the propulsive agents employed in the units of the Cunard fleet was completed.

The *Servia* marked the next important forward step, and when launched in 1881 she was the largest and most powerful steamship so far constructed with the exception of the historic *Great Eastern*. The *Servia* was 515ft. long, 52ft. broad and 40ft. 9in. deep, with a gross tonnage of 7,391 and an indicated horse-power of 9,500. Her speed was 16·5 knots, with a coal consumption of 190 tons per day.

The *Umbria* and *Etruria* (1885) followed the *Aurania*, and with their sea speed of 19·5 knots held the speed records for both the eastward and westward trips for many years. These single-screw vessels with compound steam engines were superseded in 1893 by the twin-screw express steamships *Campania* and *Lucania* with triple-expansion engines. They were vessels of about 12,950 tons gross and 27,650 I.H.P., and the last-named made record passages eastward and westward in 5 days 8 hours and 5 days 7 hours respectively. The *Campania* maintained the weekly mail service with the *Lusitania* and first *Mauretania* until the *Aquitania* was put into commission in May, 1914.

The triple-screw *Carmania* (19,524 tons gross), the first of the Cunard fleet to be fitted with steam-turbine engines, and the twin-screw *Caronia* (19,687 tons), fitted with quadruple-expansion steam engines, and both having a speed of 18·5 knots, were put into service in 1905.

Direct-driving steam turbines were also adopted as the propulsive agent in the quadruple-screw express steamships *Lusitania* and the first *Mauretania* (30,396 and 30,695 tons gross respectively), vessels which will be long remembered for their epoch-making sea speed of 26 knots and shaft horse-power of 70,000. These two famous sister ships entered the Atlantic service in 1907. The *Lusitania* was torpedoed off Kinsale Head, on the 7th May, 1915, and the *Mauretania* was sold for breaking up in April, 1935. Some further particulars of the first *Mauretania* are given in the chapter on "The Old and New Mauretanias."

The quadruple-screw steamship *Aquitania* was delivered by her Clydebank builders in May, 1914, after running sea trials during which she reached with ease a speed of 24 knots. This vessel has a length B.P. of 865ft., a breadth moulded of 97ft., a depth moulded of 64ft. 6in., and a gross tonnage of 45,647. Her four sets of direct-driving turbines were designed to give a shaft horse-power of 60,000. At the time of writing, the *Aquitania* is still doing splendid work for her owners in the North Atlantic express service.

The advent in the North Atlantic service in 1936 of the quadruple-screw geared-turbine steamship *Queen Mary* will be so fresh in the minds of our readers that only a passing reference to this famous express liner need be made here. With a gross tonnage of 81,235, this vessel holds the North Atlantic records in both directions, making the westward crossing at an average speed of 30·99 knots and the eastward crossing at 31·69 knots last year. It is expected that the still larger *Queen Elizabeth*, which will take up her service next year, will have an even greater turn of speed than the *Queen Mary*.

NOTABLE WHITE STAR LINERS.

Turning now to the historic ships of the White Star Line, the pioneer vessel was the first *Oceanic*, launched at Belfast in August, 1870, and taking up her service on the North Atlantic early in the following year. She was 420ft. long, 41ft. broad and 31ft. deep, with a tonnage of 3,707, and she embodied a number of improvements previously unknown in the Atlantic trade. Her propelling machinery consisted of two sets of four-cylinder compound steam engines supplied by Messrs. Maudslay, Sons & Field, of London, and working on a single shaft. Each set consisted of two 41-in. diameter high-pressure cylinders and two 78-in. diameter low-pressure cylinders, with a stroke of 60in. Steam was supplied by 12 boilers, having in all 24 furnaces and working

The Rt. Hon. Lord Essendon,
Director of the Cunard White Star, Limited.

Sir Percy E. Bates, Bt., G.B.E.,
Chairman of the Cunard White Star, Limited.

Sir Thomas Brocklebank, Bt.,
Director of the Cunard White Star, Limited.

Sir Thomas Royden, Bt., C.H.,
Director of the Cunard White Star, Limited.

at 65lb per sq. in. pressure. The speed of this vessel was about 14 knots, with a coal consumption of 65 tons per day.

Following the *Oceanic* came a long list of notable vessels. Specially noteworthy were the first *Britannic* and *Germanic*, built in 1874 and 1875. These vessels had a speed of over 16 knots, and reduced the time of the Atlantic passage to less than 7½ days. The *Germanic*, with new engines and boilers, made the passage in 6 days 21 hours in August, 1896. No further development in the direction of high speed was attempted by the White Star Line until, in 1889, they placed in service the successful 20-knot vessels *Teutonic* and the first *Majestic*, their first twin-screw steamships, both of which, almost up to the advent of the *Olympic* in 1911, were regularly employed between Southampton and New York.

In 1899 an important stage was reached by the completion of the second *Oceanic*, a vessel surpassing in dimensions any previously constructed and the first ship to exceed the *Great Eastern* in length. No attempt was made in her design, however, to emulate the high speed attained by the contemporary Cunard and German record-breakers. It was considered that a speed of 20 knots was sufficient to make the vessel a reliable seven-day ship, and in this respect she amply fulfilled expectations. Following the *Oceanic*, a return was made to slower-speed ships of 16 to 17 knots, but the increase in size was maintained. The largest vessel of the Line prior to the completion of the *Olympic* was the *Adriatic*, built in 1907, her dimensions being 709ft. 3in. by 75ft. 6in. by 56ft. 9in., and speed 17 knots.

The triple-screw steamship *Olympic*, of 46,439 tons gross, took up her service on the 14th June, 1911, and at that time was the largest merchant ship in the world. Her propelling machinery was notable as perhaps the most outstanding example of the " combination " of reciprocating engines with a Parsons low-pressure turbine. Each wing propeller was driven by a set of reciprocating engines, and the central propeller by a low-pressure turbine. Steam was supplied by 24 double-ended and five single-ended boilers, designed for a working pressure of 215lb. The indicated horse-power of the reciprocating engines was 30,000 and the shaft horse-power of the turbine engine 16,000. On her sea trials the results obtained greatly surpassed expectations, and the designed speed of 21 knots was exceeded. The *Olympic*, except during the Great War, remained in the North Atlantic service until she was sold to the ship-breakers in 1935.

Following the war, the White Star Line acquired the second *Majestic* (ex *Bismarck*), and she left Southampton for Cherbourg and New York on her maiden voyage on the 10th May, 1922. This vessel, when she took up her service, was the largest merchant ship afloat, her gross tonnage of 56,641 exceeding that of the *Olympic*. She had accommodation for about 1,060 first, 545 second and 2,392 third-class passengers, and her quadruple-screw machinery was designed to develop 62,000 S.H.P. and give a service speed of 23 knots. As a result of adopting oil fuel, however, with the consequent saving of time spent in cleaning fires, it was possible to maintain without difficulty a much higher power and speed. The turbines were of the Parsons type, constructed in Germany under licence, and steam was supplied by 48 water-tube boilers of the Yarrow-Normand type, working under forced draught at a pressure of 260lb per sq. in. The *Majestic* was sold to the British Admiralty in 1936, and was renamed H.M.S. *Caledonia*. She is now stationed in the Firth of Forth as a training ship for youths who are about to enter the Royal Navy.

More recently the White Star Line took a leading part in the adoption of the Diesel engine for the North Atlantic service, examples being the twin-screw motorships *Britannic* and *Georgic,*

completed in 1930 and 1931. They have a gross tonnage of 26,943 and 27,759 respectively, and both are capable of a speed of 17½ knots. These two fine motorships are continuing to give good service in the fleet of the Cunard White Star, Ltd.

THE PRESENT FLEET, SERVICES AND PERSONNEL.

The accompanying table gives particulars of the present fleet of the Cunard White Star, Ltd. The services in which the vessels are engaged include the express mail from Southampton to New York, *via* Cherbourg ; Liverpool to Boston and New York; Liverpool to Canada ; London to New York ; and London to Canada *via* Havre and Southampton. Other ports served on these routes are Cobh, Dublin, Belfast, Greenock and Galway. Patrons of ocean cruising are also well catered for. In addition to a voyage round the world, there are trips to the Mediterranean and Northern Europe ; while American travellers may journey under the Cunard White Star flag to the West Indies, South America, and even to the Mediterranean and Northern Europe.

The present directors of the Cunard White Star, Ltd., are Sir Percy E. Bates, Bt., G.B.E. (chairman), the Rt. Hon. Lord Essendon, Sir Thomas Royden, Bt., C.H., Sir Thomas Brocklebank, Bt., Mr. Frederick A. Bates, Mr. Robert Crail, Mr. Frank Charlton, Mr. William Richard Roberts, Mr. Arthur B. Cauty and Mr. Sidney J. Lister, the last-named being general manager.

The brain centre of the wonderful organisation, which for nearly a century has been an important factor on the North Atlantic and in the trade of Merseyside is, as it ever has been, Liverpool ; and to-day the Cunard Company with its associated undertakings—Cunard White Star, Ltd., Commonwealth and Dominion Line, Ltd., and Thomas & John Brocklebank, Ltd.—controls shipping approaching one million tons.

THE PRESENT FLEET OF THE CUNARD WHITE STAR, LTD.

Name.	Type.	Year Completed.	Gross Tonnage	Speed (knots)
Alaunia	Twin-screw geared-turbine s.s.	1925	14,030	15½
Andania	do.	1922	13,950	15½
Antonia	do.	1922	13,867	15½
Aquitania	Quadruple-screw turbine s.s.	1914	45,647	24
Ascania	Twin-screw geared-turbine s.s.	1925	14,013	15½
Aurania	do.	1924	13,984	15½
Ausonia	do.	1922	13,912	15½
Britannic	Twin-screw motorship	1930	26,943	17½
Carinthia	Twin-screw geared-turbine s.s.	1925	20,277	17
Franconia	do.	1923	20,175	17
Georgic	Twin-screw motorship	1931	27,759	17½
Laconia	Twin-screw geared-turbine s.s.	1922	19,695	17
Lancastria	do.	1922	16,243	17
Laurentic	Triple-screw " combination " s.s.	1927	18,724	16
Queen Elizabeth	Quadruple-screw geared-turbine s.s.	1940	85,000*	29*
Queen Mary	do.	1936	81,235	28½
Samaria	Twin-screw geared-turbine s.s.	1922	19,597	17
Scythia	do.	1921	19,761	17
Mauretania	do.	1939	35,739	22

*Estimated.

19 Passenger-carrying Liners aggregating 520,551 tons gross.

THE BUILDERS OF THE "MAURETANIA."

THE great and historic establishment of Messrs. Cammell, Laird & Co., Ltd., at Birkenhead, is one of the oldest engaged in shipbuilding and marine engineering in the United Kingdom. It is also the largest industrial undertaking on the banks of the Mersey, and the prosperity of the town of Birkenhead depends almost entirely upon the amount of work on hand in its numerous departments. The firm was founded by Mr. William Laird about 115 years ago for the building of ships and boilers, and since that time the keels of 1,045 ships have been laid by them—an achievement which but few other shipbuilding companies (if any) can equal. Engine works were added in 1857.

EARLY RECORDS.

Laird Brothers (by which name the firm were known until 1903) were pioneers in the use of iron as a shipbuilding material, their first iron vessel having been built in 1829. This was a lighter, 60ft. long by 13ft. 4in. broad, and having a measurement of 50 tons. They were also pioneers in steel shipbuilding, for in 1858 they constructed the steel paddle steamship *Ma Robert* (Fig. 1), in which Dr. Livingstone, the great explorer, carried out his memorable work on the Zambesi. This historic vessel, it is interesting to record, was a year earlier than the first steel ship (the *Windsor Castle*) built on the Clyde.

The first steamship constructed by the Birkenhead firm was the *Lady Lansdowne*, a cross-channel vessel for the City of Dublin Steam Packet Company, and a type of craft with which they have been particularly successful throughout their long career. She was launched in 1833. Five years later—in 1838—they constructed the first screw steamship to cross the Atlantic—the *Robert F. Stockton*. They were destined to enjoy a wide and varied experience in the building of Atlantic steamships during the century which elapsed between the completion of the *Robert F. Stockton* and the advent of the giant *Mauretania*.

The celebrated Confederate cruiser *Alabama* (Fig. 2) was launched by Messrs. Laird in 1862. She was a steam vessel of 1,000 tons and with propelling machinery of 300 H.P., giving a speed of about 11 knots. She did great damage to American mercantile shipping between the banks of Newfoundland and Martinique, and succeded in destroying the *Hatteras*, a Federal vessel engaged in the blockade of Galveston. The *Alabama* was eventually destroyed by the Federal ironclad *Kearsarge* in 1864.

SHIPS FOR THE MERCHANT SERVICE.

The firm have played an important part in the development of practically every type of ship for the merchant service, their output ranging from large ocean-going passenger and cargo liners to cross-channel steamships, dredgers, and small vessels for river and ferry services. In recent years the firm have built for the Cunard White Star Line (the 19,597-ton 17-knot intermediate Atlantic liner *Samaria*), the Blue Star Line (including the famous cruising liner *Arandora Star*), the Pacific Steam Navigation Company, Messrs. Thomas & James Harrison, the Booth Steamship Company, the Ellerman Lines, the Elder Dempster Lines, Messrs. John Holt & Co. (Liverpool), Ltd., the Canadian National Railways, and many other prominent shipowners. Of vessels for the transport of refrigerated cargoes the firm have made a special study ; a large number of passenger and banana-carrying steamships to the order of the United Fruit Company and of Messrs. Elders & Fyffes, and large motorships for the meat trade of the Blue Star Line, etc., having been turned out. The firm have also built oil-tankers for many of the important companies owning such vessels, including the Anglo-Saxon Petroleum Company, the British Tanker Company, the United Molasses Company, and Messrs. Hunting & Son.

Typical of the dredging craft constructed in the Birkenhead establishment are the large sand-pump hopper dredgers launched for the Mersey Docks and Harbour Board, the controlling authority of the Port of Liverpool. One of these vessels can lift 10,000 tons and others about 3,500 tons of sand per hour, and are thus outstanding in their class. Smaller craft for which the firm have been responsible include passenger and vehicular ferry steamships with either screw or paddle-wheel machinery, train ferries, tugs, hoppers, etc. For example, the train ferry and ice-breaker *Leonard* (Fig. 3) was launched in 1914 for service on the River St. Lawrence. This vessel had a length overall of 326ft. and a beam of 65ft., and had three propellers—two aft, and one forward to assist in breaking up the ice. The main steam propelling machinery indicated 3,200 H.P.

NAVAL WORK.

For nearly 100 years the firm have taken a leading part in the design and construction of warships, their connection with the British Admiralty having begun so long ago as 1840. In the early sixties they were largely instrumental in bringing about the introduction of armourclad turret ships, which may be regarded as the precursors of the modern Dreadnought.

For the British Admiralty alone the firm have built at Birkenhead over 160 ships, among these being H.M.S. *Rodney* (the largest battleship so far completed for the Royal Navy), the cruiser *Achilles* (which set up a record on a run from Gibraltar to England), and the large aircraft-carrier *Ark Royal* (which has just recently been completed). They have on hand at the time of writing the battleships *Prince of Wales* and *Temeraire*, the cruisers *Dido* and *Charybdis*, two destroyers, four submarines and two escort vessels for the British Government, as well as a large set of propelling machinery for the battle-cruiser *Renown*, now undergoing an extensive refit at Portsmouth Dockyard.

The firm have also been closely associated with the development of the torpedo-boat destroyer, being one of the three shipbuilding concerns whose designs were accepted by the British Admiralty (in the year 1893) for the first vessels of this type ever constructed. Since that time over 70 destroyers and flotilla-leaders have been launched at the Birkenhead establishment, some of them being the pioneers in their respective classes.

Before the commencement of the Great War, the firm turned their attention to the construction of submarines, and since that time a number of vessels of this description have been constructed and satisfactorily completed for the British Government, the propelling machinery having also been manufactured by the firm at Birkenhead.

Besides the ships constructed for the British Admiralty, a number of war vessels have been built at the Birkenhead Works for foreign governments, including the Argentine, Russian, Bolivian, Brazilian, Chilean, Dutch, Greek, Portuguese and Peruvian Governments.

SHIP-REPAIRING WORK.

In addition to new-construction work, a very important ship-repairing business is carried on by the firm on Merseyside. Owing to the numerous graving docks and wet basin, of which mention is made later, vessels of the largest size using the port can be dealt with both expeditiously and economically. Special attention has been given to the equipment of these docks as regards cranage, and electric, pneumatic and hydraulic power. The most modern facilities are provided for dealing with oil-ship repairs, the installation including an oil-separating plant of large capacity, which enables the cleaning of tanks to be undertaken immediately after the ships enter the docks.

A special feature is made of the repair and overhaul of Diesel machinery.

THE BIRKENHEAD WORKS.

As already indicated, the shipbuilding and marine engineering works of Messrs. Cammell, Laird & Co., Ltd., at Birkenhead rank among the largest and most modern in the United Kingdom, having an area of 108 acres and a frontage on the River Mersey of 3,100ft. There are 10 building berths, ranging

Mr. Robert Stewart Johnson,

Managing Director of Messrs. Cammell, Laird & Co., Ltd.

Mr. William Lionel Hichens,

Chairman of Messrs. Cammell, Laird & Co., Ltd.

Mr. F. O. John, M.Inst.C.E., Mem. Council I.N.A.,
Technical Manager and Naval Architect.

Mr. James Hamilton,
Shipbuilding Manager.

Mr. W. H. McMenemey, Mem. Council I.N.A.,
Engineering Manager.

up to 1,100ft. in length, and all are provided with overhead cranes and the latest devices for the rapid handling of materials. The works are in direct communication with the L., M. & S. and the G.W.R. main lines.

Situated in the premises are seven graving docks, the largest of which is over 860ft. long, and a fitting-out basin having a water area of 15 acres and ample quay space for the accommodation of the largest vessels. The entrance to the basin is 140ft. wide, and it is closed by a sliding pontoon. In addition to a fixed crane having a lifting capacity of 150 tons, there is a 200-ton floating crane, which can be speedily brought alongside any vessel in the basin when heavy armament, machinery or boilers have to be shipped.

The works throughout are equipped not only for the use of electric power, but for compressed-air and hydraulic power where this can be efficiently used. A very large installation of low-pressure electric mains is also provided for electric welding in all departments, and a special study is being made of developments in this method of construction in the shipbuilding and other departments.

Over 100,000 tons gross of new vessels can be produced annually at the shipbuilding yard, while the engineering works are capable of turning out annually machinery and boilers equivalent to over 450,000 horse-power. When fully employed, occupation is found for about 10,000 workpeople on the building berths and in the various workshops.

Fig. 1.—The Steel Exploration Paddle Steamship " Ma Robert," 1858.

Fig. 2.—The Confederate Cruiser " Alabama," 1862.

Fig. 3.—The Canadian Triple-screw Train-ferry Steamship and Ice-breaker " Leonard," 1914.

THE OLD AND NEW "MAURETANIAS."

A SOUVENIR number devoted to the new *Mauretania* of the Cunard White Star, Ltd., could hardly be regarded as complete without more than a passing reference to her famous namesake—the great Tyne-built express liner which for over two decades held pride of place on the North Atlantic passage.

Launched from the yard of Messrs. Swan, Hunter and Wigham Richardson, Ltd., at Wallsend on the 20th September, 1906, the first *Mauretania* was one of two similar ships ordered by the Cunard Steamship Co., Ltd., to meet the early German challenge in the North Atlantic passenger trade, the other

the fastest Atlantic westward speed record of her 22-year-old Cunard rival by just over nine hours. The brave old *Mauretania*, with a record of something like 2,000,000 miles of fast steaming behind her (including several years of strenuous war service) and still relying on her original Scotch boilers, pluckily responded to the challenge, and, although foiled by adverse weather conditions, it almost appeared at one point as though the attempt might prove successful. In crossing from Cherbourg to Ambrose in the official time of 4 days, 22 hours, 44 minutes, the Cunarder averaged a speed of 26·85 knots for the 3,162-mile run ; and although she was 5 hours 2 minutes behind the *Bremen's* time it

Photograph by]   **Fig. 1.—The Old " Mauretania " on Trial, November, 1907.**   [the late J. S. Dodds.

vessel being the *Lusitania*, built by Messrs. John Brown & Co., Ltd., at Clydebank. Both these vessels entered their regular service in 1907, and were then the largest, most powerful and fastest merchant ships in the world. The propelling machinery of each developed 70,000 S.H.P. (no less than 1¾ times that of any previous merchant-marine installation), and gave a sea speed of 26 knots.

As already recorded in this volume, tragedy marked the end of the *Lusitania*, when she was torpedoed and sunk off the South Coast of Ireland in 1915 ; but her companion vessel survived for greater glories, and so recently as July, 1935, made her last voyage to the shipbreakers' yard at Rosyth.

THE FIRST " MAURETANIA'S " RECORD-BREAKING PERFORMANCES.

Shortly after taking up her service on the North Atlantic, the old *Mauretania* broke the speed records of all rivals, and continued to hold every record both on the eastward and westward runs until the advent of the German liner *Bremen* in 1929. With her greater size, much increased power, and with her modern water-tube boilers supplying high-pressure, superheated steam to geared turbines, the German challenger put up a sensational performance on her maiden voyage, beating

was 3 hours 50 minutes better than the veteran's previous best. On the homeward run which terminated on the 21st August, 1929, the *Mauretania* covered the 3,098 miles from New York to Plymouth in 4 days, 17 hours, 49 minutes, at an average speed of 27·22 knots, beating her own record by more than two hours and coming within 3 hours 19 minutes of the *Bremen's* time eastward. The struggle, of course, was an unequal one : the naval architectural and marine engineering skill of 1907 could not hold its own against that of 1929. It is curious to recall, however, that at that time, even in technical circles in Germany, the belief was fairly general that the *Mauretania*, in some mysterious way, had been rejuvenated and was still capable of offering the *Bremen* doughty opposition : indeed *The Shipbuilder and Marine Engine-builder* received more than one request from German correspondents for information on this intriguing subject.

On the North Atlantic, in the mail and passenger service for which she was designed, the *Mauretania's* remarkable regularity in maintaining high speed had never been previously matched by that of any other vessel. In fair weather and foul, she maintained the same high average speeds. During one year she made 30 consecutive trips at an average speed of 25·5 knots, a sustained performance which had never been surpassed nor even approached by any other Atlantic liner of her day. An immensely popular ship right to the end, stories are related of almost incredible bursts of speed in emergency, as when steaming to the assistance of a vessel in distress. In her long period of usefulness, she probably carried more distinguished people and more millionaires than any other contemporary vessel.

The foregoing brief historical account of the first *Mauretania*, which has been largely taken from a leading article published in *The Shipbuilder and Marine Engine-builder* in May, 1935, proves conclusively that she earned for herself a name which will always live in the annals of North Atlantic shipping.

THE OLD SHIP'S WAR RECORD.

Apart from her service on the North Atlantic and on ocean cruises, the first *Mauretania* had a remarkable war record.

Commissioned early in 1915, her magnificent furnishings were taken out and her apartments reconstructed for transport work. In June of that year she made her first voyage under these conditions to Mudros, loaded with British troops for the Gallipoli Peninsula. Then she became a hospital ship, carrying wounded from Gallipoli to this country ; and, later, she again became a trooper, transporting the Canadian forces to Europe. After a prolonged stay in the Clyde, the vessel re-entered the sphere of operations as an armed cruiser, with six big guns and a full naval crew, and equipped, in addition, for the transport of thousands of reinforcements. After the termination of the war, she was employed conveying the American troops to the other side of the Atlantic. Throughout her war career, the old *Mauretania*, by her great speed, successfully penetrated various submarine zones, often with limited escort. She was one of the five troopships which steamed by themselves, no convoy being able to maintain her speed.

Photograph by]   **Fig. 2.—The New " Mauretania " leaving the Mersey for her Sea Trials, May, 1939.**   *[Stewart Bale, Liverpool.*

THE OLD AND NEW " MAURETANIAS."

	The Old.	The New.		The Old.	The New.
Year of completion	1907	1939	Number of propellers	Four.	Two.
Length overall	787ft. 0in.	771ft. 5¾in.			
Length B.P.	760ft. 0in.	732ft. 0in.	Boilers	25 cylindrical	6 Yarrow water-
Breadth extreme	87ft. 10in.	89ft. 6in.		multitubular,	tube type,
Depth moulded	60ft. 6in.*	65ft. 0in.†		195lb pressure,	425lb pressure,
Load draught, summer freeboard	36ft. 2¼in.	30ft. 10½in.		forced draught,	725 deg. F.
Gross tonnage	31,938‡	35,739		coal-fired	final steam
Passenger accommodation :—				(later oil-fired).	temperature,
First-class	560	486			oil-fired.
		(cabin)			
Second-class	475	390			
		(tourist)	Electrical installation...............	4 turbo-genera-	4 turbo-gener-
Third-class	1,300	502		tors each of	ators each of
				375 kW. at	800 kW. at
Total	2,335	1,378		110 volts.	225 volts.
Crew	812	594			
			Speed in service, knots	26	22
Total complement ...	3,147	1,972	Highest average speed for Atlan-		
			tic crossing (coal), knots......	26·06	
Number of staterooms	664	602	Highest average speed for Atlan-		
Propelling machinery...............	Parsons direct-	Parsons single-	tic crossing (oil), knots	27·22	25½
	driving tur-	reduction			(trial trip)
	bines.	geared tur-			
		bines.			

*To shelter deck.   †To main deck.   ‡Original gross tonnage.

THE NEW "MAURETANIA."

What of the second *Mauretania*? Her comparative particulars are set forth in the accompanying table. She has not been built for speed, but to meet a demand for comfort and luxurious travel in keeping with the best modern traditions. In point of size she is very similar to the old ship, and in regard to power she would appear to have a substantial reserve for a 22-knot schedule.

She has the advantage of over 30 years' scientific progress in the combined arts of naval architecture and marine engineering; the best has been put into her design, construction and equipment; and we may therefore look to her with the greatest confidence to maintain the high prestige of the amalgamated Cunard White Star interests on the North Atlantic.

.   .   .   .

Below is reproduced the painting of the first *Mauretania* which hangs in the tourist-class smoking room of the *Queen Mary*. It represents the old ship arriving at Rosyth on the 4th July, 1935, to be broken up.

From a painting by]   *[Charles Pears, R.O.I.*

Fig. 3.—The Old " Mauretania " arriving at Rosyth to be Broken Up.

THE DESIGN—GENERAL AND STRUCTURAL.

PRELIMINARY CONSIDERATIONS.

WHEN, towards the latter half of 1936, the Cunard White Star, Ltd., were concerning themselves with further outlay on new tonnage for their North Atlantic fleets, it was not only the express service which claimed their attention. Already they had satisfied themselves that this particular service for passengers and mails could best be carried on with two 1,000-ft. liners operating on a weekly sailing schedule between Southampton and New York and capable of a minimum 28½-knot service speed in all but the most severe weather conditions. The *Queen Mary* had made her *début* on the Atlantic in May of that year ; and, following her satisfactory performance, it was but a matter of time and circumstance before a similar ship was ordered. The second step in this bold scheme duly materialised in October, 1936, when Messrs. John Brown & Co., Ltd., of Clydebank, builders of the *Queen Mary*, were again successful tenderers for the *Queen Elizabeth*, which they are now completing afloat for service in the spring of 1940.

Meanwhile, it was fully realised that two such express liners, although greatly attractive to the travelling public, did not by any means meet the full range of demand of passenger traffic between the two continents. There are a great many voyagers who are not primarily dependent on fast crossings, and who prefer to prolong within reason the pleasures of an ocean crossing, particularly when it is made with all the comforts available in a modern luxury liner.

It was with these facts in view that the company sought to strengthen their second-line services, and drew up a scheme for a proposed vessel which, while certainly smaller and of less speed than her giant contemporaries in the North Atlantic express service, would nevertheless compare favourably in the matter of appointments and equipment with any passenger-carrying unit afloat.

This vessel was intended for trade between the Thames and New York, and the size of ship deemed most suitable for the service was very similar to that of the old Tyne-built *Mauretania*, to which reference has been made in the previous chapter of this volume, while the power to be developed by two sets of geared steam turbines driving twin screws was to be sufficient for a minimum service speed of 22 knots with substantial reserve.

With the salient features of the proposal thus formulated, the owners were in a position to proceed further, and asked four of the leading shipbuilders to submit designs and tenders to fulfil definite requirements. The proposals of Messrs. Cammell, Laird & Co., Ltd., were accepted, and the order was placed with them on the 30th December, 1936.

HULL DESIGN.

The design characteristics of the ship as built are indicated by the data in the accompanying table, and also by the general-arrangement plans reproduced on Plates II., III. and IV.

The view of the *Mauretania* on Plate I. indicates the very imposing exterior model achieved. The appearance in a general sense is not unlike that of the *Queen Mary* with the terraced formation of the rounded bridge front and the long sweep aft of the superstructures. The topside painting scheme is, of course, the same.

The two masts are widely placed and rake well aft. They are of robust steel-plate construction, and some idea of their dimensions is conveyed by the fact that the ladder to the crow's nest on the fore mast is internal.

The two funnels, both working, are also of imposing size, and are raked aft to the same degree as the masts. Their section is elliptical. A departure from previous practice has been made in that the funnels are specially stiffened internally to obviate the necessity for guys.

No radical departure has been made from orthodox practice in the design of lines. The under-water form was based on tank model tests, and the speed-length ratio, taken in relation to the load water-line, is ·875 for a speed of 24 knots.

Above water, the sides are carried up sheer without tumble-home amidships, while the forward sections show a good flare at the bows. A feature is the provision of anchor recesses

PARTICULARS OF THE TWIN-SCREW PASSENGER AND CARGO LINER "MAURETANIA."

Length overall	771ft.	5¾in.
Length B.P.	732ft.	0in.
Breadth extreme	89ft.	6in.
Breadth moulded	89ft.	1in.
Depth moulded to C deck (bulkhead deck)	38ft.	6in.
Depth moulded to promenade deck	73ft.	6in.
Mean load draught	30ft.	10½in.
Gross tonnage		35,739
Net tonnage		20,170
Number of passengers :—		
Cabin-class		486
Tourist-class		390
Third-class		502
Total		1,378
Number of officers, crew and personnel		594
Total complement		1,972
General-cargo capacity, cu. ft.		390,000
Insulated-cargo capacity, cu. ft.		92,000
Service speed, knots		22
Mean speed on trial, knots		25½

forward, which give a very neat housing for the main bower anchors.

The raked stem is straight in contour, with a long shallow cutaway of the fore-foot. The keel and lower-strake endings are taken by a cast-steel member continued to the load water-line, but above this level the stem takes on the rounded-plate or " soft nose " construction familiar in modern practice. An excellent impression of the stem is conveyed by the photograph reproduced in Fig. 5 of the chapter dealing with the launch and completion of the vessel.

The after-end lines are faired in to a well-proportioned cruiser stern, which overhangs 24ft. abaft the after perpendicular on the load water-line, and affords adequate protection for the rudder.

It is perhaps notable that the deadwood in this case has been cut away and a rudder of the semi-balanced type fitted. A view of the rudder in place is shown in Fig. 13 of the chapter on " Launch and Completion," while the details of its construction and arrangement are shown in Fig. 19 of the chapter on " Construction of the Hull." The rudder is arranged on two gudgeons on the stern-post by pintles, and supported by a thrust block fitted below the tiller crosshead at *D*-deck level. The principal radial thrust is taken at the transom by the gland bearing incorporated in the stern-frame casting. At its widest portion, the rudder has a width of 22ft., and in longitudinal section is of aerofoil form.

Similar attention to detail is to be noted in other underwater appendages. The bilge keels, as may be seen from the midship section in Fig. 1 of this chapter, are of V-plate construction, while the propeller shafts are fully enclosed by bossings designed to offer minimum interference with stream-line flow.

One of the most interesting refinements is the flushing of the under-water plate butts and seams with a special mixture of Aranbee composition, supplied by Messrs Rowan & Boden, Ltd., of Glasgow. A section of the side plating so treated is shown in Fig. 2. From considerations of resistance, the advantage is two-fold, firstly in that it eliminates eddy-making at the plate edges, and, secondly, there is a definite reduction of wetted surface—small, it is true (probably of the order of one per cent.), but worthy of consideration in a high-powered ship. It seemed reasonable to doubt whether such composition fillets would remain intact under onerous conditions of service at sea, but tests carried out in connection with the Cunard White Star Line's *Queen Mary* have demonstrated that this special Aranbee composition will adhere perfectly. In January, 1938, when this vessel was in dry-dock, the plate edges were flushed at certain selected places. Three months later, a fillet situated between wind and water was chipped away, and the bare steel underneath showed a " clean surface," free from corrosion. At sub-

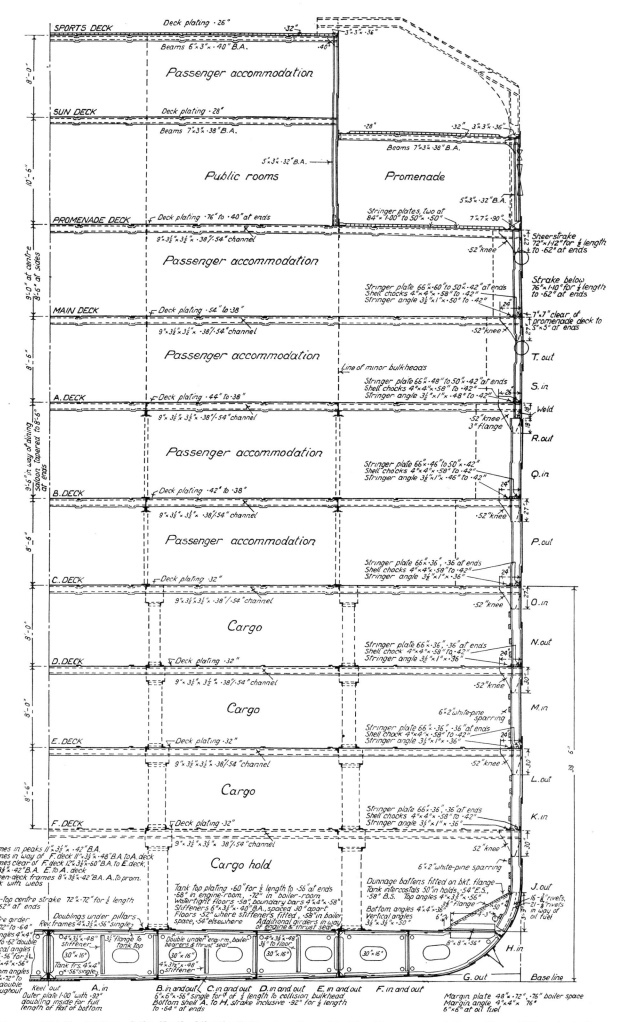

Fig. 1.—Midship Section of the North Atlantic Twin-screw Geared-turbine Passenger and Cargo Liner " Mauretania."

Plate A—Cabin-class Grand Hall.

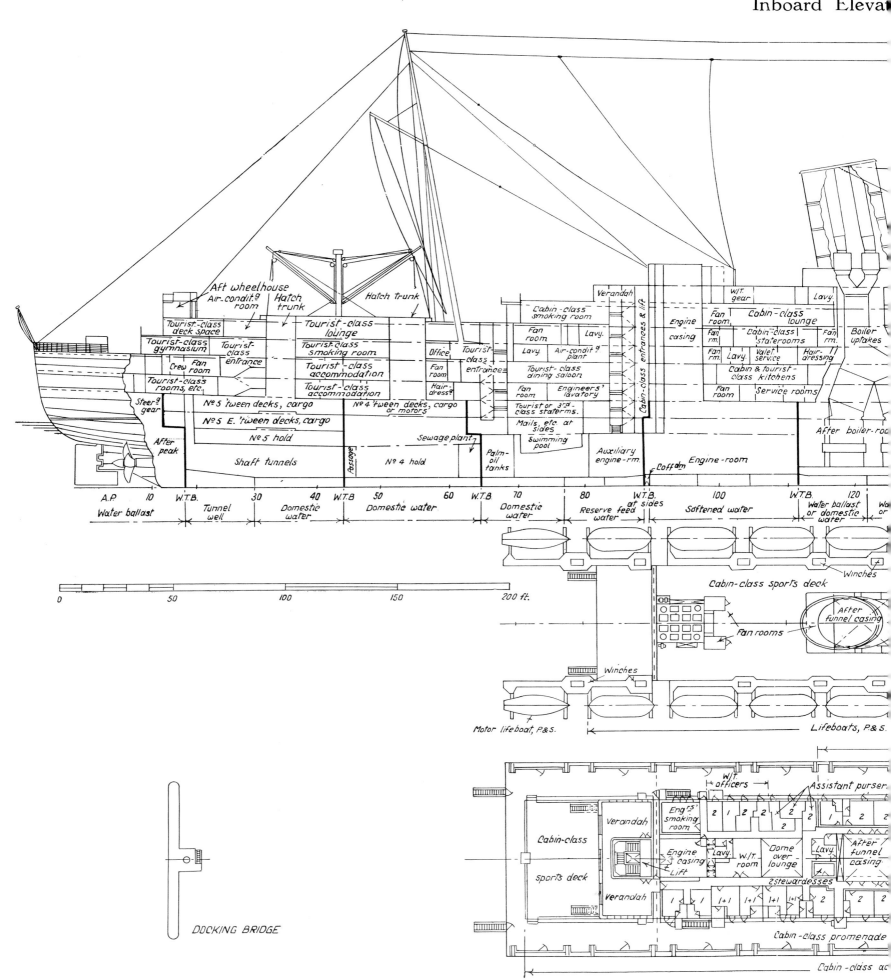

ORTH ATLANTIC LINER "MAURETANIA."

d Deck Plans.

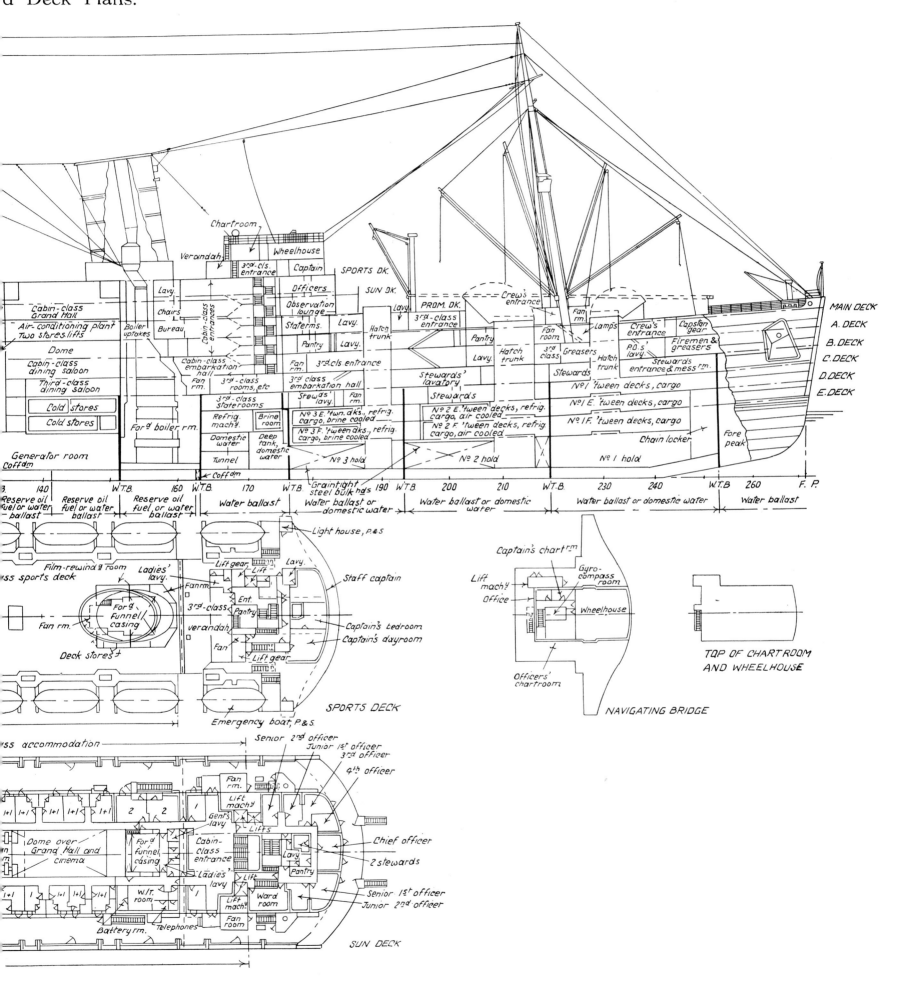

THE CUNARD WHITE STAR TWIN-SCRE
De

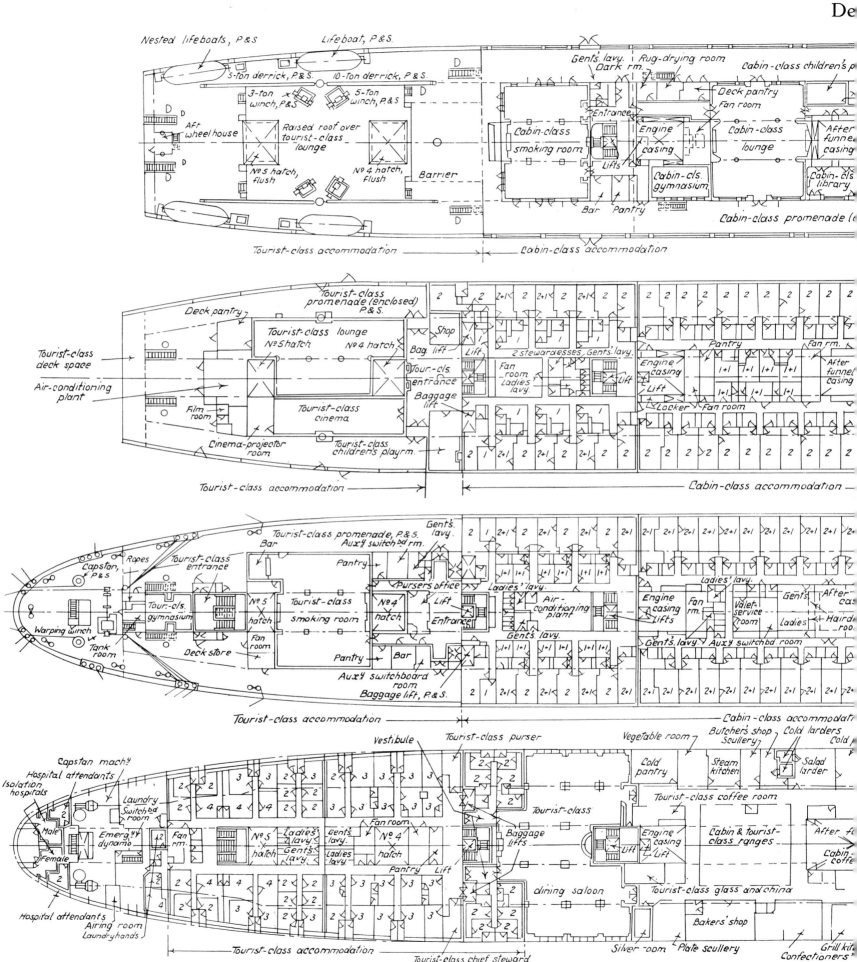

RTH ATLANTIC LINER "MAURETANIA."

ns.

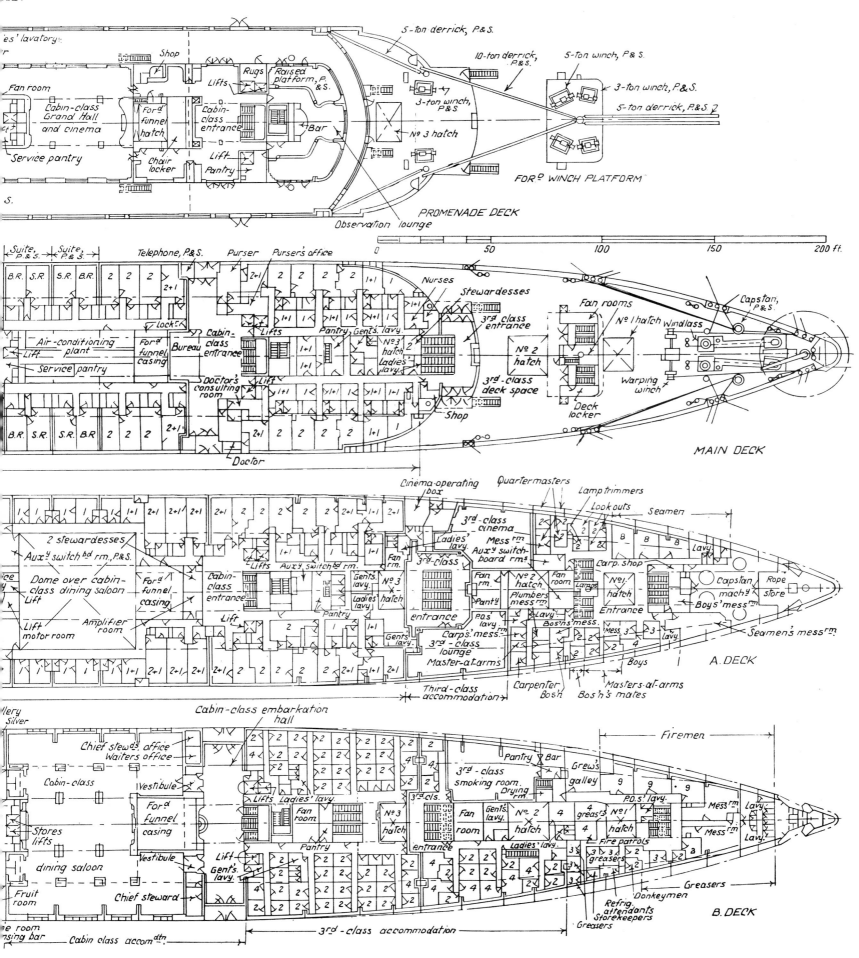

PROMENADE DECK

MAIN DECK

A. DECK

B. DECK

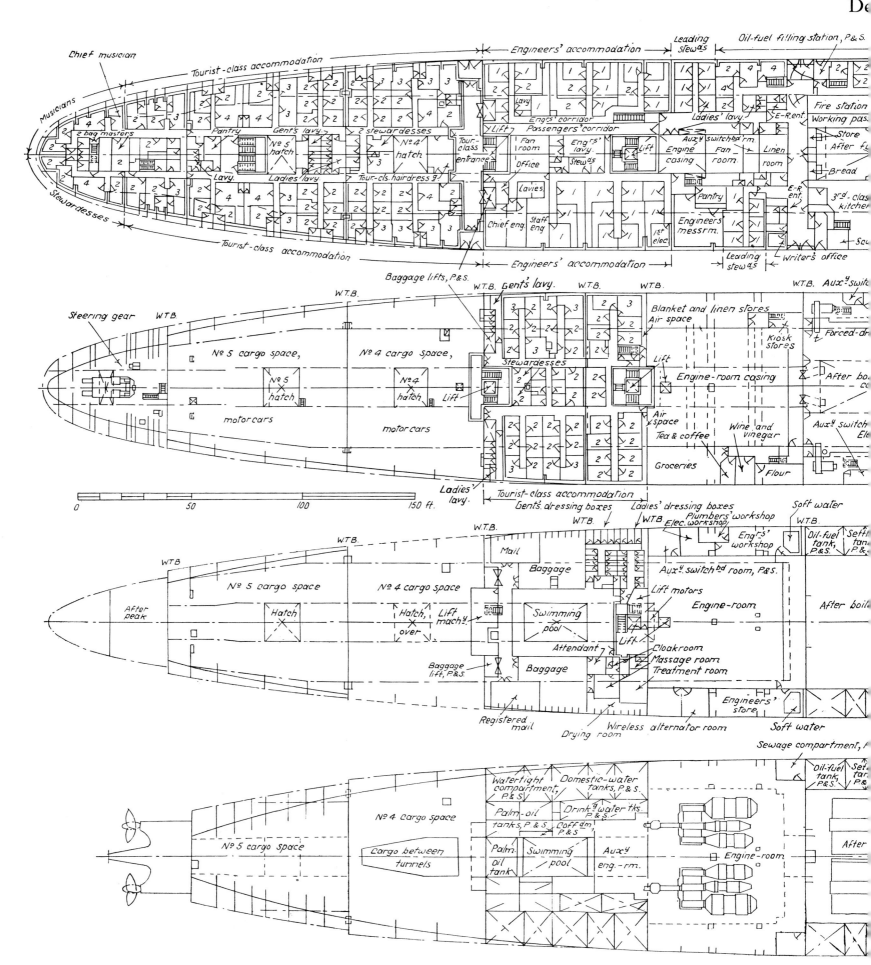

RTH ATLANTIC LINER "MAURETANIA."

ns.

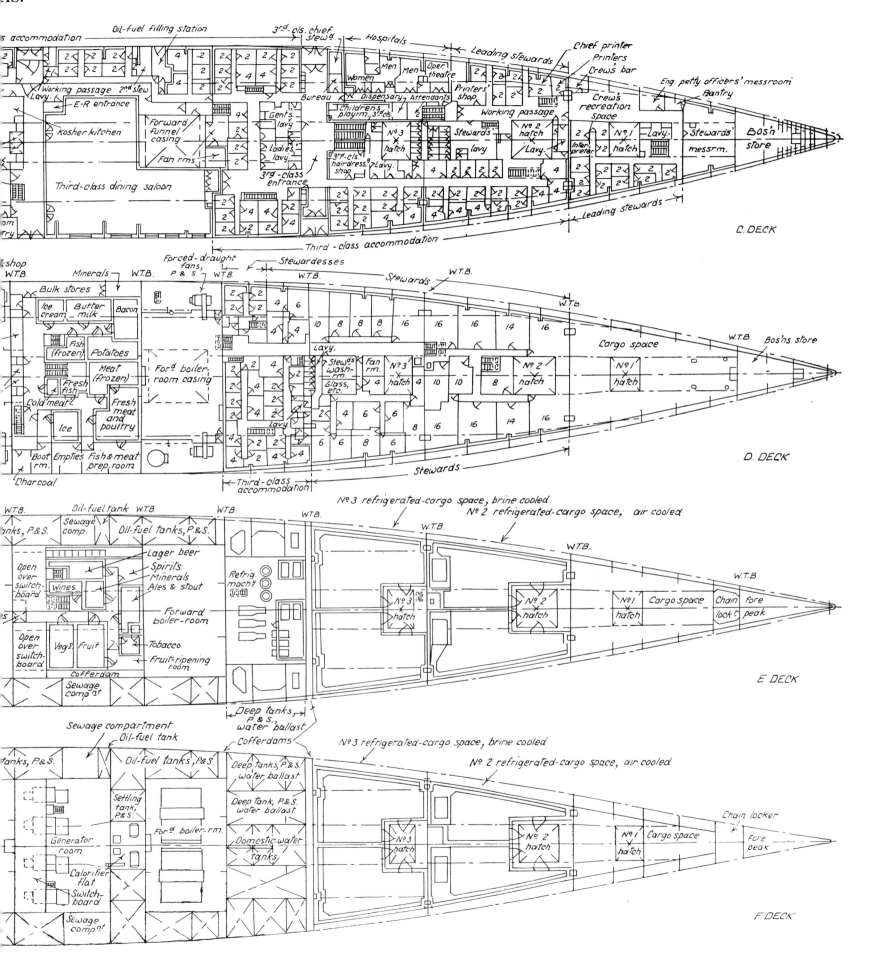

C. DECK

D. DECK

E DECK

F DECK

Plate B—Cabin-class Swimming Pool.

sequent dry-dockings (July, 1937, and January, 1938), examination revealed all fillets intact. That the owners were well satisfied with the results of the tests is borne out by the fact that they ordered Aranbee flushing treatment for all the underwater butts and seams of the *Mauretania*, this work being carried out a short time before the launch.

GENERAL ARRANGEMENT.

The detail of the internal arrangements may be studied from the inboard elevation and deck plans reproduced on Plates II., III. and IV.

The vessel has 10 decks, designated, from above, the sports, sun, promenade, main, *A, B, C, D, E* and *F* decks. The first two mentioned are superstructure decks, while the promenade deck extends from the bridge front to within 57ft. of the stern and the main deck from the bow to within 47ft. of the stern. Decks *A, B* and *C* are continuous all fore and aft, while *D, E* and *F* are partial lower decks, the last-named being worked in way of the forward hold only. The 'tween-deck heights are in the main 8ft. or 8ft. 6in., increased to 9ft. 6in. in way of the cabin-class dining saloon on *B* deck.

The main watertight subdivision is to the current Board of Trade regulations, which are based on the recommendations of into 33 compartments, appropriated to the carriage of domestic fresh water or water ballast, reserve boiler-feed, soft water, and reserve oil fuel or water ballast. There are also two pairs of double-bottom tanks at the sides amidships arranged as heeling tanks.

The main oil-fuel capacity is provided by wing bunkers reaching to *D*-deck level, and fitted at the sides for the full length of the forward boiler-room, generator compartment and after boiler-room spaces.

On the fore side of No. 1 boiler-room bulkhead, and arranged at the sides of and below the refrigerating-machinery space, is a further group of deep tanks for water ballast and domestic fresh water, while abaft the main engine-room is another group allocated to drinking water, domestic water and palm oil. The end peak tanks, of relatively small capacity on account of the fineness of the form, are arranged for water ballast.

The accommodation for passengers in the *Mauretania*, fully dealt with in a later chapter of this volume, provides for three separate classes, designated cabin, tourist and third-class respectively.

The broad scheme of arrangement shows the accommodation for cabin-class passengers in the upper 'tween decks and superstructure amidships, the principal group of public rooms being

Fig. 2.—View of Under-water Shell showing Plate Edges flushed with Aranbee Composition.

the International Convention for the Safety of Life at Sea (London, 1929). It has been effected by 12 transverse watertight or oiltight bulkheads carried to *C* deck and spaced as shown on the inboard elevation on Plate II. The degree of subdivision represents a two-compartment standard, or, in other words, the vessel will not immerse beyond the margin-line to *C* deck with any two adjacent compartments bilged. The margin of safety may be considered as further increased by certain arrangements not taken account of in the flooding calculations, *viz.*, the fitting of a transverse watertight division on the after side of the cable-locker forward, the presence of wing oil-fuel bunkers abreast the machinery spaces, and the high degree of subdivision of the double-bottom structure.

The watertight doors fitted to openings in the main bulkheads below the bulkhead deck number 11, and, in addition to local control, all are capable of remote operation on the Stone hydraulic system, as fully described in a later section of this volume.

The cellular double bottom extends for the full length between the peak bulkheads, and, except for a short rise at each end, has a uniform depth of 4ft. 9in. It is subdivided by watertight (or oiltight) transverse and longitudinal divisions on the promenade deck and the staterooms on the main and *A* decks. Verandahs, with adjoining open deck space, are arranged at the after end of the sun deck, and also on this deck is a group of special staterooms. Above this level, the sun-deck house roof has been utilised to form a large open sports deck. The further appointments for the cabin-class passengers include the main dining saloon, situated on *B* deck, and the swimming pool, placed low down in the hull below the water-line.

Accommodation for the tourist-class passengers is grouped at the after end of the vessel, with the public rooms on the main and *A* decks, dining saloon on *B* deck, and staterooms on *B, C* and *D* decks. A games deck is available on the promenade deck aft.

The third-class accommodation is distributed forward on *A, B, C* and *D* decks, with special access to a games area on the sports deck forward.

The very greatest care has been bestowed on the appropriate arrangement of living quarters for officers and crew.

The captain's suite is on the sports deck forward and the deck officers' rooms immediately below in the house on the sun deck. The accommodation for engineer officers is on *C* deck in a central position convenient to the engine-room access, while the crew's quarters are located right forward on *A*, *B* and *C* decks, and the stewards and kitchen staff on *D* deck.

For the stowage of cargo there are available five cargo holds and corresponding lower 'tween-deck spaces, grouped three forward and two aft.

Detailed from forward, No. 1 cargo hold, as well as the three tiers of *D*, *E* and *F* 'tween decks above, is arranged for general cargo. No. 2 hold is for general cargo, and has a steel centre-line grain division, while No. 2 *E* and *F* 'tween-deck spaces are divided into port and starboard compartments, which are insulated and provided with air-circulating arrangements suitable for the transport of fruit. No. 3 hold is a general-cargo space, and has also a steel centre-line division, while a centre-line division is also fitted in the corresponding *E* and *F* 'tween decks above, these spaces being insulated and fitted with brine grids to give conditions suitable for the carriage of refrigerated produce.

At the after end, No. 4 hold is extended to the underside of *D* deck and fitted for general cargo, and the 'tween-deck space immediately above is allocated to the transport of motor-cars.

No. 5 hold and the corresponding *D* and *E* 'tween decks above are further general-cargo spaces, except that the uppermost space is adaptable for extending the garage accommodation should the need arise.

The total capacity for general cargo aggregates about 390,000 cu. ft., and the insulated-cargo space available in the eight compartments arranged on the port and starboard sides of Nos. 2 and 3 'tween decks on *E* and *F* decks is about 92,000 cu. ft.

The hatchways are necessarily trunked right down to the compartments which they serve, and Nos. 1 and 2 hatchways are fitted with hinged steel covers at the level of the main weather deck forward.

For the stowage of the ship's cold stores, a group of 17 insulated chambers is fitted on *D* and *E* decks amidships, having a total capacity of approximately 15,500 cu. ft.

STRUCTURAL DESIGN.

The *Mauretania* has been constructed to the highest class of Lloyd's 'Register of Shipping for the classification ✠100 A.1, with freeboard, by that society, and to fulfil the requirements of the Board of Trade for the granting of a foreign-going passenger certificate.

The general design of structure and the scantlings of the main members are indicated by the midship section in Fig. 1.

The design is on the normal scheme of transverse framing associated with a cellular double bottom and four rows of pillars.

The promenade deck (depth 73ft. 6in. moulded at side) forms the upper flange of the strength girder over the greater part of the length, and from longitudinal-strength considerations the length-depth ratio is as low as 10.

The section at amidships is fairly full, due to a moderate rise of floor and easy turn of bilge. As mentioned previously, the ship side is carried plumb to the promenade deck, and there is no overhang of deck.

The centre girder in the double bottom is watertight or oiltight for the greater part of its length. At each side four longitudinal girders are incorporated in the double-bottom structure, which has solid floors at every frame.

The tank-top plating is carried across level, from side to side, and the margin plate is fitted horizontal, with a short flange to give a normal attachment to the bilge strake and also to form a shallow bilge.

The bilge keels, as indicated previously, are of built-up V-section, and have a depth of 24in.

The main frame spacing is 36in., reduced to 27in. forward of the three-fifths length and 24in. in the peaks. The main frames generally are 11 or 12-in. bulb-angle sections extending from the bilge to *A* deck, at which level they are butt-welded to 'tween-deck frames of 8-in. bulb-angle section carried to the promenade deck. From considerations of transverse stiffness, deep plate webs are introduced at regular intervals to reinforce the side framing at upper levels.

The deck beams generally are 9in. channels, lapped on to the frames and stiffened by plate knee connections. In way of the passenger decks, the beams are pocket-joggled to enable the decks to be flush-plated. The decks are worked with a normal sheer, but have no camber except at the exposed weather decks, where the round of beam is 6in. in the full width.

As mentioned earlier, the decks are supported by four rows of pillars, these struts being of hollow built construction from the tank top to *C* deck, and of 4-in. diameter tubes fitted in conjunction with I-section fore-and-aft girders from *C* to *A* decks. The line of thrust is continued by an arrangement of minor bulkheads, and the outer line of pillars coincides with the side wall of the superstructure deckhouse.

The side frames and bottom frames are out-joggled to suit a normal arrangement of " in and out " shell strakes, the plating generally being ·92in. thick for the half-length amidships, but considerably reduced at the ends. The flat keel is 1in. thick and doubled for the full length of the flat of bottom.

The superstructure, which consists of a two-tier inset deckhouse of considerable length, incorporates three expansion joints to alleviate working stresses transmitted through the main hull. The 'tween-deck height from the promenade deck to the sun deck is 10ft. 6in. in way of the cabin-class public rooms, but clear of the deckhouse the sun deck is stepped down by 2ft. to form the roof of the covered promenade at each side of the promenade deck. This arrangement also gives a suitable head-room for the open sun-deck promenade above, which passes under the guide channels of the gravity davits. These latter may be regarded as strength members, affording lateral bracing for the superstructure.

CONSTRUCTION OF THE HULL.

IN approaching the hull construction of the *Mauretania*, the builders—Messrs. Cammell, Laird & Co., Ltd.—were fortunate in having at their disposal useful experience in the building of large vessels. Several ships of heavy launching displacement had already been built on their No. 6 berth, as mentioned later in the chapter on the launch and completion of the vessel, and the foundations, after-end arrangements and cranage facilities were therefore suitable without modification for the projected liner.

The construction was largely along orthodox lines, employing mild steel and riveted connections, and practically the whole of the steel used was delivered from the South Wales rolling mills of Messrs. Guest Keen Baldwins Iron & Steel Co., Ltd., of Port Talbot.

In accordance with the usual modern methods, as much groundwork as possible was done, using hydraulic riveting machines for such items as keel structure, garboard strakes and inner-bottom floors and connections. The riveting of work

Fig. 1.—Laying the Keel (24th May, 1937).

After preliminary investigation for launching, a keel declivity of $\frac{9}{16}$ in. per foot was chosen, and building operations were commenced on the 24th May, 1937, when the first keel plates were laid. Thereafter, the work proceeded smoothly, the vessel being brought to the launching stage in the comparatively short period of 14 months.

Figs. 1 to 18 accompanying this chapter show the progressive stages of hull construction within this period, and, at the same time, serve to illustrate various structural details.

in place was generally accomplished by portable pneumatic tools, these being largely of the well-known Thor pattern, produced by the Independent Pneumatic Tool Co., Ltd., of London.

It may also be appropriate to record at this point that drilling and milling machines, supplied by Messrs. James Archdale & Co., Ltd., of Birmingham, have been extensively used by the shipbuilders in the construction of the hull and propelling machinery.

A certain amount of electric welding was also employed in

building up the structure, notably for such items as ventilating trunks and pillaring connections, while the upper side frames were also butt-welded on to the main framing. Electrodes for welding work were supplied by the Murex Welding Processes, Ltd., of London.

CASTINGS.

One of the most striking features of large-liner construction is undoubtedly the size of the castings necessary for efficient end arrangements. The contract for the hull castings of the *Mauretania* was entrusted to the Darlington Forge establishment of the English Steel Corporation, Ltd., a foundry at which orders of a similar nature have been executed in the past for

27-ton steel castings, and together form a rigid spectacle-frame measuring 29ft. between the boss centres.

The rudder-frame was manufactured in two pieces, the lower portion consisting of a cast-steel frame, and the upper portion of a forged-steel stock fitted with a bronze liner and connected to the frame through a massive bolted coupling. The total weight of the rudder assembly is about 70 tons.

For the stem arrangement a three-piece steel casting having an overall length of 57ft. 6in. and a finished weight of 8¾ tons was delivered from the same foundry.

Details of the scantlings and the design of the stern-frame, rudder-frame and shaft-bracket casings are indicated by the drawings reproduced in Figs. 19 and 20.

Fig. 2.—Double-bottom Structure in course of Erection.

such important vessels as the old *Mauretania*, *Olympic*, *Aquitania* and, more recently, for the huge Cunard White Star Atlantic liner *Queen Mary*.

The total weight of steel required for the production of the castings of the new ship was in the neighbourhood of 300 tons.

The stern-frame, the main portion of which is seen in course of erection in Fig. 5, was manufactured in three pieces, and has a total finished weight of 38 tons.

The shaft brackets, one of which is shown in Fig. 13, are each

PAINTWORK AND PROTECTIVE COMPOSITIONS.

With the shell plating largely completed and caulked some weeks before the launch, commencement was made with the external paintwork.

To prevent corrosion of the ship's structure, Anodite rust-preventative composition was applied for the priming coats of the *Mauretania*. Practically the whole of the steelwork—both inside and outside—was coated with the material. This vessel is the third large liner of the Cunard White Star fleet

Fig. 4.—Framing Well Advanced and " D "-deck Beams Erected.

Fig. 3.—Tank Top Plated and Side Framing begun.

Fig. 6.—View from Forward, showing " A " Deck Plated.

Fig. 5.—Lining-off Cast-steel Stern-frame.

Fig. 8.—View from Aft—Superstructure Completed.

Fig. 7.—Promenade Deck at Plating Stage.

Fig. 9.—Fabricating the Double Bottom.

Fig. 10.—After-end Structure, showing Bossed Frames.

Fig. 11.—View from Aft—Structure advanced to " C " Deck.

Fig. 12.—Upper 'Tween Decks, showing Joggled Beams and Web-frame Stiffening.

Fig. 13.—Starboard-side Shaft-bracket Casting.

Fig. 14.—Twin Scimitar Bronze Propellers fitted prior to the Launch.

Fig. 15.—Superstructure Front erected to Sports-deck Level.

Fig. 16.—Broadside View a Fortnight before the Launch.

Fig. 18.—Steelwork on Superstructure Front completed.

Fig. 17.—Sports Deck, from Aft, showing Superstructure Expansion Joints and Boat-davit Members.

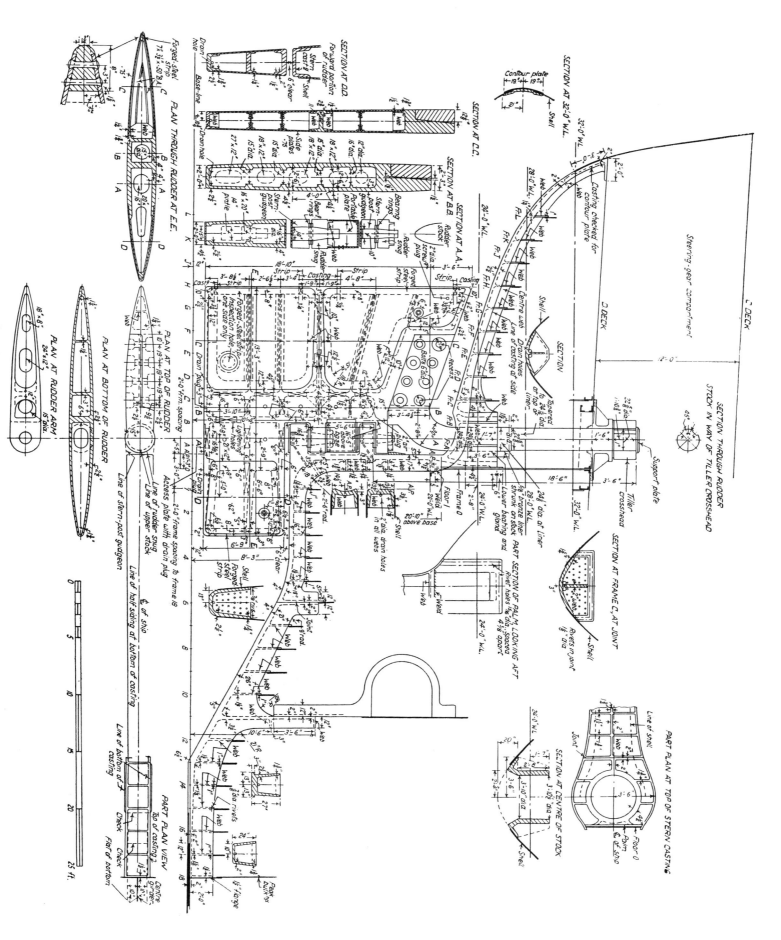

Fig. 19.—Details of Stern-frame and Rudder-frame Castings.

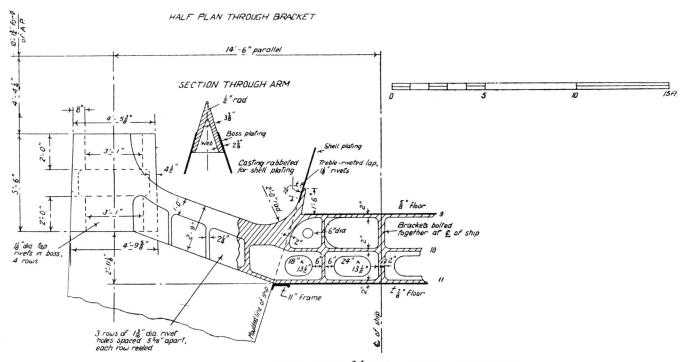

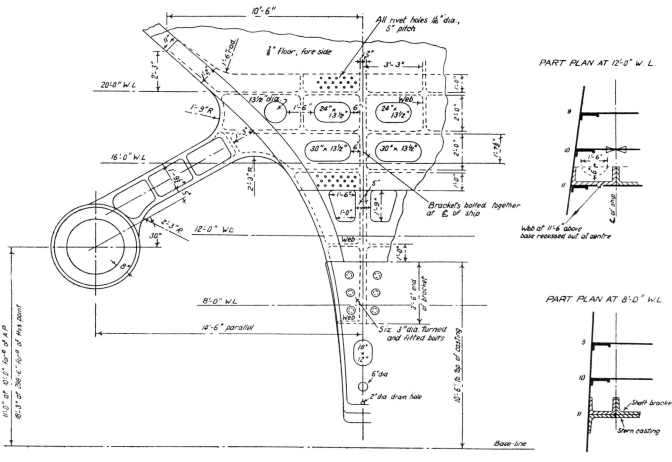

Fig. 20.—Details of Shaft-bracket Castings.

to be protected by this composition, which is the product of Messrs. Goodlass, Wall & Co., Ltd., of Liverpool.

The anti-corrosive and anti-fouling compositions applied to the under-water portions were the products of the old-established Merseyside firm of J. & W. Wilson, Ltd., of Liverpool, who were also responsible for the topside and superstructure paints.

In the region of the stern, the special ApeXioR No. 3 compound of Messrs. J. Dampney & Co., Ltd., of Newcastle-on-Tyne, was applied. This coating offers adequate protection against

damage by erosion due to electrolytic action of bronze propellers in salt water, and obviates the use of zinc strips for the same purpose.

Internally, Bitumastic enamel and Bitumastic solution, specialities of Messrs. Wailes Dove Bitumastic, Ltd., of Newcastle-on-Tyne, found extensive application for steelwork protection inside the double-bottom and deep tanks, inside bilges, on the tank tops in way of machinery spaces, and numerous other locations. The aggregate amounts used were $21\frac{1}{2}$ tons of enamel and 435 gallons of solution.

Fig. 1.—The " Mauretania " ready for Launching.

LAUNCH AND COMPLETION.

INTRODUCTORY.

IN addition to constituting an outstanding event in the lives of many people resident in the immediate vicinity of the Mersey, the launch of the *Mauretania* created immense interest in the United Kingdom and other countries. The association of the name *Mauretania* with the famous express liner of other days, for which a large section of the ocean-travelling public had a great regard, no doubt helped to increase the interest aroused by the launch of the new vessel, which is the largest mercantile ship built in England.

The launching ceremony was very gracefully performed by Lady Bates, wife of Sir Percy E. Bates, Bt., G.B.E., chairman of the Cunard White Star, Ltd., on the 28th July, 1938, in the presence of a great and enthusiastic assembly of people. A novel touch introduced into the ceremony was the unveiling by Lady Bates of the name of the vessel, which is in large raised-up letters on each side of the bow. The illustration given in Fig. 1 is reproduced from a photograph taken at the precise moment Lady Bates named the ship in the traditional manner by breaking a bottle of wine across the stem. This illustration gives a good impression of the magnificent appearance of the vessel as she lay on the launching ways before commencing the brief movement into the water, in preparation for which such extensive arrangements had been made.

The fact that the launch proceeded without the slightest deviation from the carefully planned arrangements is an indication of the amount of thought expended by the builders on the various problems to be met in connection with the launch. Messrs. Cammell, Laird & Co., Ltd., have had considerable experience in the building and launching of large ships, the predecessors of the *Mauretania* from the same berth including H.M. battleship *Rodney* (33,900 tons standard displacement), the Cunard White Star liner *Samaria* (19,597 tons gross) and, more recently, H.M. aircraft-carrier *Ark Royal* (22,000 tons standard displacement). The launching weight of the *Rodney* was, indeed, somewhat in excess of the launching weight of **16,457** tons of the *Mauretania*.

LAUNCHING ARRANGEMENTS.

The launching arrangements generally were in accordance with the shipbuilders' usual practice, in which the normal method of using two launching ways is followed. In the preliminary investigations made prior to laying down the vessel, a depth of water of 11ft. 6in. was assumed for the purposes of calculation of maximum pressures between the ground-ways and the ship's structure and of other important data. This figure for the height of water on the way-ends was the minimum value which was anticipated, and was considerably exceeded on the actual day of the launch, the height of the tide being such as to give 13ft. 3in. of water over the way-ends. Under this more favourable condition of tide, the maximum pressure between the ground-ways and the sliding-ways did not at any time during the launch exceed 2·52 tons per sq. ft.

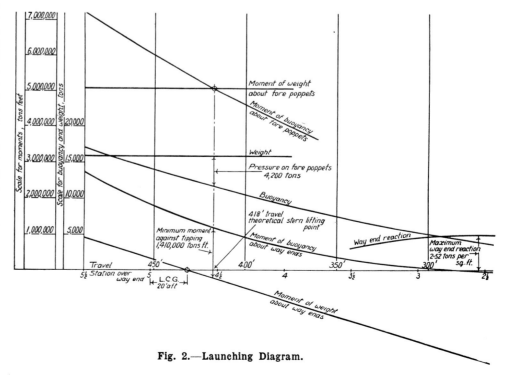

Fig. 2.—Launching Diagram.

The principal technical data, derived from calculations using the 13ft. 3in. figure for the water over the way-ends, is given in the accompanying table, while the launching curves are reproduced in Fig. 2.

LAUNCH PARTICULARS (AS FOR ACTUAL LAUNCH).

Declivity of keel of ship	·5625in. per ft.
Declivity of chord of ways........................	·6140in. per ft.
Overall length of standing ways	777ft. 0in.
Camber of ways in 754ft.	15in.
After-perpendicular from after-end of standing ways	86ft. 0in.
Fore-perpendicular from fore-end of standing ways (fore poppet)	65ft. 3in.
Length of sliding-ways...........................	641ft. 4in.
After-perpendicular to after-end of sliding-ways (after poppet)	36ft. 6in.
Breadth of sliding-ways (each way)	7ft. 0in.
Area of sliding surface............................	8,979 sq. ft.
Initial mean pressure on grease................	1·84 tons per sq. ft.
Spread of ways (centre to centre)	25ft. 1in.
Launching weight of ship (including sliding-ways and make-up of ways)	16,457 tons
Depth of water on way-ends	13ft. 3in.
Travel at stern-lift point.........................	418ft. 0in.
Corresponding pressure on fore poppets	4,200 tons.
Minimum anti-tipping moment	1,410,000 tons-ft.
Maximum pressure over after-end of ways (calculated as for rigid structure)	2·52 tons per sq. ft.
Corresponding travel..............................	272·5ft.
Time taken from commencing to move to point of dropping off way-ends	50 seconds.

The releasing arrangements comprised four hydraulic triggers, two being provided on each set of ways at distances of 241ft. and 450ft. from the after-perpendicular. The hydraulic piping system serving this gear was arranged so that the pressure could be released simultaneously from all four triggers when it was desired to free the vessel. In accordance with the necessity for providing for any emergency, the builders fitted hydraulic rams in positions at the forward end of the vessel, to be used in helping to start the hull moving down the ways if she were inclined to stick when the triggers were released. It was found, however, that this emergency gear was not required, as the ship began sliding immediately upon the release of the hydraulic holding arrangements.

For many years Messrs. Cammell, Laird & Co., Ltd., have followed the practice of using cradle or sling plates, carried from side to side of the vessel under the keel, to hold the heads of the fore-poppet stilts. These plates, in conjunction with soft-wood packing between the cradle plate and the shell plating of the ship, offer the most efficient and easily erected means of taking

the large way-end pressures which are brought about after the stern lifts during the launch of a heavy ship.

The method described in the foregoing, and which was adopted in the case of the *Mauretania*, offers further advantages in that it avoids the necessity for any elaborate structure riveted or welded to the shell of the ship. In addition, it provides a very desirable measure of flexibility between the hull and cradle when the stern begins to lift. This latter attribute is one which has been found particularly advantageous by the builders in launching into the Mersey.

If the presence of " batter," or fall-in towards the ship's centre-line of the tops of the cradle stilts, should make it necessary to adopt means for preventing the heels of the stilts spreading, it is usual to fit tray plates under the poppets and on top of the sliding ways, in conjunction with athwartship tie-plates which pass under the keel-plate and connect the port and starboard-side ways together. In the case of the *Mauretania*, however, as may be seen from the photograph of the fore-poppet reproduced in Fig. 3, the cradle stilts were practically vertical, making it unnecessary to provide tie-plates at the heels. Cross wire lashings and spread shores were considered to be sufficient for the purpose.

Although it was found possible in this way to simplify the construction of the fore-poppet, the cradle-plates and the timber supports used had to be of an extremely massive type to withstand the very considerable poppet pressure of 4,200 tons which was brought about when the stern lifted. To meet this severe load, the fore-poppet construction adopted consisted of

Fig. 3.—The Fore-poppet—Port Side, looking Aft.

Fig. 4.—The After-poppet—Port Side, looking Forward.

four separate cradle-plates of heavy scantlings, each with shelf-plates attached. These shelf-plates had to take almost the entire upward thrust on the poppets, owing to the stilts being arranged vertically. For this reason, the shelf-plates were each strengthened by three deep brackets above the plate, in conjunction with longitudinal tie-plates, and also by two deep brackets on the underside and at the ends of the shelf-plate. These last-mentioned brackets formed, with the shelf, a socket into which the poppet supports were wedged.

The timber stilts of the poppet were thus in four separate supporting members on each side of the ship, each support consisting of 12in. by 12in. timbers securely bolted together to form a 7ft. wide by 5ft. fore-and-aft compression member between the tops of the sliding-way packing and the cradle shelf-plates. These separate supports were securely tied together fore and aft by ribbands on the inboard and outboard sides. A cushioning effect was provided for the heels of the poppet supports by fitting soft-timber packing on top of the sliding ways, the thickness varying from about 12in. at the fore end to about

Photograph by]

[W. Cull, Birkenhead.

Fig. 5.—Bow View of the " Mauretania " when Commencing to Move.

Fig. 6.—The '' Mauretania '' at about Mid-travel down the Ways.

6in. at the after end. When the stern began to lift, this packing, together with that between the cradle-plates and the shell plating, served to distribute the load as evenly as possible over the full length of the fore-poppet, instead of being entirely concentrated at the fore end.

For a vessel of the launching weight of the *Mauretania*, it was very advisable that there should be a good margin of strength in the construction of the fore-poppet. With this in mind, the builders, in designing this part of the launching arrangements, provided a structure such that the whole load which was anticipated could be taken by the two foremost sling-plates and supports and a reasonable factor of safety still maintained. This assumed case of the total poppet pressure bearing on the two foremost plates is one which might conceivably arise where the cushioning effect of the packing had not functioned sufficiently well to avoid some such heavy concentration of load at the forward part.

The question of the necessity for internal shoring was carefully investigated. It was found, however, that very little shoring was required to bear the pressures which it had been calculated would be brought about during the launch. The structure in the region of the most serious pressure, *viz.*, in way of the fore-poppet, was adequately stiffened by a conveniently placed transverse bulkhead and also by various strong beams in the vicinity. For the purpose of withstanding the maximum pressure on the bottom of the vessel, the floors and framing, it was decided, were sufficiently strong to take the fairly moderate pressure coming upon them. The shoring eventually required was limited to a row of strong timber shores which was provided over each launching-way throughout the machinery spaces between the tank-top plating and the various decks immediately above.

An item in the launching arrangements which attracted a great deal of interest was that no land drags or other similar

Photograph by]   *[F. Hopwood, Liverpool.*

Fig. 7.—The " Mauretania " dropping off the Way-ends.

Immediately abaft the four main cradle-plates referred to previously, seven narrow sling-plates were arranged, one on each frame. Vertical supports, each consisting of seven 12in. by 12in. stilts arranged athwart the sliding-ways, were wedged up under small shelf-plates, which were attached, with deep brackets, to the sling-plates. Between the after end of this series of supports and the amidship portion of the *Mauretania*, vertical timbers were arranged, as necessary, in conjunction with longitudinal ribbands where the height between the sliding-way packing and the hull of the ship permitted these to be worked.

A similarly strong construction to that adopted forward was used in building the after-poppet. In this case, sling-plates were not required, as it was possible to build the poppet stilts vertically between the sliding-ways and the twin-screw bossing. The system of supports used, *viz.*, that of 12in. by 12in. stilts for the full width of the ways on each frame and tied together by fore-and-aft ribbands, may be seen in Fig. 4.

checking mediums were required. Messrs. Cammell, Laird and Co., Ltd., are among the few leading shipbuilders in the world who are fortunate in having an expanse of open water fronting their building berths which is sufficiently large to enable them to launch ships and allow them to come to rest by the braking effect given by the water resistance alone. The Mersey is about one mile wide at the builders' yard, and is of ample depth for launching purposes, even in the case of the largest ships.

The movement of the vessel during the launch proceedings, from first commencing to slide slowly down the ways to the final stage in which she was moored alongside the fitting-out quay of the builders, may be followed from the numerous photographs reproduced herewith. Fig. 5 gives a bow view of the *Mauretania* when just commencing to move, while Fig. 6 shows her after having travelled approximately half the length of the ways. The vessel is shown at the moment of dropping off the way-ends in Fig. 7. She is shown after having been brought under the

Fig. 8.—The " Mauretania " after having been picked up by Tugs.

Fig. 9.—The " Mauretania " in process of being Moored at the Fitting-out Berth.

Photograph by] [Hutchinson, Liverpool.

Fig. 11.—Machinery on Board and Casings in Process of Completion.

Fig. 10.—One of the Yarrow-type Boilers being lifted on Board.

Fig. 13.—The Rudder after being fitted in Dry-dock.

Fig. 12.—The Fore Mast being lifted on Board.

Fig. 14.—One of the Amis Models.

control of tugs in Fig. 8, following which she was safely manœuvred into the fitting-out basin. Fig. 9 is a view of the *Mauretania* as she was in process of being moored at the quayside in readiness for the work of completion.

An indication of the efficiency with which the launching arrangements were carried out is that the work of transferring the *Mauretania* from her building berth to the required position in the fitting-out basin was entirely completed within a period of one hour.

POST-LAUNCH CONSTRUCTION.

The steel structure of the *Mauretania* was well advanced at the time of the launch ; and in the main engine-room, boiler-rooms and generator room the various seatings were practically complete in readiness to take the different parts of the machinery installation which were to be lifted on board when the vessel was alongside the fitting-out quay. There were no large parts of the propelling machinery on board at the time of the launch.

The various stages in her fitting out afloat are illustrated in the photographs reproduced in Figs. 10 to 13. Fig. 10 illustrates one of the Yarrow-type boilers being lifted on board. Fig. 11 is a view of the sun and sports decks, taken at a stage when the deck planking was in process of being laid. It will also be noticed that, at this relatively early stage in fitting out, the machinery and boilers are on board and the casings in place, together with the lower parts of the main funnels. Fig. 12 shows the fore mast being lifted on board by means of the 200-ton floating crane.

On the 14th May, the *Mauretania* was transferred from the fitting-out basin of the builders to the Gladstone Dock, in which final preparations were made in readiness for her preliminary trials. In addition to the work which might be termed the finishing touches carried out during the time the vessel was in dry-dock, one important task—that of shipping the rudder—was reserved for this late stage in the completion. Fig. 13 shows the rudder in position after being fitted.

MODELS.

Two completely-rigged models of the *Mauretania* have been constructed by Messrs. I. R. Amis, Ltd., of London, to the order of the Cunard White Star, Ltd. They have been made to the working drawings from which the ship herself has been constructed, and the scale adopted, *viz.*, $\frac{1}{6}$in. to one foot, has given the models an overall length of 10ft. 9in. These models, one of which is shown in Fig. 14, formed an important part of the publicity released concerning the *Mauretania*, one of them having been televised from Olympia in September, 1938, during the Wireless Exhibition, while the other was shipped to New York in March, 1939, for exhibition at the World's Fair.

A fully-equipped model of the *Mauretania* has also been constructed by Messrs. Bassett-Lowke, Ltd., of Northampton, to the order of Messrs. Cammell, Laird & Co., Ltd., and will form an outstanding feature in the showrooms of the shipbuilders at their office headquarters in Birkenhead. This model, which is illustrated in Fig. 15, has been built to a scale of $\frac{3}{16}$in. to one foot.

Fig. 15.—The Bassett-Lowke Model.

GENERAL EQUIPMENT.

THE installation of deck auxiliary machinery on board the *Mauretania* is electrically driven throughout, and, in the design and arrangement of the various parts of this equipment, full advantage has been taken of the most recent developments in the many branches of engineering represented.

STEERING GEAR.

The steering gear has been manufactured by Messrs. Brown Brothers & Co., Ltd., of Edinburgh, and is of their four-cylinder, electro-hydraulic design, with duplicate power units. These units each consist of a constant-speed, non-reversing electric motor driving a V.S.G. high-pressure, variable-delivery pump. Owing to the simplicity of the design and the robust construction of these pumps, which have been manufactured by the Variable Speed Gear, Ltd., of London and Newcastle-on-Tyne, they are particularly suitable for marine service. The driving motors, which have been provided by Messrs. Laurence, Scott and Electromotors, Ltd., of Norwich, are of the makers' standard marine type, except for certain minor modifications made to meet the Cunard White Star Line's requirements. These motors each develop 120 B.H.P. at a speed of 500 r.p.m. The arrangement of the steering gear may be seen from the plan reproduced in Fig. 1, while the electric motors may be seen from the photograph reproduced in Fig. 2.

Starting gear has been supplied by Messrs. Allen West and Co., Ltd., of Brighton, in the form of two open panels, the starters being of the automatic type and provided with an alternative source of supply through a change-over switch on each panel. These change-over switches are normally closed on their selected supplies, and starting of the equipment is effected by closing the main switch. The warning and alarm signals fitted to the switchgear include a fault lamp which is illuminated and a running lamp which is extinguished in the event of failure of the running contactors. Audible warning is also given if the equipment stops while the main switch is closed. In addition, each item of the equipment is provided with means of hand operation, so that the motors can be started without a supply to the operating coils.

Each power unit is capable of meeting all normal steering requirements, so that, under ordinary sea-going conditions of service, one unit is held in reserve. The time required to move the rudder from hard-over to hard-over under the normal conditions of single-unit steering is 30 seconds. On the occasions when specially rapid manœuvring is required for docking purposes, or in negotiating restricted or tortuous channels, both power units can be used, this having the effect of practically doubling the speed of action of the steering gear. The change-over from the employment of a single motor to both power units or *vice versa*, or from one unit to the other, can be carried out instantaneously by direct control of the appropriate motors.

The four hydraulic cylinders are arranged in pairs at the sides of the rudder-stock, the rams of each pair being coupled together through double bearings in which pivot the vertical pins of the ball crossheads. The last-mentioned, which are bronze-bushed, are free to slide on the circular arms of the tiller, which is keyed to the rudder-stock. The rams are 13in. in diameter and the stroke is 50·4in. The torque which is exerted on the rudder-stock is 700 tons-ft. at the working pressure, the transmitting medium being a first-class mineral oil.

A further refinement is provided in that the arrangement of hydraulic stop valves allows for an emergency which might arise if damage to the cylinders were sustained. In the event of damage or other difficulty occurring in any of the hydraulic cylinders, the sections involved may be isolated from the pressure systems and steering maintained by only one pair of cylinders. The arrangement, which is a standard feature of the makers' electro-hydraulic steering installations, is such as to give four possible combinations of two cylinders each, in addition to the normal condition of operation with all four cylinders.

The steering gear is controlled from the navigating bridge by telemotor equipment of the patent type developed by Messrs. Brown Brothers & Co., Ltd., while an alternative mechanical means of control is available from a pedestal on the docking bridge aft.

The rudder, as mentioned elsewhere, is of the double-plate stream-lined type, with cast-steel frame and forged-steel stock. The whole weight of the rudder, rudder-stock and tiller, in addition to the radial thrusts on the stock, is taken by a combined rudder-carrier and bearing, which has also been supplied by Messrs. Brown, and which is fitted immediately below the tiller. The carrier consists of a massive cast-steel pedestal secured to the deck, and provided with a heavy bronze bush in which the rudder-stock rotates. The tiller rests on a heavy bronze thrust ring on the top of the pedestal. The radial bush and thrust ring are made in halves, and special arrangements are provided to facilitate examination or renewal of these parts without disturbing any other fittings. Efficient lubrication of both the radial and thrust bearings is maintained from oil boxes attached to the tiller.

ANCHORS, CABLES AND OTHER MOORING EQUIPMENT.

The three main bower and spare anchors of the *Mauretania* are of Hall's latest improved pattern, supplied by Messrs. N. Hingley & Sons, Ltd., of Dudley, Staffs., and each weighs 183¼ cwt.

The total weight of the anchors and the associated ship's cable, which comprises 330 fathoms of Tayco stud-link chain cable, is in the region of 96 tons. This cable has been manufactured by Messrs. Samuel Taylor & Sons (Brierley Hill), Ltd., of Brierley Hill, Staffs., and is of $3\frac{3}{16}$-in. diameter steel having an ultimate tensile strength of 31 to 35 tons per sq. in. The equivalent size of the earlier type of iron chain cable which would have been required is $3\frac{3}{8}$-in. diameter.

The steel-wire warping, towing and streaming lines with which the ship is provided have been manufactured by British Ropes, Ltd., of London, etc.

ANCHOR AND WARPING GEAR.

The equipment provided for handling the anchors and steel cables consists of a complete set of electrically-driven combined cable-lifting and warping capstan gear, made by Messrs. Clarke, Chapman & Co., Ltd., of Gateshead, Co. Durham. The cable pull available at the two gypsy heads on the main deck forward is 67 tons at 20ft. per minute, while the two warping capstan heads also fitted are each capable of a pull of 25 tons at 50ft. per minute.

For warping purposes aft there are two Clarke-Chapman vertical capstan heads capable of a pull of 25 tons at 50ft. per minute, the motors and gear for these units being installed below *A* deck.

The control for the cable-lifting gear and the forward and after capstans is of the Clarke Chapman-Ward Leonard booster type.

In addition to the foregoing equipment, two Clarke-Chapman electrically-driven worm and spur-geared warping winches have been provided. One of these winches is fitted forward on the main deck, while the other is on *A* deck aft. Each winch develops a pull of 12 tons at 50ft. per minute, and is arranged to run at speeds up to approximately 200ft. per minute with slack rope. Extended shafts are fitted in each case, the centres of the warping ends being 20ft. 3½in. apart in the case of the forward winch and 21ft. 9½in. in the after winch. Two warping ends are fitted on each winch, each being 2ft. 2½in. in diameter and 2ft. 3½in. in length, and fitted with cast-iron whelps. The motors for driving the winches each develop 56 H.P. at 385 r.p.m. and are of the makers' special built-in type. Control is by means of the Clarke Chapman-Ward Leonard booster system, which consists in each case of a booster motor-generating set of the enclosed, ventilated, drip-proof type and placed below deck for each winch. A watertight master regulator is provided in each case on the open deck beside the winches. Starting switches are arranged in each control position to allow the motor-generating sets to be started and stopped from above the deck on which they are installed. An ammeter is also placed in each control

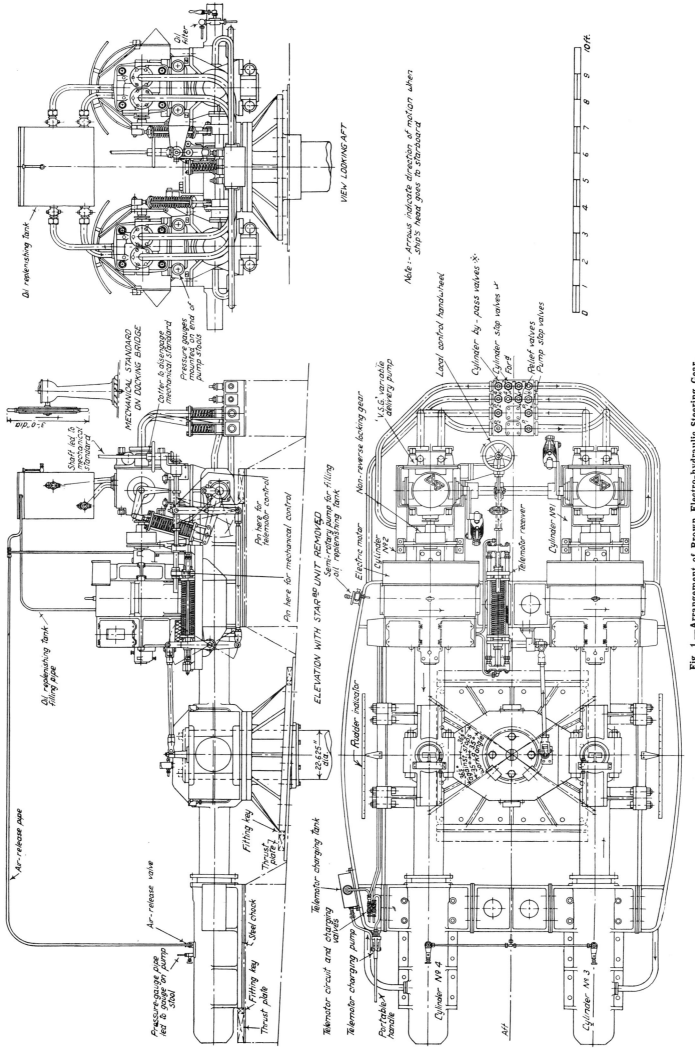

Oil replenishing tank

Oil filter

VIEW LOOKING AFT

MECHANICAL STANDARD ON DOCKING BRIDGE

Totter to disengage mechanical standard

Pressure gauges mounted on end of pump stools

Shaft led to mechanical standard

3'-0" dip

Pin here for telemotor control

Pin here for mechanical control

ELEVATION WITH STAR'BD UNIT REMOVED

Semi-rotary pump for filling oil replenishing tank

Oil replenishing tank filling pipe

Air-release pipe

22.625" dia.

Air-release valve

Fitting key

Thrust plate

Steel chock

Pressure-gauge pipe led to gauge on pump stool

Fitting key

Thrust plate

Telemotor charging tank

Telemotor circuit and charging valves

Telemotor charging pump

Portable handle

Cylinder Nº 4

Aft

Cylinder Nº 3

Note :— Arrows indicate direction of motion when ship's head goes to starboard

Local control handwheel

Cylinder by-pass valves

Cylinder stop valves

Ford

Relief valves

Pump stop valves

V.S.G. variable delivery pump

Non-reverse locking gear

Electric motor

Cylinder Nº 2

Telemotor receiver

Cylinder Nº 1

Rudder indicator

0 1 2 3 4 5 6 7 8 9 10 ft.

Fig. 1.—Arrangement of Brown Electro-hydraulic Steering Gear.

position, and a pilot lamp is arranged to light when the generating set or booster is running.

WINCHES.

The deck machinery includes 14 electrically-driven winches of the standard Scott pattern of the manufacturers —Messrs. Laurence, Scott and Electromotors, Ltd. Of this equipment of winches, 10 are used for the purposes of handling cargo. The arrangement of the winches on the promenade deck forward and on the top of the fore mast-house

Fig. 2.—Steering Gear, showing Laurence-Scott 120-B.H.P. Electric Motors.

Leonard (motor-generator) system of working for large windlasses and capstans, and gives the widest and most flexible control of speed. Automatic control is arranged so that with heavy loads the speed falls ; and in the case of unduly large overloads, the winch stalls in exactly the same way as does a steam winch in similar circumstances. It is not a constant-current system, both voltage and current being controlled ; so that with light loads high speeds are obtained with comparatively

may be seen from Fig. 3. Six of the winches are each of 3 tons working load and develop 28 B.H.P. at 450 r.p.m., two are each of 5 tons working load and of 36 B.H.P. at 260 r.p.m., and the remaining two are each of 5 tons working load and develop 44 B.H.P. at 290 r.p.m.

The last-mentioned winches are of the special Scott motor "reducer" type, illustrated in Fig. 4. These units are worked on a system which is a development of the well-known Ward-

low current input, and with heavy loads the current increases and the speed decreases down to a stalled condition on overload. The consumption of electric power is much lower than with winches worked under a constant-current system. Very slow creeping speeds are obtainable at light loads, for the purpose of drawing cargo out into a position from which it can be lifted through the hatchway without incurring damage. Valuable or fragile cargoes may be gently handled with great convenience, as slow

Fig. 3.—The Scott Winches on the Promenade Deck Forward and on Top of the Fore Mast-house.

Fig. 4.—One of the Scott Motor " Reducer " Winches.

lowering speeds are obtainable at both light and full loads.

The remaining cargo winches referred to previously are provided with the Scott system of " creeping control " and with the makers' latest form of load discriminator. This type of control enables speeds to be obtained, both in hoisting and lowering, down to about one-tenth of the full-load speed, while also permitting high light-hook and lowering speeds to be used.

The equipment also includes four Scott winches, each of 3 tons working load and developing 11½ B.H.P. at 198 r.p.m., which are reserved for handling baggage and stores. These items, in addition, are arranged to work under the system of " creeping control " referred to in the previous paragraph.

DERRICKS.

The five cargo hatchways of the *Mauretania* are served by four derricks, each for a working load of 10 tons, and six derricks, each for a working load of 5 tons. These derricks are all of the tubular-steel type.

CARGO HATCHWAYS.

The cargo hatchways throughout the ship, with the exception of Nos. 1 and 2 hatchways on the main deck forward, have all been fitted with Cocks reinforced wood hatch covers having mild-steel galvanized open-end bands on the covers. These have been supplied by Cocks Reinforced Hatchcovers, Ltd., of Cardiff.

REFRIGERATING INSTALLATION.

The refrigerated chambers for cargo and ship's stores which are referred to in the chapter on the design have been insulated by Messrs. Cammell, Laird and Co., Ltd., the insulating medium being Eldorado compressed cork, supplied by the Cork Insulation & Asbestos Co., Ltd., of London. In connection with this work, it may be mentioned that the shipbuilders have employed Aquaseal, provided by Messrs. Berry, Wiggins and Co., Ltd., of London, for the purpose of sealing the sections of the cork insulation. The timber used in connection with the insulation has been treated with Toritna wood preservative, supplied by the Dry Rot & Fire Prevention Co., Ltd., of London.

The compartments are served by refrigerating plant manufactured by Messrs. L. Sterne & Co., Ltd., of Glasgow, which is capable of eliminating over 3,000,000 B.Th.U. per hour, and is the largest installation yet fitted in any of the Cunard White Star liners.

The refrigerating machinery includes three CO_2 compressors of the Haslam single-acting, vertical, enclosed marine type, each driven by a variable-speed electric motor of 142 H.P. Each compressor is complete with a condenser and liquid precooler, these being of the float-operated type, and the compressors are interconnected so that any unit can be used to do the work of either of the others, although in normal circumstances each compressor will be reserved for a particular service. The duties of the compressors comprise the maintenance of the required temperatures in the refrigerated-cargo chambers and cold storerooms, and the cooling of water in connection with the air-conditioning installation. The last-mentioned cooling is effected by direct expansion of the CO_2, and this part of the refrigerating services requires the elimination of 1,655,000 B.Th.U. per hour. The compressors and condensers are served by two circulating pumps of the vertical-spindle type, which are situated in No. 1 boiler-room. These pumps, each of which delivers 66,000 gallons of brine per hour, are driven by a 20-H.P. electric motor in each case.

Brine for the coils in the refrigerated-cargo and provision chambers is supplied from two evaporators in an insulated room at the forward end of the refrigerating-machinery compartment, and is circulated by three horizontal electrically-driven pumps installed in the evaporator room, the motors for these units, however, being in the refrigerating-machinery room. For the purpose of clearing the air locks, a booster brine pump has also been fitted.

As mentioned previously, the eight refrigerated-cargo

Fig. 5.—Allen West Control Pillars for Refrigerating Plant.

compartments have a total capacity of approximately 92,000 cu. ft. Four of these are cooled by the Sterne latest type of cross-current air-coolers, designed to maintain a temperature of 10 deg. F. for frozen produce, or for higher temperatures for the storage of fruit, eggs, etc. Each of these cargo spaces has its own independent battery and fans to enable entirely different commodities to be stowed in the various compartments. Air is delivered from ducts buried in the insulation of the roof, and returned through ducts which are fitted down each side of the insulated 'tween decks. Provision is made for changing the air. The remaining four refrigerated-cargo chambers are fitted with brine grids on the decks above, ship sides, and the end bulkheads. Special de-frosting arrangements are incorporated to ensure rapid and complete thawing of the snow on the brine grids and air-cooling batteries.

A point of interest in connection with the installation is that the patent Triple Seal piston rings and scrapers of the Standard Piston Ring & Engineering Co., Ltd., of Sheffield, have been adopted in the refrigerating machinery.

The starters for the motors driving the compressors and water-circulating pumps, already referred to, and for the 15-H.P. and 5½-H.P. motors driving the brine-circulating pumps, as well as for the 3-H.P. motors of the air-circulating fans,

have been provided by Messrs. Allen West & Co., Ltd., of Brighton. Some of the control pillars containing the starting gear may be seen in the view of the refrigerating-machinery room reproduced in Fig. 5. The starters for the compressors are of the hand-operated drum type, and are arranged with a double-pole line contactor and over-current release with time lag. A visual indicator showing the position of the starter is provided, and means are arranged for preventing the starter drum being left in a position with some resistance in the motor circuit. A "stop" button is fitted for stopping the motor. The starter housing is hose-proof and of very robust design.

The starters for the motors of the water and brine-circulating pumps are of the same type as those for the compressor starters, while those for the circulating-fan motors are of the face-plate type, fitted with under-voltage release on the starter arm and a rotary-type field regulator. The starters are provided with an over-current release, two main-circuit fuses, and a double-pole isolating switch.

In addition to the main refrigerating plant, there are numerous small compressors, manufactured by Messrs. L. Sterne and Co., Ltd., and which are described in the chapter dealing with the passenger services.

"Mauretania" Entering the Liverpool Dock System *en route* to Gladstone Dock, 16th May, 1939.

EMERGENCY ARRANGEMENTS.

LIFE-SAVING APPLIANCES.

THE lifeboats which have been provided for the *Mauretania* are of three types, as may be seen from the accompanying table, which gives a summary of the equipment. The contract for the supply of these boats has been fulfilled by Messrs. Hugh McLean & Sons, Ltd., of Renfrew.

LIFEBOAT EQUIPMENT.

No.	Type.	Dimensions.	Complement.	
			No. of Persons in each.	Total No. of Persons.
2	Motor lifeboats...	30ft. in length	45	90
14	Oar-propelled lifeboats with auxiliary Diesel engines	30′ 0″ × 10′ 6″ × 4′ 6″	93	1,302
8	Oar-propelled lifeboats	30ft. in length	68	544
24	Grand total			1,936

All the lifeboats are constructed of double-skin Burma teak planking, with the interior finish also of teak, and in every way they comply with the latest requirements of the Board of Trade.

The two motor lifeboats are each fitted with a Thornycroft type-RJ/2, two-cylinder Diesel engine of 21 B.H.P.; while the 14 lifeboats fitted with auxiliary propulsion have each a Thornycroft RJ/1-type Diesel engine of 9 B.H.P. One of these last-mentioned units is illustrated in Fig. 1. Both types of engines are fitted with self-contained reducing and reversing gear, which forms part of the engine unit. The oil-fuel and lubricating-oil strainers on both the 18 and 9-B.H.P. units have been supplied by Auto-Klean Strainers, Ltd., of London, while the bearings of the engines are of the Tandem D.E. Plus type of the Eyre Smelting Co., Ltd., of London.

An interesting feature of these engine installations is their enclosed system of fresh-water circulation. One advantage of such a system lies in that the power units may be run while the boats are in the davits, so that they will be in operation when the craft reach the water. When they are afloat, the enclosed system is cooled by sea-water, which circulates through a copper coil in the tank of the enclosed circulating system.

In addition, it has been possible to ensure that the engines will start, even under the coldest climatic conditions, by the provision of an electric heater in the steel house in which each of the motor-lifeboat engines is installed, and also in the insulated engine casing which surrounds the auxiliary engines of the remaining power-propelled lifeboats. The heaters are connected by a plug to the ship's circuit, and this heating connection is automatically released during the launching of the boats.

The two motor lifeboats are each fitted with a complete wireless installation, supplied by the Marconi International Marine Communication Co., Ltd., of London. The wireless equipment is fitted in the steel house containing the engine in each lifeboat.

The davits in which the lifeboats are carried are of two types, each adapted to suit the different conditions of available space for boat-stowage purposes.

Of the 12 boats on each side of the ship, nine are arranged at a height above the sun deck which gives ample headroom right to the ship-side rail for passengers using that deck. These boats are carried in Taylor gravity davits of the patent type developed by Messrs. Samuel Taylor & Sons (Brierley Hill), Ltd., and of which 18 sets have been provided. These davits (Fig. 2) consist of sloping trackways formed of double rolled-steel channels suitably braced to make a single element, down which the cradles run, carrying the lifeboats from the stowed to the lowering position. The movement of the lifeboats is initiated and maintained by gravity, and is controlled

by suitable winches. The cradles each consist of two parts, *i.e.*, an arm and a carriage. The arm is pivoted to the carriage in such a manner that, as the cradle moves down the trackway, the arm swings outboard, carrying the boat with it into the lowering position. As the carriage reaches the outboard position, it experiences a retardation which affects the movement of the lower part of the arm, while the speed of the upper part of the arm, from which the boat is suspended, is maintained. As a result, when the carriage reaches the outboard position, the impact on the gear and on the ship's structure caused by the destruction of momentum is much reduced.

An important refinement of this type of gravity-davit gear is the keel support which is incorporated in each carriage. During the recovery operation of the davits, the keel support is automatically raised immediately before the boat reaches a stowed position and engages with the keel of the craft, thereby relieving the falls, etc., of load.

At the after end of the promenade deck, two sets of Columbus mechanical davits have been provided on each side of the ship. The two after sets are each arranged to serve two lifeboats, these being stowed one above the other in the davits, while the

Fig. 1.—One of the Thornycroft RJ/1-type 9-B.H.P. Diesel Engines fitted in 14 Lifeboats.

two forward sets are of the ordinary single-boat handling pattern. The Columbus davits, which are shown in Fig. 3, are also the product of Messrs. Taylor.

The steel-wire rope falls used on all these davits have been supplied by Messrs. Martin, Black & Co. (Wire Ropes), Ltd., of Coatbridge, and are of 2⅝-in. and 2-in. circumference. The falls are of galvanized best plough steel, and have been specially treated during manufacture to prevent corrosion and also to give ropes which will not mark the white enamel of the lifeboats and the surrounding gear. These ropes are similar in construction and quality to those supplied by Messrs. Martin, Black & Co. for similar use in the *Queen Mary*, and also to those at present being manufactured for the *Queen Elizabeth*.

To facilitate the recovery of the boats after having been lowered from the davits, 22 electrically-driven boat-hoisting winches have been supplied by Messrs. Samuel Taylor and Sons (Brierley Hill), Ltd. The electric motors for these winches are of the vertical series-wound type of the British Thomson-Houston Co., Ltd., of Rugby, and each motor develops 10 H.P. at 1,180 r.p.m. The controllers for the motors are of the drum type, fitted with a contactor circuit-breaker with over-current and under-voltage releases. An isolating switch is provided. The circuit-breaker is interlocked with the controller drum, so that all current breaking takes place on the contactor. The boat winches are fitted with hand-operated gear so that the boats can be recovered without the use of motor power.

Loud-speakers, operated from the bridge, are fitted at the boat stations.

In accordance with the requirements of the Board of Trade, the capacity provided by the lifeboats is supplemented by buoyant apparatus, and this part of the life-saving equipment has been supplied by Linkleters Patent Ship Fittings Co., Ltd., of North Shields. The outfit comprises 24 buoyant apparatus appliances of the makers' Simplex type, each being 6ft. 9in. by 4ft. 3½in. by 9in. in dimensions. Each appliance is capable of supporting 22 persons, so that a total capacity of 528 persons is provided for by the buoyant apparatus.

Ample lifelines and handholds are supplied, while the sparring and keels or runners are arranged so as to permit efficient ventilation of the apparatus, even if the units are stowed in tiers. The method adopted for securing the sparring is such

sliding and 10 horizontal sliding doors, which are all of the Board of Trade type No. 5.

It is interesting to note that the watertight-bulkhead doors in the new *Mauretania*, as in the case of those in her famous old namesake, have been fitted with the hydraulically-controlled system developed by Messrs. J. Stone & Co., Ltd., of Deptford, London. The number of watertight doors controlled by this power system is 11, as compared with the 38 doors similarly controlled in the first *Mauretania*. The smaller number of doors in the new ship is accounted for by the fact that she is, of course, oil-fired, whereas the old ship was originally coal-fired, this needing a very extensive subdivision below the water-line to arrange the large number of coal bunkers required. Later, when the first *Mauretania* was converted to burn oil, the number of watertight bulkheads was reduced.

The central control of the system in the new ship is from the bridge and is divided into two sections, as may be seen from Fig. 4. One section deals with all the doors in the hold spaces and the other controls those in the passenger-accommodation 'tween decks. The separate sections may be operated independently or simultaneously, in order that, in an emergency,

Fig. 2.—Sun-deck Promenade, showing Taylor Gravity Davits.

Fig. 3.—Tourist-class Promenade, showing Columbus Davits.

as to greatly facilitate removal for inspecting the tanks on the occasions of periodical survey of the life-saving equipment. The robust construction of the appliances is indicated by the fact that, during a Board of Trade drop test, a Simplex buoyant apparatus was twice allowed to fall from a height of 60ft. into the water without in any way affecting the efficiency of the unit.

WATERTIGHT DOORS.

Great attention has been paid to the watertight subdivision of the *Mauretania* so as to provide the highest possible degree of safety, but it was inevitable in the arrangements made for the efficient working of the vessel that a certain minimum number of openings had to be provided in some of the transverse watertight bulkheads, although the desirability of facilitating access was never at any time considered as of the same importance as the necessity for maintaining the intactness of the various watertight divisions. The openings which have been arranged are fitted with power-controlled watertight doors. These doors have been supplied by Messrs. Donkin & Co., Ltd., of Newcastle-on-Tyne, the equipment comprising one vertical

the doors in the holds may be immediately closed as a primary precaution, while the doors in the passenger spaces may be left open to permit free intercommunication between compartments right until danger becomes imminent.

For the information of the officer in charge on the navigating bridge, an electrically-operated indicator has been installed which shows the position and identification number of each watertight door. The closed doors are indicated by the illumination of the individual numbers, these being engraved on coloured discs in the instrument.

Operating power for the system is provided by a pump, a duplicate of which is arranged as a stand-by. The pumps are each capable of developing sufficient fluid, at a pressure of 700lb per sq. in., to close all watertight doors in less than one minute from the commanding officer's order to do so. The pressure control gives an operating load in excess of 6 tons in the hydraulic cylinders, thus making the doors capable of crushing through obstructions.

An important feature of the installation in the *Mauretania* is the hydraulic manual-control gear, this being the first British vessel to be so equipped. The type of hydraulic manual-control gear developed by Messrs. Stone has obvious advantages over the normal type of mechanical hand-gear. If the latter type of hand-gear had been adopted, it would have been necessary for two men to operate each door ; so that 22 men, operating at 11 different stations, would have been required to control the 11 doors. The further disadvantages which are incurred by fitting mechanical hand-gear include the necessity for a sometimes complicated system of shafting which requires to be kept in efficient working order, and the disturbance created in the positions where the shafting for the hand-gear runs through the passenger accommodation.

The hydraulic manual-gear installed in the *Mauretania* is shown in Fig. 5, and consists of three-throw, hand-operated pumps fitted above the margin-line (C) deck. These pumps are connected by separate small-bore pipe-lines to the 11 water-

division. The movement of the doors by local operation is recorded on the indicator fitted on the bridge.

The watertight-door control system of Messrs. Stone has been fitted in many of the world's largest liners, including the *Queen Mary*, with 38 doors. This system is also being installed in the *Queen Elizabeth*, in which 47 doors will be power-controlled in this manner.

There are, in addition, watertight doors giving access through the bridge front on the main-deck level, and similar doors through the bridge front at the promenade-deck level. These doors are of the patent embossed type of Messrs. Mechans, Ltd., of Scotstoun, Glasgow. A recess is stamped all round the edge of the door, and contains a rubber jointing piece which engages with the steel angle frame attached to the bridge-front plating. Watertightness is ensured by means of clip handles and wedges on the door panel.

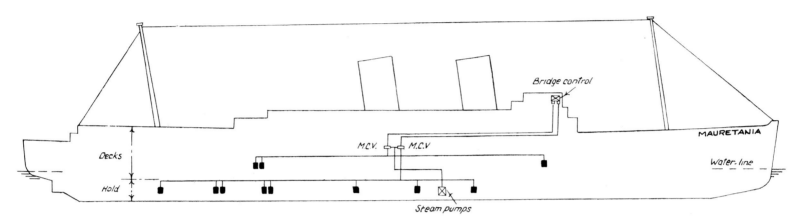

■ *Watertight bulkhead doors*   *M.C.V.   Master control valve*

Fig. 4.—Diagrammatic Arrangement showing Pumps, Master Control Valves and Bridge Control of the Stone System of Hydraulic Control for Watertight-bulkhead Doors.

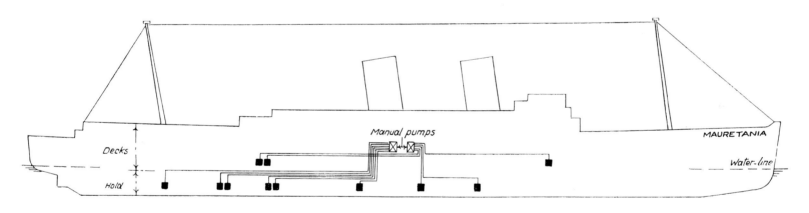

■ *Watertight bulkhead doors*

Fig. 5.—Diagrammatic Arrangement showing Control of the Watertight-bulkhead Doors by the Stone Hydraulic Manual-gear.

tight doors (one pump to six doors) and the other to the five remaining doors. At each hand-pump is a distributor column complete with valves, which control the closing of any door or doors, and a local electrical indicator, which shows when the doors are closed.

While it was anticipated that four men would be necessary to man the hand-pumps, it was found during the trials of the *Mauretania* that two men could efficiently carry out this work. Thus, instead of the 22 men required to work mechanical hand-gear to operate the 11 doors, the number is reduced to two men when the hydraulic manual-control system is employed. Further reasons for the adoption of this system are that the initial cost and the cost of maintenance are lower, while the saving in space occupied by the gear is appreciable.

It is necessary that means be provided in a watertight-door control system for local control in the event of persons being trapped in any one compartment. The doors installed in the *Mauretania* may be opened locally from either side of the bulkhead, but will automatically reclose, thus ensuring the absolute safety of the arrangements for watertight sub-

FIRE PROTECTION.

The *Mauretania* is a good example of the increasing care and attention which are being given to the arrangements made for preventing, detecting and extinguishing fire in ships.

The issues arising from the four main problems in relation to this important part of the equipment of the vessel were all closely examined at a very early stage in the design. The task of eliminating, so far as was known, the causes of fire, the extent to which the vessel might be constructed of incombustible materials, the means of localising any fire which might arise from unknown causes, and, finally, the problem of the most effective methods of detecting and extinguishing fires, were all considered. The decisions made are summarised in the following paragraphs.

(1) *Elimination of the Causes of Fire.*—In this connection, particular attention has been devoted to providing the most efficient and safe form of conduits and other casings in which to carry the electric cables, and also in the design of the various fittings to avoid overheating, etc. As mentioned in another

chapter of this volume, separate heaters have been adopted only in certain of the ship-side staterooms, and in these cases the heaters are of a special type which eliminates any risk of fire. Elsewhere, in the passengers' public rooms and staterooms and in the crew's quarters (with the exception of those spaces which are air-conditioned), the heating is effected by means of trunks which form part of a special mechanical arrangement of combined ventilation and heating.

Safeguards against the possible carelessness of smokers have been arranged in that a good supply of ash-trays and other receptacles has been provided in all public rooms, corridors and staterooms throughout the vessel.

The adoption of Diesel engines for the power-driven lifeboats obviates the necessity for carrying a large supply of highly volatile spirit on board the ship.

(2) *Use of Incombustible Materials.*—While it was recognised that it was impossible to make the whole of a large passenger vessel and her contents of fireproof materials, great care has been taken in equipping the vessel so as to ensure that full advantage has been taken of the opportunities offered. An instance of this policy is seen in that the fire-resisting doors in the ship have been supported from wooden framing, attached to the adjacent bulkheads, which has been treated by the Oxylene process. This fireproofing work has been carried out by the Timber Fireproofing Co., Ltd., of London and Market Bosworth.

In addition to the foregoing, fireproof paint has been used to a considerable extent, as detailed in the chapter on the passenger and crew accommodation.

(3) *Isolation of Fires.*—Steel fire-resisting bulkheads are fitted in accordance with the statutory regulations with regard to spacing and construction. Access openings in these bulk-

number of pipe-lines which run from the cabinet to the various spaces to be protected. By means of a small exhaust fan, air is continuously drawn from each of the various compartments and passed into visual detecting chambers in the cabinet. Any smoke which may be drawn through with the air is conspicuously illuminated by light beams, invisible in clear air, which are projected in each chamber. In addition to this visual method of detection, it should be mentioned that the air, in being drawn from the various spaces, is momentarily by-passed automatically from each pipe-line to a photo-electrically operated unit which, on the presence of smoke, causes alarm gongs to function as an audible warning signal. The air samples drawn from the different compartments may be exhausted into the fire station, thus also providing for the detection of fire by the sense of smell, while the exhaust valve is arranged to discharge the air to the atmosphere in the event of obnoxious odours arising from any cargo which may be carried.

When the presence of fire has been detected by the methods detailed, the space affected is shown on the line-number indicator on the cabinet panel, and it is immediately apparent into which compartment the Lux CO_2 cylinders are to be discharged. There are three batteries of Lux cylinders, and one of these is arranged for slow release in serving as protection to the cargo, motorcar and store spaces. The pipe-lines from the detecting cabinet to these spaces are fitted with Lux three-way carbon-dioxide valves, the positions of which are indicated in Fig. 6, for the purpose of emitting the gas supplied from the battery. The remaining two batteries of CO_2 cylinders are of the quick-release type and are manifolded to quick-opening distributing valves which feed systems of nozzles in the forward and after boiler-rooms and the turbo-generator room, so that an atmos-

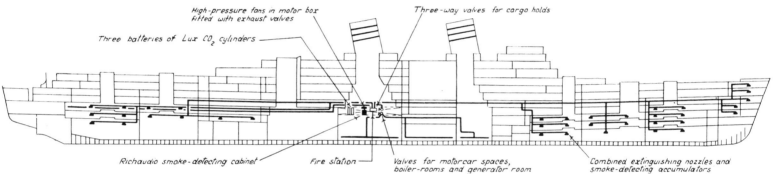

Fig. 6.—**Diagrammatic Representation of the Lux-Richaudio Combined Fire-detecting and Extinguishing System.**

heads are provided with fire-resisting doors of the Kleen-flush type, constructed by Dreadnought Fireproof Doors (1930), Ltd., of Bolton. In all, 38 single-leaf and two double-leaf doors have been fitted in the *Mauretania*. These doors present a fair, flat finish on both sides, and are finished to match the surrounding decorative treatment. Special bronze spring hinges of heavy pattern are fitted to the door leaves, together with internal triple-action shoot-bolts and lever handles of Delta metal. Special door coamings have also been supplied. The doors, and all the fittings in connection therewith, are to the British Board of Trade requirements, and were inspected and passed by surveyors of that authority at the works of the manufacturers before being fitted in the ship.

(4) *Fire-detecting and Extinguishing.*—The arrangements which have been made in connection with fire-detecting and extinguishing have depended on the different types of compartments which have had to be equipped. The large number of compartments and spaces for various purposes in the *Mauretania* have been regarded as being in two categories, *viz.*, spaces which could be easily and regularly patrolled, and compartments which were not so accessible.

The latter class includes cargo spaces, the 'tween decks for the carriage of motorcars, and storerooms. In association with these compartments (as well as the forward and after boiler-rooms and turbo-generator room, as detailed in the chapter on "Main Propelling Machinery") a Lux-Richaudio combined CO_2 smoke-detecting and extinguishing system has been provided. This installation is shown in the diagram reproduced in Fig. 6.

The Richaudio smoke-detecting system consists of a cabinet fitted in the fire station, situated on C deck, and a

phere of inert gas can quickly be produced throughout the protected spaces.

The whole of the passenger accommodation, including the public rooms, stairways and corridors, is protected by an automatic sprinkler and fire-alarm installation on the Grinnell system, provided by Messrs. Mather & Platt, Ltd., of Manchester. This equipment consists of a network of piping of varying sizes, attached to the underside of the overhead decks of the spaces concerned, and charged with water at considerable pressure. At relatively short distances apart on the pipe-lines, automatic sprinkler heads are fitted. These valves serve the dual purpose of fire-detectors and spray nozzles. Each separate unit is entirely automatic in action and is independent of others in the vicinity. Each consists of a screwed fitting, the outlet from which is kept closed in ordinary temperatures by a hemispherical glass valve, normally retained in the shut position by a strut consisting of a quartzoid bulb. This bulb is filled with a liquid which has a very rapid rate of expansion when heated; so that, in the event of a fire, the rising temperature causes the liquid to expand until the bulb is shattered. There being then no support to the glass valve, it falls away and allows the water to be discharged from the orifice with considerable force. The water is deflected by means of a fitting on the lower portion of the sprinkler into the form of a strong spray. Simultaneously, a pressostat is actuated by the freed water, causing an alarm bell to ring, and also showing on the panel of an electrically-operated indicator in the fire-station the precise location of the outbreak.

In the *Mauretania*, the sprinkler system is divided into 27 separate sections or installations, each having its own set of controlling valves and automatic alarm; so that, in the event of the system being brought into use, only a small section of the complete equipment need be shut down to replace the shattered sprinkler bulb.

One of the essential features of the installation is that a sufficient supply of water at the required pressure should always be available, and, in consequence, special consideration has been paid to this detail. The primary supply to the system in the *Mauretania* is fresh water from a tank of ample capacity, the water in the tank being under high air-pressure to ensure that it is all used when this is called for, and at sufficient pressure to give the required force to spray from the sprinklers.

Fig. 7.—Gefit Alarm Bell.

A pump is provided which, in the unlikely event of the fresh-water supply being insufficient to extinguish an outbreak, automatically comes into action and takes water from the sea, discharging it direct into the system.

A fire-alarm indicator has been provided by the Telephone Manufacturing Co., Ltd., of London, and consists of a bronze panel on which are engraved the outlines of the principal spaces on each of the nine decks to which the system applies. These outlines are equipped with a total of 99 red-lamp caps, in positions which correspond to the actual situations of the fire alarms on the respective decks. Test keys are provided which enable the apparatus to be tested locally for continuity of internal wiring, etc., of the indicator, without the necessity of visiting each alarm point throughout the ship.

Some 80 alarm bells of the type illustrated in Fig. 7 have been supplied by Messrs. Gent & Co., Ltd., of Leicester. These large under-dome design bells are tamper-proof and occupy little space on the bulkheads on which they are mounted. The same company have also supplied the " Start fire pump " indicator in connection with the fire-alarm system.

The important task of extinguishing fires which might arise at the cinematograph projectors is accomplished by Pyrene automatic film-fire extinguishers, one of which is fitted to each projector. These appliances, which have been supplied by the Pyrene Co., Ltd., of Middlesex, extinguish fires of this type instantly and automatically in any portion of the film track, and at the same time cut off the current supplied to the arc-lamp and stop the projector motor. This method prevents the possibility of re-ignition of the film. The CO_2 gas used in this automatic extinguisher is distributed throughout the film track, and is brought into action so rapidly that, in the event of a fire, any damage which may be incurred to the film is limited to only one or two frames. The latest improved models provided in the *Mauretania* are each fitted with a tell-tale indicator which shows when the CO_2-gas cylinder has been exhausted, thus obviating the risk of an empty cylinder being fitted in place by mistake. The appliance, in addition to being automatic, is extremely rapid in operation ; and as the gas used is harmless and non-injurious, the projector is capable of being brought into action again with the minimum of delay. In connection with the sound-picture equipment of the *Mauretania*, it may be mentioned that the fire shutters and light ports in all three cinema theatres have been specially designed and fitted by the Western Electric Co., Ltd., of London, to comply fully with the latest fire-control regulations on board ship.

Additional equipment supplied for use in the boiler-rooms and the turbo-generator room includes fire hoses which have been fitted with Fyrex patented nozzles manufactured by the Universal Nozzle Co., of London. These fittings offer many advantages in that the water discharged from the hose is entirely controlled at the nozzle by means of a single movement of the wrist. Instantaneous stream selection is possible, and the supply of water can be varied from a straight jet, for use with ordinary fires, to a finely-atomised water spray suitable for use against fires in the region of electrical plant, as the spray given by the nozzle has been proved during actual tests to be entirely non-conductive. The fitting makes it possible to generate a wide-spreading water curtain for the purpose of driving away smoke surrounding the source of a fire, thus giving better access thereto. Water consumption and possible damage which may be effected during the extinguishing of a fire are reduced to a minimum, as the nozzle also incorporates a shut-off valve, which allows instant control at the point from which the jet is being applied to a fire.

For the use of fire-fighters, 10 sets of Spirelmo smoke-helmet apparatus and several sets of " Salvus " self-contained oxygen breathing equipment have been supplied by Messrs. Siebe, Gorman & Co., Ltd., of London.

NAVIGATING EQUIPMENT AND WIRELESS INSTALLATION.

NAVIGATING EQUIPMENT.

THE task of navigating a large modern passenger liner is always a very responsible part of the organisation of the ship, and it is natural to find, in this connection, that the equipment used in the various duties which come under this heading is as efficient and complete as it is possible to obtain. In the case of the *Mauretania*, the navigating equipment provided is of a most comprehensive character, and comprises instruments which reflect the continued progress being made in the design and manufacture of these specialised fittings. The photograph of the interior of the wheelhouse reproduced in Fig. 1 serves to indicate the completeness of the equipment.

of 47 cells, which give a total capacity of 65 ampere-hours. An automatic alarm has been fitted to the compass equipment for the purpose of warning the officer of the watch when a change-over from the use of mains to the emergency-battery supply has been necessitated.

For steering purposes, a repeater compass of the enlarged-scale type has been mounted on a column stand in the wheelhouse, while a bearing repeater compass has been fitted in each wing of the navigating bridge. Another repeater compass has been installed adjacent to the wireless direction-finder in the wireless-telegraphy room for the use of the operator when obtaining bearings by radio. These repeater compasses are electrically controlled by the master gyro compass.

Fig. 1.—The Wheelhouse.

The vessel is equipped with a master gyro compass of the latest Mark XIV. type of the Sperry Gyroscope Co., Ltd., of London, which gives a permanent indication of the true geographical north, being entirely unaffected by the movement of the ship. This type of compass is designed to give a high degree of accuracy in service, and has, it is claimed, a directive force of more than 150 times that of a standard magnetic type. The equipment, which, with its accessories, is installed in a special master-compass room on the navigating bridge, is designed to operate primarily from the ship's main electrical supply of 220 volts D.C. In the event of failure in the main power system, the compass will automatically continue to operate by means of current supplied from an emergency storage battery which has been provided. The unit selected for this reserve purpose is a NIFE nickel-cadmium alkaline battery supplied by Nife Batteries, Ltd., of Redditch, and consists

The magnetic compasses have been supplied by Messrs. Kelvin, Bottomley & Baird, Ltd., of Glasgow. The 10-in. standard and 10-in. steering compasses provided are of this firm's Kelvite type, while a liquid-type compass has been supplied and fitted aft. The same manufacturers have also been responsible for a Kelvite heavy-duty sounding machine, driven by a 2½-H.P. electric motor and fitted complete with all the necessary accessories.

In addition to the mechanical sounding equipment referred to, the navigating staff will have available the Echometer sounding device which has been installed, this being of the type developed by the Marconi International Marine Communication Co., Ltd., of London. This instrument, which is fitted in the chartroom, gives instantaneously and accurately the depth of water under the keel of the vessel and is not affected by the speed of the ship or the weather conditions prevailing.

Use is made of waves having a frequency above the audible limit, the advantage of using these supersonic frequencies being that they can be concentrated into a beam. This means that they can be transmitted vertically from the ship's hull, with a consequent economy in power. As reception is within a sharply-defined area, it is not affected by submarine or para-

Fig. 2.—One of the Kent Clear-view Screens.

sitic noises. Two means of indication are given by the Echometer, *viz.*, a visual indicator, which, when the instrument is in operation, shows the depth of water numerous times per minute by means of a peak of light on a graduated scale, and also an automatic recorder, which, in addition to giving depth measurements, plots a graph of the contours of the sea-bed which may be kept as a permanent reference. Comparison of the known contours of the sea with those given by the instrument forms a valuable aid to the navigator in determining the position of his ship, and also serves as a check on other methods of obtaining bearings, such as detailed later in connection with the direction-finding apparatus.

To assist further in fixing the position of the ship, submarine-signalling apparatus, including auxiliary gear, for the reception of synchronous wireless and submarine signals, has been supplied by the Submarine Signalling Co. (London), Ltd., of London.

The very complete installation of electric telegraphs comprises instruments for engine, boiler and turbo-generator room intercommunication, and also docking, steering, anchor and cable equipment.

The engine-room telegraphs provide means of independent signals being sent from either side of the navigating bridge to each engine, while the usual arrangements have been made for replies. The boiler-room equipment, for which reply gear is unnecessary, consists of a pedestal-type transmitter, of a similar pattern to the bridge instruments, arranged in the engine-room and communicating with a receiver in each of the forward and after boiler-rooms. Another pedestal-type telegraph in the engine-room provides means for sending orders to and receiving replies from a similar instrument in the turbo-generator room.

The docking telegraphs comprise a twin instrument on the navigating bridge, with port and starboard orders, connected to a similar telegraph on the docking bridge, and a single-dial instrument on the navigating bridge communicating with a similar telegraph on the forecastle. Steering instructions are transmitted from a single-dial instrument in the wheelhouse to a similar telegraph on the docking bridge, while this latter unit is also provided with a change-over switch which enables orders to be sent direct to a bulkhead instrument fitted in the steering-gear compartment. For transmitting anchor and cable instructions there are two further single-dial instruments on the navigating bridge, which control similar telegraphs on the forecastle. The complete installation of telegraphs described

has been supplied by Messrs. Siemens Brothers & Co., Ltd., of Woolwich, London.

The same company have supplied a navigation-lights indicator and an electric rudder indicator, these instruments being fitted in the wheelhouse. The first of these appliances is designed to give an aural signal immediately on the failure of any of the masthead, stern or side lights, while the particular lamp which has ceased to function is also indicated by the extinguishing of a corresponding small light in the deck-plan of the ship reproduced on the front of the indicator. The electric rudder indicator consists of a switch, an indicator and a battery. The angular movements of the rudder are communicated by levers and links to the switch in the steering compartment. This switch controls the indicator installed in the wheelhouse, power being supplied from a battery fitted adjacent to the indicator. The gear is thus independent of the ordinary electric supply of the ship, while the current consumed is so small that, under normal conditions, the battery does not need renewal more than once annually. In the event of a fault in the supply from the battery, the indicator pointer disappears from sight, so that a wrong reading cannot be given.

As detailed elsewhere, other equipment provided by Messrs. Siemens Brothers & Co., Ltd., includes electrical thermometers, shaft-revolution and directional indicators, CO_2 indicators and torsionmeters.

The navigation lights are themselves electrically illuminated under normal conditions of service, but for emergency use oil lanterns have also been fitted. Both the electric and the oil lanterns are of the latest type, and have been supplied by Messrs. William Harvie & Co., Ltd., of Birmingham. The metal portions have been made of extra heavy copper.

An 18-in. searchlight is fitted in a prominent position on the superstructure.

To facilitate the look-out from the bridge during bad weather, the front of the sheltered navigating position is fitted with two 15-in. clear-view screens of the Marine Light type of Messrs. George Kent, Ltd., of Luton, Beds., one of which is illustrated in Fig. 2. It is a matter of interest that these screens—now a familiar feature of many classes of ships— were first supplied to a shipping company in 1918 to meet an order from the Cunard Line, which resulted in three screens being fitted in the old *Mauretania*.

Fig. 3.—Bulkhead-type of Loud-speaking Telephone.

The importance of convenient and reliable means of intercommunication between the various executive departments has been fully realised, and the greatest care has been exercised in the choice and arrangement of the equipment to ensure the efficient working of this essential service. The equipment comprises a system of loud-speaking telephones and also intercommunicating telephones, both sets of these instruments

Fig. 4.—The Marconi Bridge Radio-telephone Installation.

Fig. 5.—Transmitting Room.

having been supplied by the Telephone Manufacturing Co., Ltd., of London.

The loud-speaking telephones (Fig. 3) provide communication between the following positions :—The wheelhouse to the forecastle, crow's nest, fire station, steering-gear compartment, docking bridge, after wheelhouse, wireless-telegraphy office, engine-room, chief engineer's room and chief steward's room ;

engine-room to the switchboard platform in the turbo-generator room, fire-station, chief engineer's room, swimming pool, and Nos. 1 and 2 boiler-rooms ; the switchboard platform to the steering-gear compartment ; and the chief engineer's office to the engine-room and the wheelhouse.

The intercommunicating installation consists of two systems, *viz.*, groups (*a*) and (*b*), which serve the following apartments :—

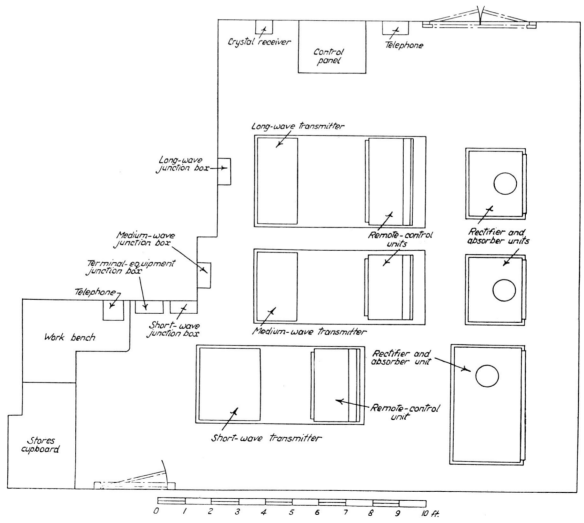

Fig. 6.—Arrangement of Transmitting Room on the Sun Deck.

the forward refrigerating and air-conditioning plant room to the after air-conditioning plant room ; the forward air-conditioning plant room to No. 1 boiler-room ; the turbo-generator room to the air-conditioning plant space in the tunnel ; the

Group (*a*).—Captain's room, staff captain's room, chartroom, chief engineer's room, chief electrician's room, engineers' office, purser's room, cabin-class bureau, tourist-class purser's office, third-class purser's office, printers' shop, wireless-telegraphy receiving room, doctor's room, dispensary, isolation hospital, chief steward's room, ship's side doors, fire-station and amplifier room.

Group (b).—Chief steward's office, second steward's room, tourist-class chief steward's room, third-class chief steward's room, kitchen clerk's office, butcher's shop, meat-handling space, main-deck midship service pantry, provision stores, main bar, cabin-class smoking-room bar, wine cellars, and fire station.

The low-power services generally are supplied with current from two 25-volt motor generators with a stand-by battery, which supply current to telephones, clocks, telegraphs, bells, etc., the distribution being by means of a ring main carried round the vessel.

The sound signalling apparatus with which a large passenger liner such as the *Mauretania* is equipped must meet several requirements, in addition to fulfilling the essential function of making known the ship's presence at satisfactory distances from other vessels and from the shore. The sounds emitted also indicate approximately the size of the vessels from which the signals are heard, this being particularly desirable while navi-

Marine Communication Co., Ltd., of London. International conventions stipulate the minimum requirements to be observed in connection with this aspect of modern ship equipment, but it may be said that the installation provided for this vessel expresses in generous measure not only the letter but the spirit of the regulations. It also caters for every requirement of ship organisation, and provides telegraph and telephone-communication services for the passengers. The *Mauretania* is able to maintain communication by either telegraphy or telephony with ships and telephone subscribers in any part of the world.

When the original *Mauretania* was equipped with wireless-telegraphy apparatus, there was not a single wireless direction-finder at sea, and she became noteworthy as being the first merchant ship in which wireless was used for direction and position-finding. The Marconi-Bellini-Tosi system was installed experimentally early in 1912, and many important discoveries were made by the Marconi engineers during tests undertaken on Atlantic crossings in this famous old vessel—in particular in connection with the effect of the metalwork of the ship on the performance of the equipment.

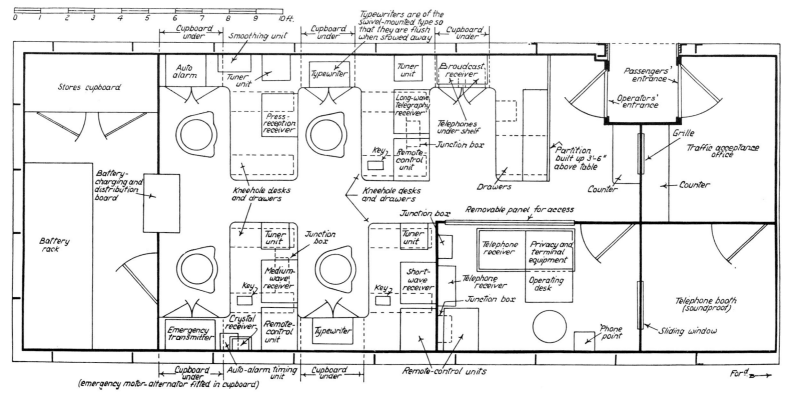

Fig. 7.—Arrangement of Main Wireless-control Room and Telephone Booth on the Sun Deck.

gating in fog. On the other hand, the whistles have to be such as not to disturb the passengers unduly.

For the *Mauretania* there are provided Tyfon whistles, which have been manufactured by Kockums Mekaniska Verkstads Aktiebolag, of Malmö, and supplied by the Industrial and Mining Supplies Co., Ltd., of London. The equipment comprises two whistles of the T 425 DVEK type, having a specially low note which cannot in any circumstance develop into a high shrill overtone. They are steam-operated and have a pitch of note of 100 vibrations per second. In order to ensure that the tone of the units will be clear and of full strength from the commencement of the signal, the whistles are partly steam-jacketed, so that every important part of the sound-producing equipment is kept constantly warm.

The whistles are electrically-operated from switches on the navigating bridge, while equipment is also installed so that signals may be automatically emitted at any required interval of time and of variable duration.

WIRELESS INSTALLATION.

The *Mauretania* has been equipped with the latest type of Marconi wireless-telegraphy apparatus, which incorporates the results of recent research and developments. The wireless equipment has been provided by the Marconi International

The new *Mauretania* is equipped with comprehensive and specially-designed apparatus to enable the following services to be carried out :—

(a) Reception of Press messages ;
(b) Long-wave telegraphy ;
(c) Medium-wave telegraphy ;
(d) Short-wave telegraphy ;
(e) Short-wave commercial telephony ;
(f) Continuous distress watch ;
(g) Direction-finding ;
(h) Emergency transmission on 600 metres.

To provide the foregoing services, nine aerials and three separate transmitters are employed, one transmitter for each of the short, medium and long-wave channels. The medium and long-wave transmitters are suitable for telegraphy only, but the short-wave transmitter is suitable for both telegraphy and telephony.

In addition to these services, the *Mauretania* is equipped with a bridge radio-telephone installation, which enables the officers of the ship to speak by radio-telephony to the shore and to tugs when docking is in progress. The telephone transmitter used, which may be seen in Fig. 4, is of the well-known TW12 type and works on a wave range of 100-250 metres. It can also be arranged to transmit on 600 metres, if required.

There are four separate telegraphy receivers, *viz.*, one each for short, medium and long waves, and one for Press reception. All these receivers are of the same type and can be used for any of the four services, but they are normally reserved for particular channels. The arrangement of the apparatus enables three separate telegraphy services to be carried on at the same time. Thus, for instance, during a transatlantic voyage, the ship is able to maintain communication with another vessel, with the American coast, and with the British coast simultaneously.

These three services are completely independent of the news service. It is perhaps not generally realised that ships of the class of the *Mauretania* are in these times so closely in touch with the world that news reception alone may account for about 8 hours per day of the working time of the wireless installation.

In addition, there is the short-wave telephone service, which enables passengers to communicate with telephone subscribers on shore. Booths have been arranged near to the telegraph office and the lifts, so as to be readily accessible to passengers receiving incoming calls. The telephone equipment is a compressed replica of an inter-Continental wireless-telephone installation, and will permit passengers to communicate with any subscriber either ashore or in a similarly equipped ship in any part of the world in complete privacy, and with the assurance that no unauthorised listener can possibly overhear the conversation. Another feature of the wireless installation is that the telephone transmitter will enable broadcasting to be carried out from the ship and relayed by the broadcasting systems on both sides of the Atlantic.

The latest pattern direction-finder, of the Marconi-Bellini-Tosi type, with fixed aerial and rotating goniometer, has been installed. This has been designed primarily for use on the bridge, and is housed in a robust casting which is mounted directly upon the deck. It presents an appearance similar to that of an ordinary binnacle, and is so constructed that the direction-finding scale is inclined towards the observer and affords clear and accurate observation of the bearings. The second scale on this instrument has been coupled to a repeater which forms part of the gyro-compass equipment, as mentioned earlier in this chapter, so that true Great Circle bearings may be directly observed. A loud-speaker is contained in a panel below the scale. The room on the navigating bridge in which the direction-finder is fitted has direct access to the chartroom. It has been completely lined with copper, and any incoming conductors have been fitted with filters. This thorough screening protects the circuits from electrical interference from the ship, and thus greatly

facilitates operation, with a resultant improvement in the performance.

The auto-alarm equipment is an important part of the wireless installation, and maintains an automatic 600-metre watch continuously for the 24 hours of each day. In the event of an alarm call being received, this instrument rings bells to call the attention of the radio officer and the officer of the watch, while a loud-speaker may also be used for this purpose, if required. This auto-alarm is of unusually robust construction, and a special test unit is incorporated so that the sensitivity can be checked at any time. A standard spark emergency transmitter, tuned to 600 metres, is installed adjacent to the alarm. This equipment is designed to work from an emergency battery. The advantages of the wide frequency band of spark transmitters for real emergency work are fully recognised, and the design of the transmitter makes it especially suitable for this purpose.

Seven radio officers are carried in the *Mauretania* to enable the various wireless services to be speedily and efficiently performed.

Power for the transmitters and receivers is provided by three dynamos, the total power required for the simultaneous working of all services being less than 30 H.P.

With the exception of the complete wireless installation which is fitted in each of the port and starboard motor lifeboats, as mentioned in the chapter dealing with life-saving appliances, the wireless apparatus occupies four positions in the ship. The three alternators are arranged in a special alternator room on *E* deck ; the transmitters are accommodated in the transmitting room (Figs. 5 and 6) on the sun deck ; the direction-finder is arranged on the navigating bridge ; and the remaining equipment, including all receivers, emergency transmitter, automatic alarm, etc., is installed in the main wireless-control room on the sun deck (Fig. 7). There are, in addition to the foregoing, the radio-telephone booths for the use of passengers, as already mentioned.

The whole of the equipment, with the exception of the direction-finder, is controlled from the main wireless-control room. This includes starting and stopping machines, adjusting the power and type of emission of the transmitters, keying, etc. There is provided telephone communication between the wireless-control room and the other three wireless positions, and also communication with the pursers' and the ship's inter-communication system.

A Monarch air-extractor ventilator, supplied by the Monarch Controller Co., Ltd., of London, is fitted in connection with the wireless battery room.

MAIN PROPELLING MACHINERY.

ALL the propelling machinery of the *Mauretania* has been constructed and installed by Messrs. Cammell, Laird and Co., Ltd., of Birkenhead, and incorporates the latest features in marine high-pressure and high-temperature boiler and turbine practice. The complete set of main engines and boilers was designed and constructed within a period of 2½ years, and a primary aim throughout has been the maintenance in service of a rigid sailing schedule, together with maximum fuel economy. In order to achieve this, the closest co-operation has been necessary between the Technical Staff of the Cunard White Star, Ltd., and the Engineering Department of the builders.

The main turbines are of the combined Parsons reaction and impulse type, and are designed for an initial steam pressure of 350lb per sq. in. gauge and a steam temperature of 700 deg. F., together with a condenser vacuum of 0·5lb per sq. in. absolute. Each main turbine unit consists of one high-pressure, one intermediate-pressure and one low-pressure turbine working in series. Each turbine drives a separate double-helical pinion which engages with the main gear-wheel. Astern power is provided by a single three-row high-pressure stage incorporated in the forward end of the intermediate-pressure ahead-turbine casing, together with a single three-row low-pressure stage in the forward end of the low-pressure ahead turbine. The high-pressure and intermediate-pressure ahead turbines are fitted with the Parsons end-tightened type of reaction blading, while the low-pressure ahead turbines are fitted with the radial-clearance type of reaction blading. In the last-mentioned turbines, the blading is arranged on the two-flow principle, with the steam inlet at the middle. The astern turbines are provided with impulse-type blading, and are designed to develop approximately 50 per cent. of the normal ahead power.

The reaction blades in the ahead turbines are made of low-carbon stainless-iron and are assembled in sectors, held at the roots by a foundation wire and brazing, and secured by side-locking strips. All the reaction-blading material for the turbines was supplied by Messrs. C. A. Parsons & Co., Ltd., of Newcastle-on-Tyne, in finished form ready for insertion in the rotor and casing-blade grooves. The nozzle plates in the astern portions of the turbines are made of phosphor bronze with cast-in vanes of Hecla A.T.V. stainless steel, supplied by Messrs. Hadfields, Ltd., of Sheffield. The impulse blades are also of Hecla A.T.V. stainless steel, and are fitted individually into the rotor and casing grooves. This special material is able to withstand high steam temperatures for lengthy periods, and has a high-resistance to the corrosive and erosive actions of contaminated steam. On completion, all the turbine rotors were dynamically balanced to eliminate vibration.

Thrust " dummies " are fitted to the ahead turbines, with the exception of the low-pressure turbines, which are of the double-flow self-balancing type, and any unbalanced axial thrust is taken up by Michell-type thrust bearings. Electric fore-and-aft movement indicators and alarms are attached to the forward ends of the Aspinall patent governors for the purpose of giving warning if excessive axial movement of the turbine rotors does occur.

The high-pressure portions of the turbine casings are constructed of cast steel, while cast iron has been used for the low-pressure casings. A view of one set of main engines on the erecting bed is shown in Fig. 1, while Fig. 3 shows the engines installed on board the vessel. All the steel turbine casings for the *Mauretania* have been supplied by the Atlas Steel Foundry and Engineering Co., Ltd., of Armadale ; while Messrs. Harland and Wolff, Ltd., of Govan, Glasgow, have been responsible for the cast-iron casings. The turbine casings are rigidly bolted at the after ends to the gearcase, the forward ends being supported on cast-iron pedestals which rest on strong steel-plate structures built up from the inner bottom of the ship. Provision has been made for isolating the high-pressure turbines and supplying steam directly to the intermediate-pressure ahead turbines in emergency conditions, and, if necessary, the low-pressure turbines can also be isolated. Each of the turbines is fitted with an Aspinall patent duplicate emergency cut-out governor, provided by Aspinall's Patent Governor Co., of Liverpool, which causes

steam to the turbines to be shut off in the event of the turbine r.p.m. exceeding a predetermined figure. The governors control the main bulkhead steam valves through the medium of the lubricating-oil system, and steam is also automatically shut off in the event of an undue drop in lubricating-oil pressure.

Shell B.C.9 lubricating oil was used exclusively during the tests of the main propelling machinery, and the same grade of lubricant will be used in the engines, turbo-generators and steering gear under service conditions.

MAIN REDUCTION GEARING.

The reduction gearing is of the conventional double-helical single-reduction type, with pinions about 17in. in diameter, driven at 1,446 r.p.m., and engaging with the main gear-wheels, which are approximately 14ft. 6in. in diameter and drive the propeller shafting at 140 r.p.m. The gear-wheels, which are of exceptional dimensions, weigh about 85 tons each, and are actually larger than those fitted in the Cunard White Star liner *Queen Mary.* All the pinions are connected to their respective rotors by flexible claw-type couplings, and the teeth of the gears are 1in. pitch, with a helical angle of about 30 deg. The gears were cut on hobbing machines embodying patent creep-mechanism, and having special arrangements for maintaining a constant temperature. The pinions and gear-wheels are enclosed in substantial cast-iron gearcases, and turning gear for the main engines is secured to the after end of the gearcases. The 8-ft. diameter turbine-turning wheels are mounted on the forward thrust-shaft couplings, and are driven by Laurence-Scott 30-H.P. electric motors through spur and worm-reduction gearing.

One of the gearcases, the castings for both of which were supplied by Messrs. Harland & Wolff, Ltd., is illustrated in Fig. 2, while a finished gear-wheel is shown in Fig. 4. The cast-iron centres of the gear-wheels were provided by Messrs. Harland & Wolff, Ltd., while the forgings for the gear-wheel spindles and wheel rims were the product of the English Steel Corporation, Ltd., of Sheffield. The last-mentioned company have also supplied the pinion, turbine-rotor spindle and propeller shaft forgings. The Atlas Steel Foundry & Engineering Co., Ltd., have provided nozzle boxes, worm-wheels and main valve castings for the machinery installation. The Northern Aluminium Co., Ltd., of London, etc., have supplied a considerable number of details, such as gearcase inspection doors, hand-hole covers, grids for the main-engine forced-lubrication system, etc.

TURBINE-LIFTING GEAR.

To facilitate main-turbine and gearing overhauls, a very complete lifting equipment is provided. This consists of lifting girders fitted in the engine-room and designed to carry the two overhead geared travellers, on which are arranged the geared lifting blocks for dealing with the heavier units up to 30 tons. There are also 12½-ton and 7½-ton geared blocks for smaller lifts, and one pair of 3-ton and one of 1-ton chain blocks are carried for minor work. All these blocks have been supplied by Messrs. Herbert Morris, Ltd., of Loughborough. The lifting girders fitted in the ship, as well as all the special lifting girders for handling the turbine casings and rotors, together with the gearing and gear casings, have been made and fitted by Messrs. Cammell, Laird & Co., Ltd. In addition to this equipment, a great number of large-size eyebolts, shackles and special wire-rope slings have been provided for the ship. Special lifting gear is also arranged for the condenser doors, and further equipment is designed to traverse any part of the main engines to the base of the engine-room casing.

PROPELLERS AND SHAFTING.

The propeller thrust is carried by the latest type of Michell single-collar thrust blocks, manufactured by Michell Bearings, Ltd., of Newcastle-on-Tyne, and each block is fitted immediately aft of the gearcases. The propeller shafting is made from solid mild-steel forgings, and is supported, in each line, by 12 ring oiling bearings. The aftermost bearing in each line is arranged to take a trailing collar and has a hinged cap for ease of inspection. The shaft bearings are water-cooled by an upright

Fig. 1.—Starboard Turbines and Gearing on Erecting Bed.

Fig. 2.—Starboard Gearcase.

Fig. 3.—View of Engine-room, looking Aft.

centrifugal tunnel water-service pump, which has been manufactured by Messrs. Drysdale & Co., Ltd., of Yoker, Glasgow. This pump also supplies the stern-tubes, which are, in addition, provided with a supply of lubricating oil delivered by a special mechanical lubricator having five feeds and coupled to a $\frac{1}{2}$-H.P. worm-geared motor. This lubricator, which has been supplied by Messrs. C. C. Wakefield & Co., Ltd., of London, also delivers oil under pressure to the rudder pintles.

The propellers have been provided by the Manganese Bronze and Brass Co., Ltd., of London, and are of the Scimitar type, with four blades. Each is made of this company's special high-tensile Parsons manganese bronze, is 19ft. 3in. in diameter, and weighs approximately 24 tons. The propellers were machined, dressed and finished to a high degree of accuracy in regard to pitch and thickness, and then statically balanced on completion. Ford electrical torsionmeters, with distant-reading indicators, have been supplied by Messrs. Siemens Brothers & Co., Ltd., of Woolwich, London, and one is fitted to each line of propeller shafting.

CLOSED FEED-WATER SYSTEM.

A diagrammatic arrangement of the closed-feed system is reproduced in Fig. 5, and it will be seen that there are two main condensers, each underslung below its respective low-pressure turbine. These are of the Weir two-flow regenerative type, manufactured by Messrs. Cammell, Laird & Co., Ltd. Each condenser has a cooling surface of 19,700 sq. ft., and houses 7,300 tubes $\frac{3}{4}$in. diameter by 14ft. $2\frac{7}{16}$in. long. The tubes are of solid-drawn aluminium-bronze supplied by I.C.I. Metals, Ltd., of Witton, Birmingham. Both ends of the tubes are secured in their tube-plates by John Crane flexible metallic packing and screwed ferrules of aluminium-bronze—all provided by Crane Packing, Ltd., of Slough, Bucks. The condensers are designed to maintain a vacuum of 29in. Hg. with a sea temperature of 60 deg. F., the circulating pumps being Drysdale Upright-type units driven by Laurence-Scott 115/125-H.P. motors at 550 to 300 r.p.m.

Each condenser is provided with a large reservoir at the base, and a Weir automatic closed-feed controller admits additional feed into the condenser or discharges it from the condenser to the feed tanks, according to the power demand.

Fig. 4.—The 85-ton Main Gear-wheel.

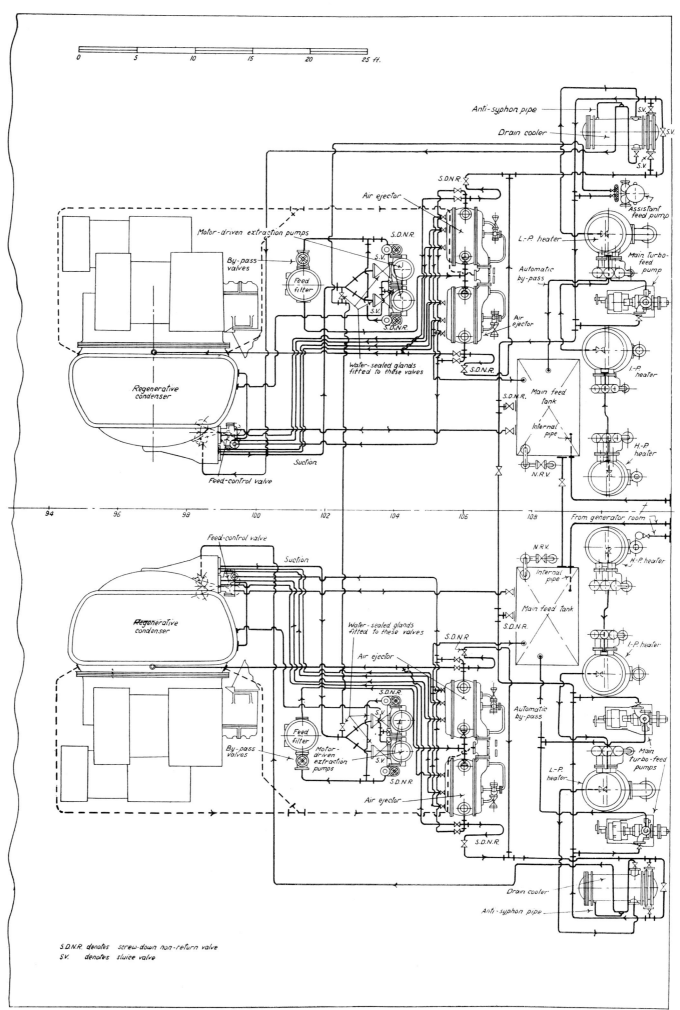

Fig. 5.—Arrangement of Closed-feed System in Engine-room.

Fig. 6.—Hocking Climax Feed Filter.

Thus, any water admitted into the condenser is effectively de-aerated. The condensate is withdrawn from the condenser by Weir Lo-Hed vertical-spindle pumps, each pump being capable of delivering a maximum of 245,000℔ of water per hour when drawing from a vacuum of 29in. Hg. and delivering against a pressure of 27·7℔ per sq. in. The pumps run at 1,200 to 1,350 r.p.m. and have two stages, the impeller in the first stage being of Monel, while the second-stage impeller is of gun-metal. Two pumps are installed (one normally working and one stand-by) for each set of engines. Two Climax low-pressure feed-water filters, manufactured by Messrs. Hocking & Co., Ltd., of Liverpool, are fitted on the discharge side of each set of extraction pumps, each filter being capable of handling up to 240,000℔ of feed-water per hour. A Climax filter is illustrated in Fig. 6.

Weir steam-jet air-ejectors are provided—one set working and one set stand-by—for each main condenser. These ejectors are of the Weir Maxivac type, No. 5 size, and have three stages. The ejector coolers are circulated with the condensate discharged from the extraction pumps, and steam is supplied to the nozzles at 250℔ per sq. in. gauge and 700 deg. F. temperature.

On leaving the ejector coolers, the condensate from each condenser passes through a Weir four-flow drain cooler having a surface of 320 sq. ft. and capable of raising the temperature of the feed-water from 83 to 103 deg. F. The heating medium consists of the drains from the low-pressure heater.

The cooler drains flow to the main condensers at approximately 130 deg. F. The main condensate passes from the drain coolers to the main turbo-feed suction. Three Weir turbine-driven multi-stage feed pumps are installed, two normally working and one stand-by, and each pump is capable of delivering 230,000℔ of feed-water per hour against a discharge pressure of 565℔ per sq. in. gauge. They are supplied with steam at 320℔ per sq. in. gauge, superheated 250 deg. F., the turbines being of normal Weir design with Monel blading and shrouding. An over-speed safety governor and an automatic pressure regulator are provided.

The pumps are of the two-stage barrel-casing type, with Monel impellers and diffuser rings. The turbo-feed pumps discharge the feed through the Weir low-pressure feed-water heaters, each having a surface of 900 sq. ft., and capable of raising the temperature

of 230,000℔ of feed-water per hour from 103 to 187 deg. F. The heaters are supplied with steam bled at 12℔ per sq. in. absolute, each heater taking approximately 15,350℔ of steam per hour. The low-pressure heaters also take the drains from the intermediate-pressure heaters, and are arranged with six flows on the water side.

Fig. 7.—Intermediate-pressure Feed-water Heater—Weir Multiflow Type.

From the low-pressure heaters the feed-water passes to two intermediate-pressure heaters, also of the Weir multiflow type, each having a surface of 600 sq. ft. and capable of raising the feed temperature from 186 to 288 deg. F. when supplied with approximately 23,250℔ of steam per hour bled at a pressure of 90 ℔ per sq. in. absolute. Views of one of the intermediate-pressure heaters are reproduced in Figs. 7 and 8. The last stage of feed-heating takes place in two Weir multiflow heaters, each of 340 sq. ft. surface, and capable of raising the temperature of the feed from 288 to 350 deg. F. when supplied with approximately 15,700℔ of steam per hour bled from the turbines at 217℔ per sq. in. absolute. The high-pressure heaters are arranged

Fig. 8.—Intermediate-pressure Heater, showing Pair of Tube Elements during Erection.

with four flows on the water side, and the drains are taken to the intermediate-pressure heaters.

In addition to the main feed system, the auxiliary system is designed to operate as a closed-feed circuit, and comprises an auxiliary condenser, extraction pumps, air-ejector, feed pumps and feed-water heater. Since the condensate from the turbo-generating sets is delivered to a separate feed tank for port use, and is not contained in the closed-feed system itself, arrangements are made for the feed to be taken through the auxiliary condenser from the feed tank before passing to the

pumps are of the Weir Lo-Hed type, one steam-driven and one electrically-driven, each pump being capable of the entire duty of 40,000lb of water per hour against 25lb per sq. in. The electrically-driven pump is operated by an Allen 8·5-H.P. motor running at 1,500 to 1,650 r.p.m. A Hocking Climax duplex low-pressure feed-water filter is fitted on the discharge side of the extraction pumps, and is capable of dealing with 40,000lb of water per hour. This filter has two sections, either of which can be cleaned while the other is working, or both sections can be worked in series, if desired.

Fig. 9.—Control Station in Engine-room.

harbour-service feed pumps, to ensure that all feed-water in the circuit is fully de-aerated. The capacities of the auxiliary condenser and the auxiliary extraction pumps have therefore been increased to allow for this.

The auxiliary condenser is a Weir regenerative unit built by Messrs. Cammell, Laird & Co., Ltd., and can handle 15,000lb of steam per hour, in addition to some 30,000lb of drains per hour. It has a cooling surface of 850 sq. ft., and works with a vacuum of 26in. Hg. when the sea temperature is 60 deg. F. It is circulated by a Drysdale Upright pump capable of delivering 700 gallons of water per minute. The two auxiliary extraction

A Weir two-stage air-ejector is provided, and the feed-water is handled by one of two Weir turbo-feed pumps, similar in design to the main feed pumps. A Weir multiflow feed-heater is used to raise the auxiliary feed-water temperature from 127 to 225 deg. F. when supplied with steam at 12lb per sq. in. gauge, the maximum capacity being 30,000lb of water per hour. Two Weir direct-acting assistant feed pumps, with a capacity of 2,500 gallons per hour, have also been supplied. In connection with the Weir plant, the Atlas Steel Foundry & Engineering Co., Ltd., have provided pump casings and water-tube headers.

Fig. 10.—Four of the six Drysdale Centrex Forced-lubrication Pumps,
with Laurence-Scott Motors.

CONTROL STATION.

A feature of the machinery-space design is the preservation of a continuously straight line and level passage throughout its length. To maintain this line, and because the starting platform is arranged on the same level as the boiler furnaces and electric generators in the auxiliary engine-room, it is made in two sections with a connecting bridge joining the two halves. The various control instruments are mounted on a well-finished gauge board illustrated in Fig. 9, a clinometer being arranged on this at the centre-line of the vessel.

Fig. 11.—Monitor Pressure Alarm
(Electric Type).

Immediately below are the ammeters, voltmeters and pilot lamps connected to the four generators. Below these electrical instruments is a barometer, flanked on either side by flush-mounted clocks. One of the last-mentioned is spring-operated and the other electrically-operated.

Control of each set of main engines is effected by three large-diameter hand-wheels. One of these is for ahead working and one for astern working, while the third operates an astern-turbine isolating valve. The ahead and astern control wheels are supported on a single pedestal. In the centre of each half of the gauge board, and immediately in front of the dual-control pedestal, the electric telegraphs and the 12-in. diameter electric gongs, one of which is provided for each instrument, are arranged. The telegraph communication between the

Fig. 12.—One of the two De Laval Lubricating-oil Purifiers, with
Laurence-Scott Motor and Starter.

machinery spaces and the bridge is described in the chapter on navigating equipment. The electrical revolution indicators are located above the telegraphs, these instruments being the products of Messrs. Siemens Brothers & Co., Ltd. They are of the Elliott 12-in. dial sector pattern, and record the revolutions and direction of the engine. On either side of these instruments, steam-pressure and temperature gauges are fixed, while other gauges on the board indicate the condenser vacua, condensate temperature and main-feed temperature.

Integrating engine-revolution counters, made by Chadburn's (Ship) Telegraph Co., Ltd., of Bootle, Liverpool, are arranged on either side of the board, and an electrical thrust alarm indicator and a Monitor-type forced-lubrication alarm are also included. The latter gives visible and audible warnings of abnormal conditions. The extreme wing positions are taken up by pressure and temperature gauges for the de-superheated auxiliary-steam supply, and by the engine-telegraph gong. The board also carries the " Start fire pump " indicator and other gauges in connection with the sprinkler fire-protection system fitted throughout the ship. Just clear of the board, on the port and starboard sides respectively, are electric-telegraph instruments, arranged for communication with the boiler-rooms and the electric-generator room. This part of the system of telegraph inter-

Fig. 13.—Serck Standard Vertical
Lubricating-oil Cooler.

communication is also described in the chapter on navigating equipment.

On separate panels, fixed on the after side of the port and starboard hotwell tanks, two additional control boards are fitted. On the port side is located a Crockatt-type salinometer, which indicates by red warning lamps the presence of salt in either condenser or in the distiller discharge. Indicators reading from 0 to 3 grains of salt per gallon are provided, and also a Neon pilot lamp to show that the circuit is operating. There is a total of nine points, and the degree of salinity at which the warning lamps and alarm bell operate is predetermined by means of relay adjusters. A four-way telephone instrument is placed on the same board. On the starboard side there are three special telephones for communication with the wheelhouse, the fire station and the turbo-generator room. This panel also carries a Monitor float-alarm panel, made by Monitor Patent Safety Devices, Ltd., of Wallsend-on-Tyne. It is connected up to the hotwells, and, by the operation of Klaxon horns, gives an audible indication of any abnormal condition of the feed-water level in the hotwell tanks. The horns have been supplied by Klaxon, Ltd., of London, and are of the company's Model A.S.1.

GENERAL ARRANGEMENT OF MACHINERY AND BOILERS.

In general, the machinery arrange⁻ ment of the *Mauretania* follows the lines adopted for most modern liners comparable in size, power and speed. All the machinery is arranged in four separate watertight compartments, the main engine-room being 67ft. long and extending across the full width of the ship. In this space are the two independent sets of single-reduction geared turbines which drive the twin screws, and there are also the auxiliaries used in connection with the closed-feed system, the circulating pumps and other general-purpose units. At the after end of the engine-room, and separated from it by a screen bulkhead, is a recess housing the water-softening plant. In the wings of the engine-room, at *E* deck, are located the engineers' stores, workshop, auxiliary switchboard and wireless-telegraphy alternator room. Directly above the machinery space and forward of the engine casing is a fan room, which contains two ventilating units for supplying air to the engine-room. An engineers' lift is fitted in the engine casing, and affords rapid transport between the first platform in the engine-room and the engineers' accommodation.

No. 2 boiler-room is forward of the engine-room, and contains four of the six high-pressure water-tube boilers, with an installation of fuel-oil pumping and heating units, a fuel-oil transfer pump and a bilge pump. This space is flanked by fuel-oil storage and settling tanks, above which, at *D* deck, are four forced-draught fans for supplying this boiler-room. All the boilers are designed to work under forced-draught, closed-stokehold conditions. The forced-draught arrangement is unusual in that the boiler casings are utilised as air-supply trunks to the forced-draught fans. These casings are separated from the boiler-room space by screens, through which the fans discharge air into the closed stokehold. The fan-discharge trunks are fitted with automatic valves, so that, should a fan be stopped, the air pressure created by the remaining fans in the stokehold automatically isolates that fan.

The electric-generator room is situated between Nos. 1 and 2 boiler-rooms. This space houses the electric-generating plant, which comprises four steam-driven geared turbo-generators, each of 800 kW. capacity, and capable of supplying power for the propelling machinery auxiliaries and all other electrical requirements throughout the ship. This space also contains an installation for feeding the boilers when in port, as well as

other auxiliary machinery for general purposes and ship hotel services. The main switchboard extends across the width of this compartment, and is arranged on a platform above the generators. No. 1 boiler-room is forward of this compartment, and contains two high-pressure water-tube boilers as well as the fuel-oil pumping and heating units and other machinery. The arrangements in this space are generally similar to those in No. 2 boiler-room ; and two forced-draught fans, situated on flats above the wing fuel-oil deep tanks, discharge air into the closed stokehold. One boiler in each boiler-room is provided with de-superheaters to supply steam for auxiliary purposes. These two boilers are also fitted with a special direct-air supply to allow them to work under open-stokehold conditions in harbour.

AUXILIARY MACHINERY IN ENGINE-ROOM.

The general arrangement of the machinery in the engine-room is shown on Plate V. The expansion of the steam mains in the engine and boiler-rooms is accommodated by the use of corrugated pipes made by Messrs. Aiton and Co., Ltd., of Derby. The pipes from the superheater outlets are of 7½-in. bore, and the main steam-pipes to the turbines are of 12-in. bore. They have been designed for a working pressure of 435lb per sq. in. and a steam temperature of 725 deg. F. The use of corrugated pipes has effected a saving in the length of the main steam-pipe, with a consequent reduction in weight, space and thermal losses, and, at the same time, the reacting forces at the points of anchorage will be considerably reduced in service. The Chesterfield Tube Co., Ltd., of Chesterfield, have provided cold-drawn weldless-steel steam-pipes in sizes ranging from 7½ to 12-in. bore. The main steam-pipes, as well as the main feed systems, are arranged so that one set of engines with a group of three boilers can be operated independently of the other set. The main-steam bulkhead and emergency cross-connection valves have been provided by Messrs. Cockburns, Ltd., of Cardonald, Glasgow, and are cast in one unit ; while the Atlas Steel Foundry and Engineering Co., Ltd., have been responsible for the castings. The emergency gear is actuated by oil pressure from an Aspinall patent governor, as already mentioned, and the manœuvring valves are of the Cockburn super-balanced type, which requires the minimum effort to open and close the valves. A further feature of these valves is the arrangement of the spring crossheads, which prevents locking of the gear when the handwheel has been spun, and obviates the danger of the valve seizing due to unequal expansion of the chest and spindle. High nickel bronzes have been used for the seats, guides, lids, etc., in these valves.

Fig. 14.—Emergency Bilge and Fire-pump Starter.

The forced-lubrication systems for the two main engines are separate and independent. Three Drysdale Centrex forced-lubrication pumps are provided, two working and one stand-by, for each set of machinery, and each is capable of delivering 18,000 gallons of lubricating oil per hour against a head of 125ft. These pumps, which are each driven by a Laurence-Scott electric motor of 15/25 H.P. at 1,300/1,700 r.p.m., are illustrated in Fig. 10. The oil is drawn from the drain tank (in the double bottom) through strainers and discharged through filters to the oil-coolers, and thence to the bearings and gears. Separate valves are fitted at the bearings to regulate the flow of oil, as required, and a Monitor electric-type pressure-alarm device is fitted in each discharge system, so that, in the event of the oil pressure falling below a predetermined value, adequate warning is given. These appliances have been supplied by the Monitor Patent Safety Devices, Ltd., and an illustration of one of them is given in Fig. 11.

Two De Laval lubricating-oil purifiers, provided by the

Alfa-Laval Co., Ltd., of Brentford, Middlesex, are installed for lubricating-oil purification. Each purifier is fitted with a 2⅓-H.P. motor and a positive rotary-gear pump, driven from the purifier shaft and mounted on a bracket attached to the body of the main unit. Each machine is provided with bowl-lifting and handling gear, and is capable of dealing with 450 gallons of oil per hour, depending upon the physical properties and condition of the oil. The motors and starters for these units have been manufactured by Messrs. Laurence, Scott and Electromotors, Ltd., and may be seen in the photograph of one of the purifiers reproduced in Fig. 12.

Two lubricating-oil coolers have been supplied by Serck Radiators, Ltd., of Greet, Birmingham, for each set of main engines. These coolers are fitted with Serck patent duplex rotary valves, which enable the lubricating oil to be readily controlled in accordance with running conditions. An external view of one of these coolers is reproduced in Fig. 13. The filters on the discharge side of the lubricating-oil pumps are fitted in duplicate in each system, and are of the Auto-Klean type supplied by Auto-Klean Strainers, Ltd., of London. Each strainer has two cartridges equivalent to 80 by 80 mesh, and the only attention required during a voyage is the turning of a handle, which cleans the strainer while in use. The rated capacity of each strainer is 18,000 gallons of oil per hour.

For general-service duties, the engine-room contains a fire and wash-deck pump, a ballast pump, an emergency bilge and

new Caird & Rayner float-control feed gear is capable of operating under either condition with the minimum of adjustment. Raw feed-water is forced into the evaporators from the double-bottom tanks by a pump of the motor-driven, vertical, two-throw ram type. This pump, which has been manufactured by Messrs. Frank Pearn & Co., Ltd., of West Gorton, Manchester, is driven by a Laurence-Scott motor.

The water-softening installation for the boiler feed-water has been provided by the Paterson Engineering Co., Ltd., of London, and is located in the engine-room recess. It consists of lime-soda and Basex softeners, complete with pressure filters, and has a capacity of 1,000 gallons per hour. The lime-soda equipment includes a lime reagent container with agitators, an injection pump and motor, a reaction tank 9ft. diameter by 9ft. deep, and two 2ft. 6in. diameter pressure filters, complete with control valves, piping and filtering medium. The two Basex units, each 21in. diameter, are complete with the necessary bed of Basex softening material, brine-preparing tank and a special brine-distributing system. A rate-of-flow indicator for fitting in the delivery main, together with testing equipment, has also been provided ; while two vertical motor-driven Drysdale Rotary-Centrex pumps are fitted for supplying the plant with raw or partially-softened water.

In connection with the hot-water service throughout the vessel, Messrs. Royles, Ltd., of Irlam, Manchester, have been responsible for four of their Row's patent storage calorifiers,

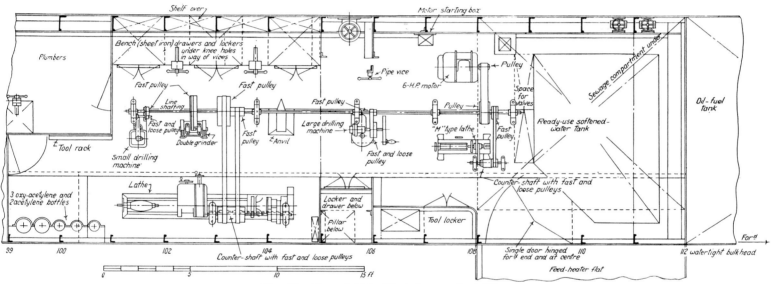

Fig. 15.—Plan of Main Workshop on Port Side.

fire pump, and, in the engine-room recess, a tunnel water-service pump. All these pumps, as well as the main circulating and forced-lubrication pumps, are of the vertical motor-driven type, and have been supplied by Messrs. Drysdale & Co., Ltd., the motors being by Messrs. Laurence, Scott & Electromotors, Ltd. The controller for the emergency bilge and fire pump, which is of a special automatic type, is by the Watford Electric and Manufacturing Co., Ltd., of Watford. This starter can be operated locally by push-buttons fitted on the front below the door, or remotely by the control box. A feature of the starter is its accessibility, and the internal slab can be lowered to the horizontal position by releasing two spring catches at the top corners. A photograph of this equipment is reproduced in Fig. 14. The other controllers are by Messrs. Allen West and Co., Ltd., of Brighton.

Make-up feed-water for the boilers is supplied from two evaporators, each capable of producing 60 tons of fresh water per 24 hours, and installed in the engine-room. These have been manufactured by Messrs. Caird & Rayner, Ltd., of London, who also provided a distiller, with a capacity of 120 tons per hour, for use in conjunction with the evaporators. The latter are suitable for working with steam at 75lb per sq. in. gauge and 450 deg. F. temperature, and are arranged for feeding with either sea or fresh water. The float-control gear is worthy of comment in that, to produce the correct ebullition height in the evaporator so as to avoid priming, a different mean water level is necessary for the sea and fresh-water working. The

fitted with Row's patent indented tubes, and specially designed and constructed for the *Mauretania*. The two hot fresh-water calorifiers are of the horizontal cylindrical storage type, each capable of raising 5,000 gallons of water per hour from 50 to 150 deg. F. when using steam at 50lb per sq. in. The two hot salt-water calorifiers are each capable of raising 6,000 gallons of water per hour from 50 to 150 deg. F. with steam at 50lb per sq. in. The shells of these calorifiers are of copper, with naval-brass tube-plates and solid-drawn copper heating tubes, and thermostatic control is employed. In the fresh-water units all parts coming into contact with water are tinned. Messrs. Worthington-Simpson, Ltd., of Newark-on-Trent, have supplied two of their ¾ VI. vertical split-casing centrifugal pumps for hot fresh-water and hot salt-water circulating purposes. The hot fresh-water pump has a capacity of 7,000 gallons per hour against a head of 30ft. when working at 1,300 r.p.m., and the hot salt-water pump has a capacity of 9,000 gallons per hour against a head of 30ft. when running at 1,400 r.p.m. Each pump is driven by a Laurence-Scott 3-H.P. constant-speed motor.

Sluice and reflux valves for the circulating water, fuel-oil, ballast and refrigerating plants have been supplied by Messrs. Hamilton, Woods & Co., Ltd., of Salford, Manchester ; while Messrs. Alley & MacLellan, Ltd., have supplied from their Worcester works 24-in. bore sluice valves in cast iron and cast steel. Messrs. James Walker & Co., Ltd., of Woking, have been responsible for quantities of their jointing specialities in connection with the machinery and boiler installations.

The largest group of associated auxiliary machinery in the engine-room is, of course, that in connection with the Weir closed-feed system, which has already been described.

VENTILATION OF MACHINERY SPACE.

Ventilation in the main engine-room is effected by two supply and two exhaust fans, all four machines having been made by the Winsor Engineering Co., Ltd., of Glasgow, and being driven by Laurence-Scott motors operated by Allen West switch-controlling gear. The inlet fans are 48in. diameter and are of the double-inlet type, each capable of delivering 50,000 cu. ft. of air per minute at $1\frac{1}{4}$in. water gauge. The driving motors are 32-B.H.P. units, with a speed variation of between 400 and 500 r.p.m. The air is supplied through air trunks led down outside the engine casing ; and, after passing through the fans, it is distributed by graded ducts situated in various parts of the engine-room, the ends of the main ducts being fitted with air diffusers which reduce the air speed and prevent draughts.

The two exhaust fans are fitted in the after-funnel casing and are arranged to draw from the forward end of the engine-room at the level of the feed-water heater flat, and also from the sewage-plant compartments at the port and starboard sides. They are each capable of handling 20,000 cu. ft. of air per minute at $1\frac{1}{4}$in. water gauge, and are driven by $10\frac{1}{2}$-B.H.P. electric motors with speed variation between 380 and 480 r.p.m.

Four 35-in. single-inlet fans, manufactured by the Winsor Engineering Co., Ltd., are fitted in the generator room. These fans are driven by Laurence-Scott $10\frac{1}{2}$-B.H.P. motors arranged for a speed variation of between 380 and 480 r.p.m. by switchgear made by Messrs. Allen West & Co., Ltd. Two of the fans are used for supplying and the other two for exhausting the air from this space, the capacity of the fans being such that 50 changes per hour are possible. Graded ducts are provided, as in the case of the engine-room.

MAIN WORKSHOP FOR ENGINEERS.

The main workshop for the engineers measures about 30ft. by 12ft., and is situated on *E* deck, in close association with the engineers' stores and the main engine-room. The machinery in this workshop is driven by a 6-B.H.P. electric motor, which rotates a line-shaft extending almost the entire length of the space. The general arrangement of the workshop is shown in Fig. 15.

The largest machine fitted is a 9-in. centre by 9-ft. V-bed Colin-type lathe, supplied by Messrs. Buck & Hickman, Ltd., of London. This machine is arranged to admit work up to about 5ft. between centres, and is designed for surfacing and screw-cutting, giving 24 changes of thread. It has a hollow spindle, and can use up to 2-in. diameter bars.

There are also a $3\frac{1}{2}$-in. centre-gap bed Drummond lathe, a No. 3 Challenge-pattern drilling machine, and a light drilling machine for smaller work. A double-wheel 12-in. by $1\frac{1}{2}$-in. grinder completes the outfit of machine tools. All the smaller machines have been provided by Messrs. Dempster Moore and Co. (Machinery), Ltd., of Glasgow.

In addition, a 3-ft. wide bench, with hand vices, drawers and shelves, extends along the side of the ship ; and at the after end of the workshop there is an oxy-acetylene welding equipment, with gas bottles arranged in 2-in. wooden battens.

FIRE PROTECTION OF MACHINERY SPACES.

The main fire-extinguishing installation in the machinery spaces consists of CO_2 gas cylinders arranged for connection to a system of solid-drawn galvanized mild-steel piping. A central fire-control station is provided, from which gas can be discharged to either of the boiler-rooms or the generator room, and the gas cylinders are located at this point. The machinery spaces are served by a total of 50 cylinders, each having a capacity of 50lb of CO_2. The cylinders have been supplied by the Walter Kidde Co., Ltd., of Northolt, Middlesex, who have also been responsible for the installation. The CO_2 capacity is designed to be large enough to cover the entire double-bottom tank top in the boiler-rooms in sufficient quantity to meet the Board of Trade requirements. Special release mechanism is provided on the

cylinders, and the piping is perforated to ensure the desired distribution of gas. One of the great advantages of this Lux system is that effective control of the plant is arranged to be external to the compartment in which a fire is likely to occur.

In addition to the CO_2 plant, there is also an auxiliary fire service in the boiler-rooms and the generator room in the form of Pyrene foam-making branch-hose units of the makers' F.B.2 size, each extinguisher being capable of producing up to 650 gallons of foam per minute. This delivery, it is claimed, is equal to two or three times that of a 30-gallon capacity foam engine of the chemical type. The branch-pipe units have the further advantage that the capacity of foam is unlimited for so long as supplies of water and the Pyrene foam-making compound are available. Each unit is provided with 60ft. of twin rubber hose and the foam is generated within the branch pipe, water and Pyrene foam compound being discharged in an atomised form. The controls are placed immediately above the units, and are linked together so that the foam and water cocks are released simultaneously. The equipment forms an invaluable protection against oil fires. For the protection of the machinery spaces, hand fire extinguishers of the Phomene foam type have been installed, these being each of two gallons capacity. The Pyrene Co., Ltd., have also supplied a number of pump-type fire-extinguishers for use in the generator room. These have the important feature that, in dealing with electrical fires, they can be used with safety on high-voltage cables, as the special liquid with which they are charged is claimed to be a non-conductor of electricity.

HEAT INSULATION.

Heat insulation is an important matter in high-temperature and high-pressure steam plant, and by numerous experiments it has been found that the best results are obtainable with a combination covering in conjunction with suitable air spaces. In the *Mauretania* the boiler-steam, water and superheater drums, where not enclosed by air casings, are covered by a layer of Newtempheit (the product of Newalls Insulation Co., Branch of Turner & Newall, Ltd.), followed by a layer of plastic magnesia, and finished off with a layer of hard-setting cement. An air space is then left between the lagging and the external cleading plates.

The superheated-steam lines are covered with Dextramite high-temperature composition (the product of the Chemical and Insulating Co., Ltd.) to a thickness of 1in., followed by two layers, each 2in. thick, of magnesia sectional covering, with joints staggered, the whole being enclosed in a covering of white asbestos cloth secured by stitching and spaced steel bands. The main-steam stop valves are lagged with magnesia non-conducting material, covered by hard-setting composition, while the boiler-feed pipes are coated with 2-in. magnesia moulds covered with asbestos cloth. The main-boiler, saturated-steam, exhaust and hot-water pipes are all insulated with magnesia block and sectional lagging.

The entire machinery installation, including the high-pressure turbine in each set, and the domestic hot-water and heating surfaces, are lagged with a layer of Dextramite high-temperature composition, followed by a layer of magnesia. The specification adopted for this insulation was one devised by the engineers of the Cunard White Star, Ltd., in collaboration with the technicians of Messrs. Cammell, Laird & Co., Ltd. For the high-pressure turbines, the outer covering, which consists of magnesia mattresses, is separated from the inner covering by an air space. Portable mattresses are provided at all joints, and the planished-steel cleading is assembled in easily removable sections. The intermediate-pressure turbine has an inner covering of plastic magnesia, followed by magnesia mattresses secured by galvanized wire netting, with steel binding strips on the bottom half. An air space is arranged between the inner and outer coverings, the latter being finished off with planished-steel plates. The low-pressure turbine casings are insulated in similar manner to the intermediate-pressure, but the thickness of lagging material is less.

All the heat-insulation work connected with the machinery spaces has been carried out by Messrs. Cammell, Laird & Co., Ltd.

Plate C—"Mauretania" in Southampton Graving Dock.

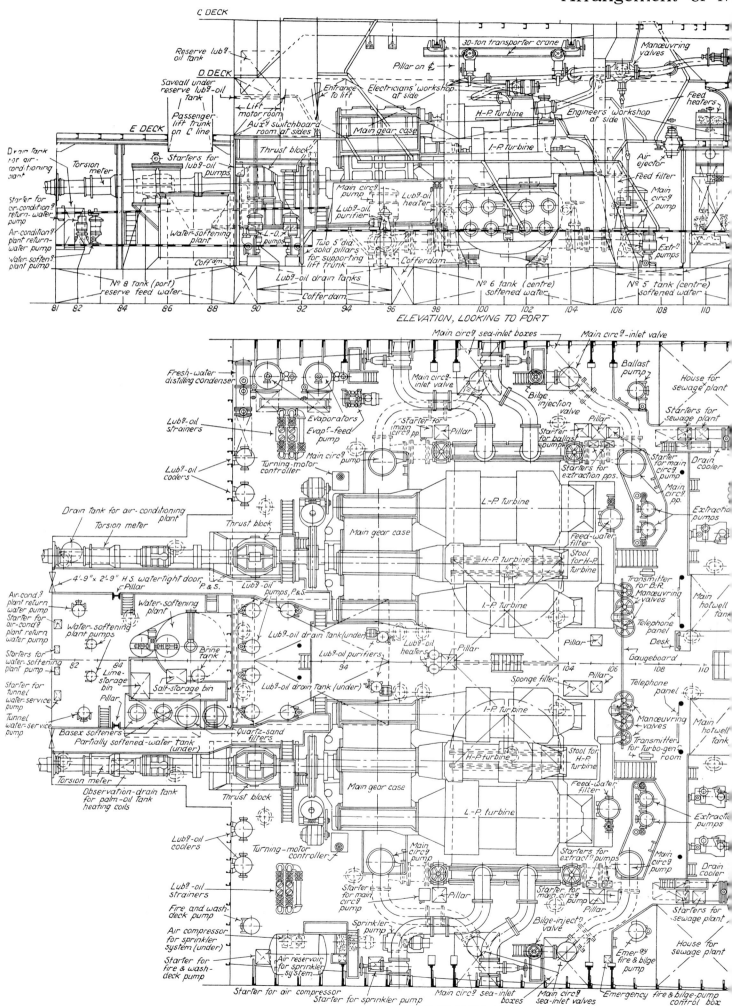

ELEVATION, LOOKING TO PORT

PLAN AT FLOOR LEVEL

RTH ATLANTIC LINER "MAURETANIA."
ry in Engine-room.

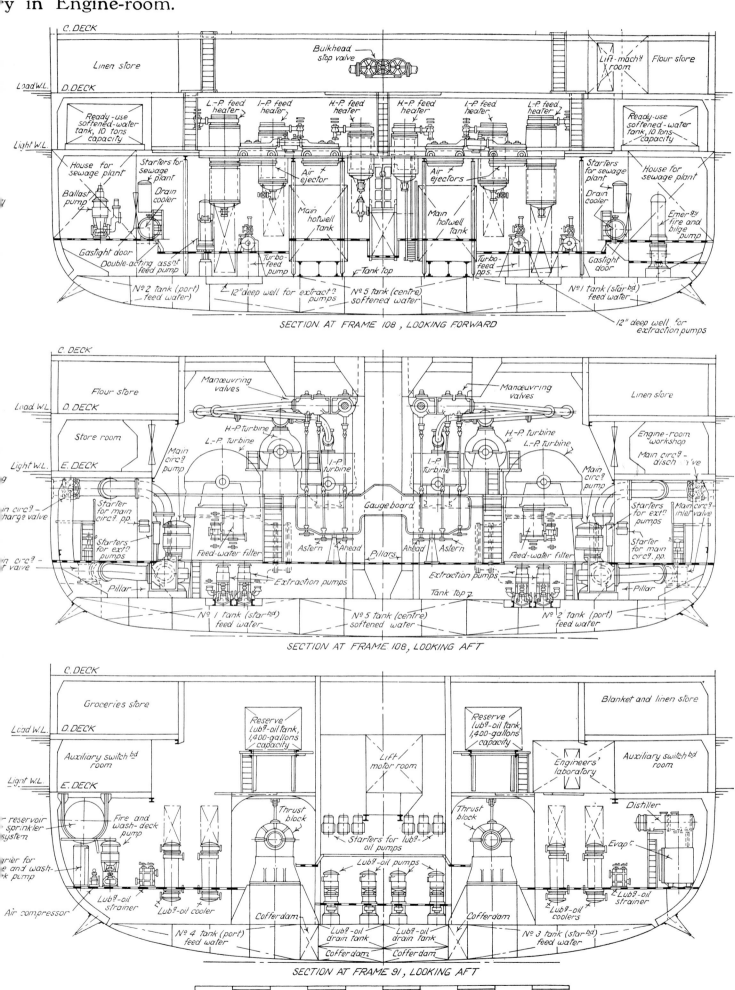

SECTION AT FRAME 108, LOOKING FORWARD

SECTION AT FRAME 108, LOOKING AFT

SECTION AT FRAME 91, LOOKING AFT

0   5   10   15   20   25   30   35   40   45   50 ft.

THE CUNARD WHITE STAR TWIN-SCREW NORTH ATLANTIC LINER "MAURETANIA."

General Arrangement of Boiler-room Installation.

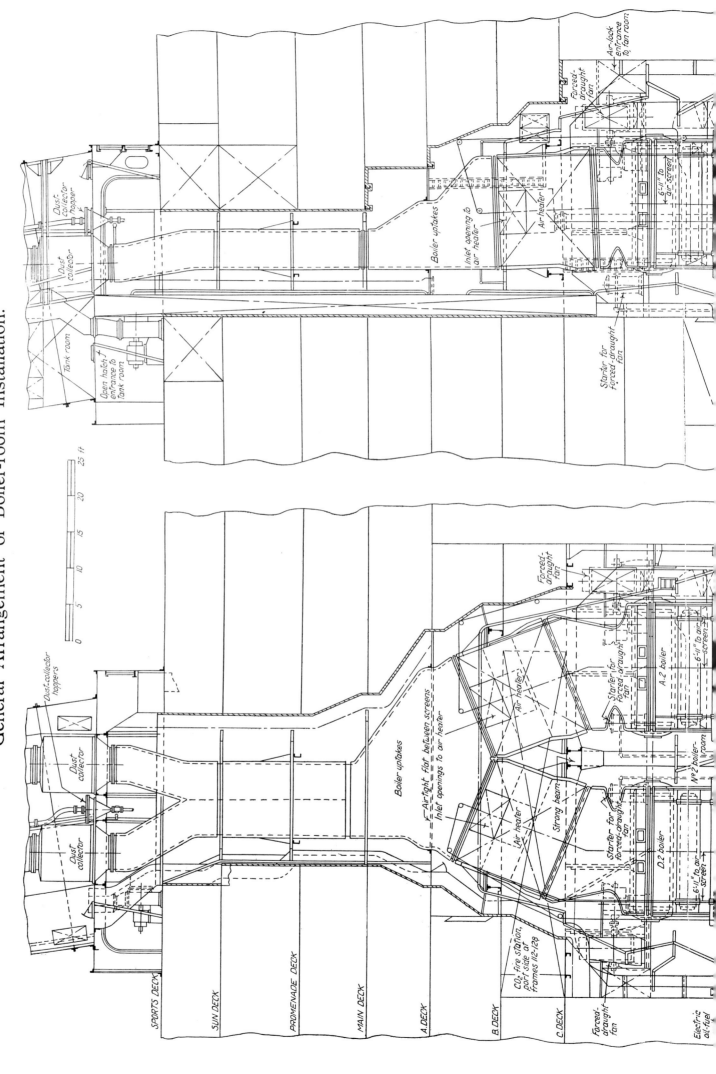

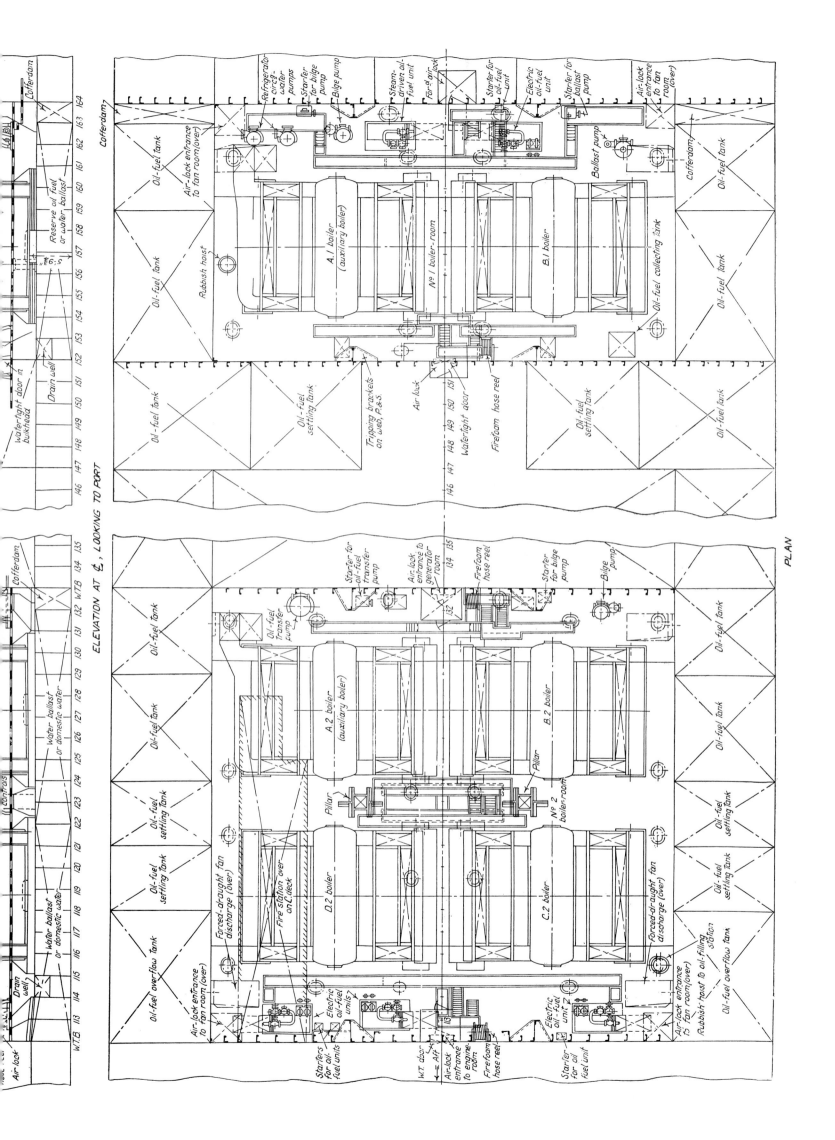

ELEVATION AT ℄, LOOKING TO PORT

PLAN

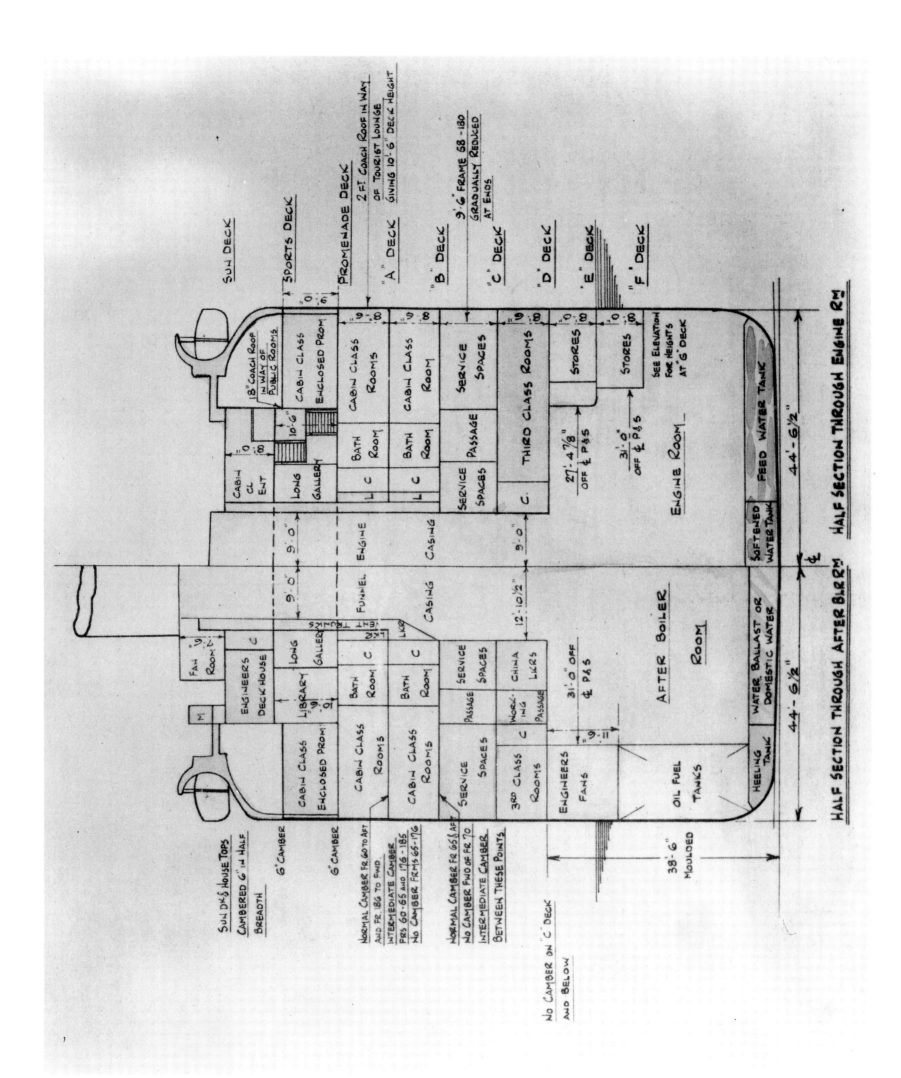

Plate D—Plan of Half-Section Transverse Arrangement.

BOILER INSTALLATION.

THE complete boiler installation consists of six Yarrow side-fired boilers of the double-flow type, with Yarrow superheaters and air-heaters, all constructed by Messrs. Cammell, Laird & Co., Ltd. The leading particulars of each unit are approximately as follows :—

Generating heating surface, sq. ft.	10,750
Superheating surface, sq. ft.	4,915
Air-heating surface, sq. ft.	14,250
Normal evaporation, ℔ per hour	68,500
Working pressure, ℔ per sq. in.	425
Final steam temperature, deg. F.	725

Each boiler has a steam drum, three water drums and one superheater drum. The steam and water drums are hollow-rolled forgings, manufactured by the English Steel Corporation, Ltd., with the ends integrally forged and machined inside and out, while a feature of these drums is their circular form. Each drum is provided with a manhole at either end for access, and straight tubes are expanded into the drums so that all parts subjected to internal pressure are of true circular section. The arrangement of one of the boilers is shown in Fig. 1.

The boiler tubes are of solid-drawn, cold-finished steel, and have been supplied by Tubes, Ltd., of Aston, Birmingham. All the fire rows are arranged with a slight set towards the furnace to allow for expansion, and the various nests of tubes are designed with a view to free longitudinal expansion. The small nest of generating tubes over the burners at the front of the boiler has four rows of 2-in. diameter tubes, terminating in a 23-in. diameter water drum ; while in the large nest of tubes above the superheater there are 13 rows of $1\frac{1}{4}$-in. diameter tubes which terminate in a 23-in. diameter water drum. At the back of the boiler the large tube bank has three rows of 2-in. diameter tubes next to the furnace, followed by 15 rows of $1\frac{1}{4}$-in. diameter tubes with a 33-in. diameter water drum at the bottom. All the generating tubes have their upper ends expanded into a 54-in. diameter saturated-steam drum. The boiler drawing shows that there is ample furnace capacity to ensure complete combustion before the gases impinge on the tubes, and it will be noted that a very large proportion of the boiler surface is exposed to radiant heat. The fire-row boiler tubes which carry the greatest evaporative load are nearly vertical and are well submerged, in addition to being readily accessible from inside the furnace.

The superheater in each boiler is located between the nests of water tubes at the front of the boiler, so that the steam-temperature variation is reduced to a minimum. The superheater is constructed of U-tubes expanded into a forged drum, with suitable divisional baffles designed to direct the steam through the several passes. The superheater tubes are steeply inclined and are self-draining, and the large drum functions as a steam receiver, giving a reserve for manœuvring purposes. All the superheater tubes are of solid-drawn, cold-finished steel, and are $1\frac{1}{8}$in. diameter, the superheater drum being 30in. diameter. All the superheater drums have been made by the English Steel Corporation, Ltd.

ApeXioR No. 1 has been applied to the internal surfaces of all the boilers to prevent pitting and corrosion.

The boiler casings are of specially robust construction, with box-section ends carrying the weight of the pressure parts. A cradle is formed at the top of the inner plate of the end casings, and supports the steam drum and the weight of the tubes and water drums. The water drums rest on an extension of the inner plate of the end casings, and are free to move outward and downward under the expansion of the tubes. The superheater is carried on another extension of the inner plate of the end casings. The hollow-box construction of the end casings serves also as a trunk, leading the heated air from the air-heaters to under the furnace floor, and thence to the air distributors and oil-burners on the boiler fronts. Thus, the casings which form the combustion chamber, in addition to the asbestos and firebrick lining, are protected by the preheated air flowing between them and the outer casing, which, in turn, is insulated with fire felt.

The air-heaters are of the tubular pattern, arranged on the contra-flow principle, each section consisting of steel tubes expanded into steel tube-plates. In the forward boiler-room the two air-heaters are built together as one block, and, similarly, the four air-heaters in the after boiler-room are formed into two blocks of two each. The gases from the furnace flow upward through the tubes, and the cold air from the stokehold enters at the top and is caused by baffles to pass three times across the tubes on its downward path to the furnace. Each air-heater inlet can be closed by means of a shutter operated from the stokehold floor, and this, in conjunction with air doors on the boiler casings, provides an air by-pass for use when raising steam. Leaving the boiler on both sides of the steam drum, the gases enter uptakes which, at their junction, are provided with dampers to regulate the proportion of gases passing into the superheater, thus giving a close control over the final steam temperature. The two dampers in the uptakes are coupled together, so that, when one is opening, the other is closing. The dampers never close completely, as a predetermined clearance is left to allow a percentage of the gas to leak past.

Each group of boilers is served by a separate funnel, the gases from two boilers being conducted to the forward funnel and the gases from four boilers to the after funnel. Each boiler has its individual dust collector ; and Messrs. James Howden & Co., Ltd., of Glasgow, have supplied six Howden Size 54 dry-upflow type dust collectors with flushing hoppers, which effectively remove from the gases soot particles, etc., before their discharge to the atmosphere. The system employed will collect all particles having a diameter of 0·0058in. or over, as well as a proportion of the smaller particles. Those escaping are so small, and their rate of settlement is so slow, that they are normally carried clear of the ship before falling to deck level.

The two outer funnels are of oval section and have the same area. The after funnel houses the dust collectors and uptakes from the four boilers in No. 2 boiler-room, and the forward funnel contains those from the two forward boilers. Both funnels receive exhaust-air trunks from the engine-room, generator room, galleys and various public rooms, while the forward funnel has a separate built-in compartment for fresh and salt-water service tanks. The funnels have been specially strengthened internally in order to dispense with the usual funnel guys, thus improving the appearance of the ship.

In the boilers fitted with de-superheaters, the superheated steam is led by four pipes connected to headers through the saturated-steam drum. The pipes are fitted with a large number of gills or fins, by which the temperature of the steam is reduced by radiation to that of the lower-temperature saturated steam.

Oil-burning Installation.

The oil-burning installation has been supplied by the Wallsend Slipway & Engineering Co., Ltd., of Wallsend-on-Tyne, and is on the Wallsend-Howden patent pressure system. The furnace equipment comprises the latest design of Wallsend-Howden burner, air distributor and burner carrier, the latter being fitted with a safety cock, by means of which it is impossible for a burner joint to be broken without first shutting off the oil supply to the burner. A special attachment on the burner carrier allows the burner body to be removed for cleaning, and a new one to be inserted and lighted up in a matter of a few seconds. The front plates of the air distributors are equipped with louvre plates, which are fitted around the burner openings, thus giving easy access to the burner nozzles and allowing observation of the flame condition. The burner carriers are of the adjustable type, and can be advanced or withdrawn from the furnace to obtain the most suitable position of the flame, thus resulting in the highest possible efficiency. The air supply to the burners is arranged in casings along the boiler front, and each air distributor has separate air controls, so that the air supply to any individual burner can be shut off if the burner is not required.

The design of the oil-burning equipment is such that any class of liquid fuel can be used efficiently. The lighting-up apparatus for steam-raising consists of an electric immersion heater for heating the oil. This is connected to the two forward boilers, the pressure of the oil being maintained by one of the

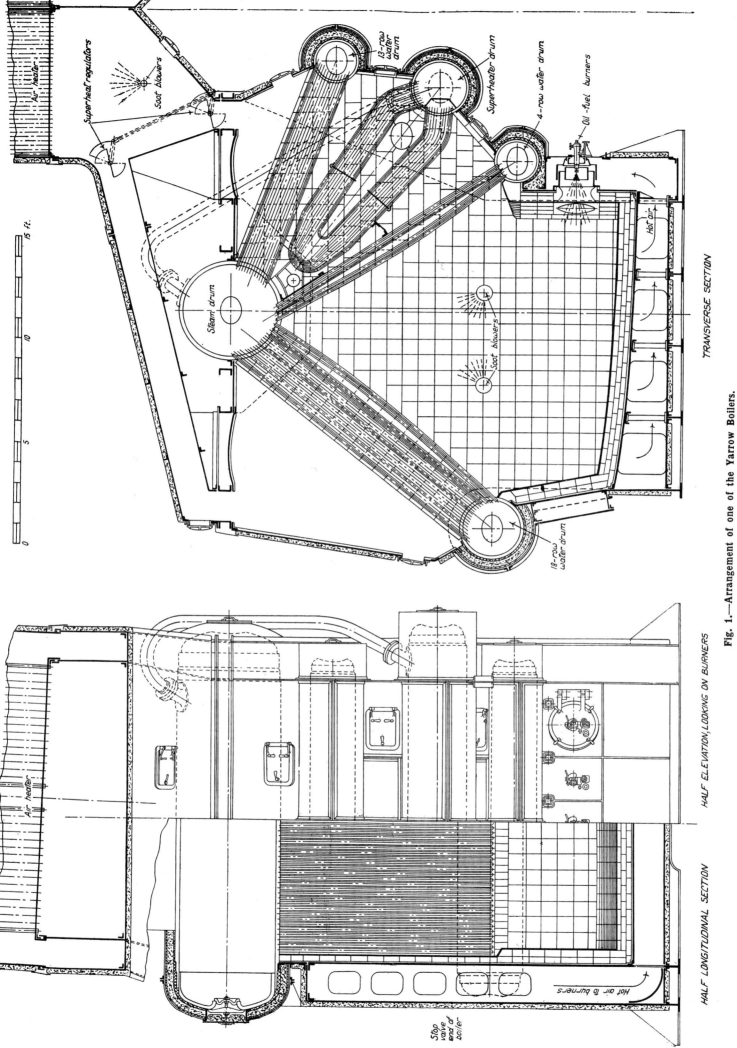

13-row water drum

Superheat regulators

Soot blowers

Superheater drum

4-row water drum

Oil-fuel burners

Air heater

15 ft.

10

5

0

Steam drum

Hot air.

Soot blowers

TRANSVERSE SECTION

18-row water drum

Air heater

HALF ELEVATION, LOOKING ON BURNERS

Hot air to burners

Stop valve end of boiler

HALF LONGITUDINAL SECTION

Fig. 1.—Arrangement of one of the Yarrow Boilers.

four under-mentioned electrically-driven fuel-oil pumps, which discharges to the electric heater and thence to the boilers.

Fig. 2.—CO$_2$ Aspirating and Measuring Unit.

Fig. 3.—Weir Robot Boiler-feed Regulator, sectioned to show Internal Parts.

For supplying oil under pressure to the burners during normal steaming, four electrically-driven and one steam-driven pumping and heating units are installed. Three of these complete units are for working purposes, the other two complete sets acting as stand-by, so that any part of the stand-by equipment can be overhauled or cleaned while the other is in operation. The electrically-driven fuel-oil pressure pumps are Size 2½A rotary-displacement units manufactured by Messrs. Stothert and Pitt, Ltd., of Bath, and each is driven by a Laurence-Scott 6-H.P. motor through high-efficiency, case-hardened steel, worm gearing. Each pump is designed to give an output of 10,000lb per hour of " C "-grade bunker fuel oil at 90 deg. F. when running at a speed of 290 r.p.m. against pressures rising to 200lb per sq. in. The starting equipment for these motors is of the drum type, by Messrs. Allen West & Co., Ltd. The steam pump is a Weir horizontal-type unit, while the fuel-oil heaters are of the U-tube type, arranged in a horizontal position.

Three of the motor-driven pumping and heating units are installed in No. 2 boiler-room; and the steam-driven set, together with the other motor-driven set, is located in No. 1 boiler-room. The motor-driven unit in No. 1 boiler-room is connected to the emergency generator.

The fuel-oil suction strainers are of the perforated steel-bag type, and one Auto-Klean fuel-discharge strainer is fitted to

Fig. 4.—Hopkinson-Ferranti Main Steam Shut-off Valve.

each of the five fuel-oil units, in the discharge from the heaters to the burners. These strainers will not require to be opened up for cleaning during a voyage, as a turn of the cleaning handle once per watch during the Atlantic passage will keep them in good order. Any foreign matter thus removed from the oil is deposited into a sump, from which it may be cleaned out when the plant is not in operation. It will be appreciated that this eliminates possible fire risk by obviating the necessity for breaking joints while the oil-burning equipment is in operation.

Quick-closing sluice valves have been supplied by Messrs. Fawcett, Preston & Co., Ltd., of Bromborough, Cheshire, for the fuel-oil suction arrangement. These consist of 6-in. and 4-in. bore valves designed so that they can be operated as standard sluice valves, or, in an emergency, closed instantaneously by remote-control trip gear. Messrs. Kelvin, Bottomley and Baird, Ltd., of Glasgow, provided 15 of their standard-pattern Pneumercator gauges for indicating the oil level in 28 fuel-oil tanks, and other 13 similar gauges for use in connection with 24 tanks carrying drinking water, domestic water and water ballast. The Pneumercator gauges are arranged in groups at convenient points and allow of rapid and accurate checking of the various tank contents.

The temperature of the products of combustion in the vicinity of the superheaters is measured by thermo-couple pyrometers supplied by Messrs. Negretti & Zambra, of London ; while the same makers have provided long-distance thermometers of the mercury-in-steel type for temperature measurements of the flue gases, air, steam and feed-water at various points throughout the installation. Each boiler is fitted with a Siemens flue-gas analysis appliance supplied by Messrs. Elliott Brothers, Ltd., of London, and worked from the ship's D.C. mains. An aspirating and measuring unit is shown in Fig. 2. Each boiler

12 being fitted. These regulators have cast-steel float boxes with forged-steel covers, Monel floats and stainless-steel float levers. The internal valves are of nickel-bronze, the needle valves being of stainless steel, with stainless-steel seats. This type of regulator is capable of maintaining a steady continuous feed to the boilers in accordance with the demand for steam, and is operated hydraulically by the discharge pressure of the feed pump under the control of the float gear, as shown in Fig. 3. The boilers are also equipped with six sets of Weir-Mumford low-level alarm gear. Each set consists of a float gear fitted

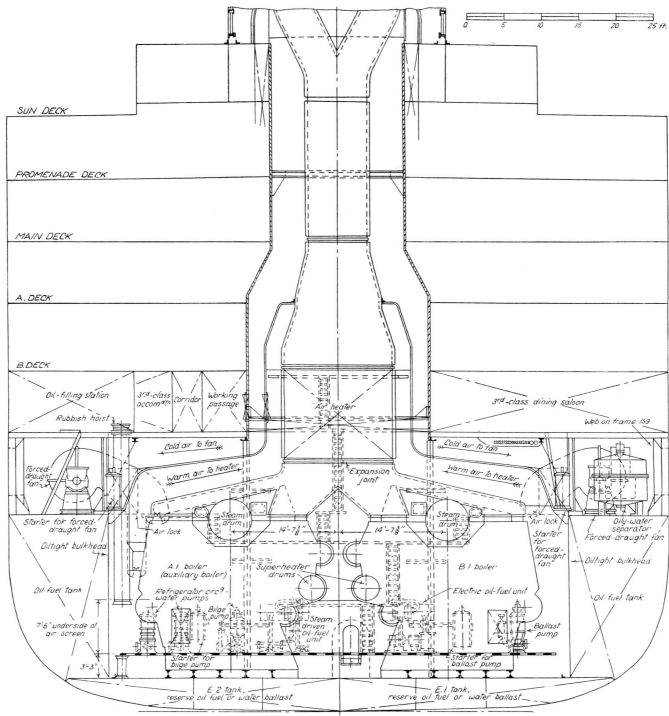

Fig. 5.—Section through No. 1 Boiler-room, looking Forward.

combustion chamber is provided with soot-blowers—for which Messrs. C. P. Parry, Ltd., of Birkenhead, have been responsible—for cleaning the boiler and superheater tubes ; while two blowers of the articulated type are fitted below the air-heaters to maintain the cleanliness of these items. The nozzles of the Parry soot-blowers are made of heat-resisting steel of which nickel forms an important constituent.

BOILER MOUNTINGS.

The admission of feed water to the boilers is controlled by Weir Robot-type automatic feed-water regulators, a total of

in a steel surge chamber inside the boiler drum. The float gear is arranged to operate a needle valve, the opening of which admits steam to a special fuel-oil shut-off valve and an alarm whistle. In the event of the boiler-water level falling below the safe minimum, the float falls, opens the needle valve, and admits steam to the fuel-control valve, cutting off the supply of fuel to the burners and also sounding the alarm whistle. The water level must be restored before the fuel valve can be re-opened, and resetting must be done by hand.

The height of the boiler steam drums above the stokehold platform necessitates the use of a special design of water gauge, and Messrs. Dewrance & Co., Ltd., of London, have provided for this purpose their patent bi-colour water-level indicators. In these indicators the position of the water level is made conspicuous and clearly defined by strongly contrasting coloured illumination of the steam and water spaces of the indicator, an arrangement of mirrors making the water-level reading visible at the firing-platform level. The water-gauge cocks to which the indicators are fitted are of the sleeve-packed type, supplied by Messrs. Richard Klinger, Ltd., of London. The drain cocks for the boiler superheaters, the steam-separator

maintained. These safety valves are the product of Messrs. Cockburns, Ltd., of Cardonald, Glasgow, and are set to blow at 435lb per sq. in. They embody the makers' special design of distance piece between the valve chest and the spring to prevent the high-temperature steam affecting the elasticity of the springs. An additional safety valve, also of the high-lift type and set to blow at 465lb per sq. in., is fitted on the saturated-steam drum. The internal valves have no wings or guides in the seats, so that there is no tendency for the valve to seize or silt up.

A Howard patent steam separator, supplied by Messrs.

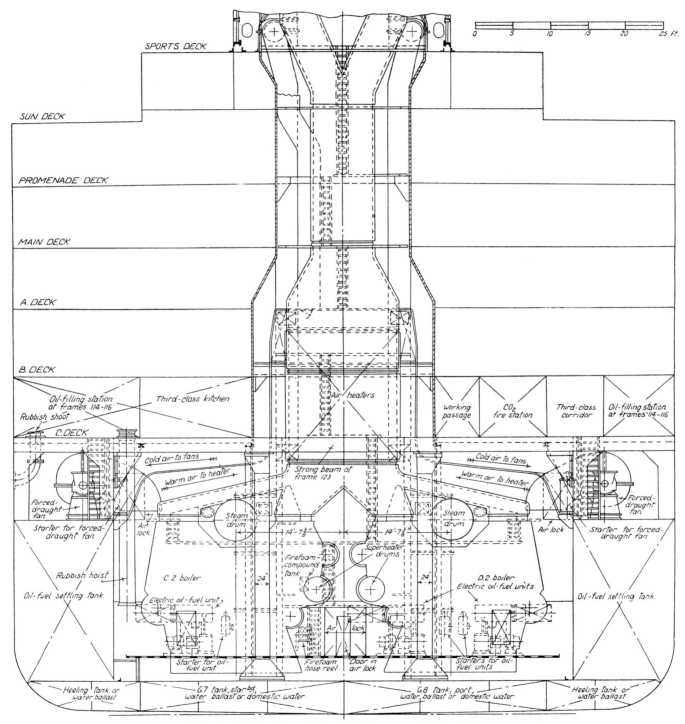

Fig. 6.—Section through No. 2 Boiler-room, looking Aft.

drain cocks and water gauges, the main steam-pipe drains, and the pressure-gauge cocks, etc., are also of the Klinger type. Features of these cocks are their suitability for high steam pressures and temperatures, and the ease with which they can be overhauled by replacing the renewable compressed-asbestos packing sleeve. This firm have also supplied a considerable amount of their well-known Klingerit jointing for use in the steam-pipe lines.

High-lift safety valves are fitted on the superheater drum of each boiler, so that, in the event of the steam pressure rising to blowing-off point, circulation through the superheater is

Warren Brothers (Middlesbrough), Ltd., is fitted in each saturated-steam drum, and the steam strainers incorporated in the main steam system are of Messrs. Cockburns' patent wirewoven mesh type. The last-mentioned firm have also provided the boiler main-steam stop valves, which are of the improved self-closing type. These valves are fitted at each superheater outlet and have external indicators showing the amount of opening. The main-steam shut-off valves are of the Hopkinson-Ferranti type, supplied by Messrs. Hopkinsons, Ltd., of Huddersfield, and one of these is illustrated in Fig. 4.

Fig. 7.—Firing Platform in Boiler-room.

AUXILIARY MACHINERY IN BOILER-ROOMS.

The general arrangement of the boiler-rooms is shown on Plate VI. and in Figs. 5 and 6, while Fig. 7 is a reproduction of a photograph taken on board the vessel.

The six motor-driven forced-draught fans are located on flats in the boiler-room wings. These fans are 48in. diameter, and are of the Howden double-inlet B-type, each being driven by a Laurence-Scott 100-B.H.P. pipe-ventilated electric motor and arranged for speed control from 585 to 1,265 r.p.m. The controlling switchgear has also been supplied by Messrs. Laurence, Scott & Electromotors, Ltd. Each fan is designed to supply 40,000 cu. ft. of air per minute against 9½in. water gauge, and is of the latest high-efficiency type suitable for operating in parallel without risk of " surging " or unequal distribution of the load. The fan power characteristic is such that overloading of the driving motor cannot occur under any possible condition of operation that may arise, as, for instance, if only one fan per boiler-room is in use.

The starboard fan room of No. 1 boiler-room is also used to house an oily-water separator. This is illustrated in Fig. 8, is of the Comyn type supplied by Messrs. Alexander Esplen and Co., Ltd., of Liverpool, and has a capacity of 100 tons per hour. No. 1 boiler-room also contains a motor-driven ballast pump capable of handling 350 tons of water per hour against a head of 70ft., and a motor-driven bilge pump capable of dealing with 200 tons of water per hour against a head of 70ft. Both these pumps have been provided by Messrs. Drysdale & Co., Ltd., of Yoker, Glasgow ; while the electric motors and controllers have been manufactured by Messrs. Laurence, Scott and Electromotors, Ltd., and Messrs. Allen West & Co., Ltd., respectively.

In order to provide the necessary suction head of sea-water, the two circulating pumps for the refrigerating plant are also located in No. 1 boiler-room. A motor-driven bilge pump similar to that in No. 1 boiler-room is installed in No. 2 boiler-room, and there is also a motor-driven fuel-oil transfer pump with a capacity of 100 tons per hour against a head of 93ft. These are Drysdale units.

Fig. 8.—Comyn Oily-water Separator.

Each boiler-room is provided with an electrically-driven friction hoist capable of lifting 3 cwt. at a speed of 180ft. per minute. These hoists are designed for the removal of ashes and refuse, and are operated by Royce motors of the totally-enclosed type. They are installed in the fuel-oil filling stations, port and starboard, and have been manufactured by Messrs. Royce, Ltd., of Loughborough.

ELECTRICAL INSTALLATION.

THE electrical installation has been carried out by the Sunderland Forge & Engineering Co., Ltd., and is on the most modern lines, complying fully with the requirements of the owners, the classification societies and the Board of Trade. The generating equipment comprises four 800-kW., 225-volt, direct-current, compound-wound turbo-generators, which have been manufactured by the British Thomson-Houston Co., Ltd., of Rugby. A photograph of one set is shown in Fig. 1, the generator-room arrangement drawing is reproduced in Fig. 2, and a photograph taken on board in Fig. 3. The turbine of each set is designed for a steam pressure of 350lb per sq. in. gauge and a total steam temperature of 700 deg. F. The condenser vacuum is 28½in. Hg. with a sea-water temperature of 60 deg. F., and steam is bled from the turbines, as required, to provide steam for other services. The generators are driven through single-reduction, double-helical

The generator room is also used to house the plant for feeding the boilers in harbour and for dealing with the exhaust from the general-service units, hotel services, etc. There are two Drysdale Upright sanitary pumps, each with a capacity of 120 tons per hour against a head of 120ft., as well as two Drysdale Rotary Centrex drinking-water pumps and two domestic-water pumps of the same type, capable of dealing with 10 and 50 tons of water per hour respectively against a head of 150ft. These pumps are of the motor-driven type supplied by Messrs. Drysdale & Co., Ltd., with Laurence-Scott motors and Allen West controllers. The fresh-water pump controllers are of the automatic type, the pumps being controlled by float gear from the overhead service tanks. A 50-ton per hour capacity domestic-water filter by Messrs. David Crawford and Co., Ltd., of Liverpool, and a battery of four drinking-water filters are also installed.

Fig. 1.—One Turbo-generating Set on Test-bed.

gearing, and the circulating-water pumps are driven from an extension of the generator shaft. The pumps have been supplied by the Mirrlees Watson Co., Ltd., of Glasgow, and have a capacity of 1,250 gallons per minute against a head of 20ft. when working at 670 r.p.m. and absorbing 9·5 H.P. The casings and impellers are of gun-metal, while the shafts are made of bronze, suitable rotary packings being fitted.

The condensers are underslung and work in conjunction with their own closed-feed system, a diagrammatic arrangement of which is shown in Fig. 4. In connection with this system, Messrs. G. & J. Weir, Ltd., have supplied four float-operated control valves for controlling the discharge from the extraction pumps, two Weir Lo-Hed vertical-spindle, electrically-driven extraction pumps (each with a maximum duty of 13,000lb of water from a suction head of 28½in. Hg.), two Weir turbo-driven pumps of similar capacity to the foregoing, and four sets of Weir steam-jet air-ejectors. Incidentally, the turbo-generator condensers can also be utilised instead of the auxiliary condenser, if the occasion arises.

The general-service units fitted in the generator room are a Weir vertical double-acting fuel-oil transfer pump, a vertical duplex steam-driven general-service pump by Messrs. J. H. Carruthers & Co., Ltd., of Polmadie, Glasgow, and a Drysdale Upright motor-driven, two-stage dust-collector pump. The watertight-door pump is also located in the generator room, as well as an air-compressor capable of supplying 300 cu. ft. of air at 120lb per sq. in., the compressor having been manufactured by Messrs. Alley & MacLellan, Ltd., of Polmadie, Glasgow. The Alfa-Laval Co., Ltd., have supplied a De Laval lubricating-oil purifier for dealing with the oil from the turbo-generators.

The generator room forms a separate compartment between the boiler-rooms, communication between the engine and generator rooms being established by means of telegraphs and suitable indicating instruments. The main switchboard is located on a flat immediately above the turbo-generators, and is divided into port and starboard sections, each section being capable of independent operation. Remote-control and instru-

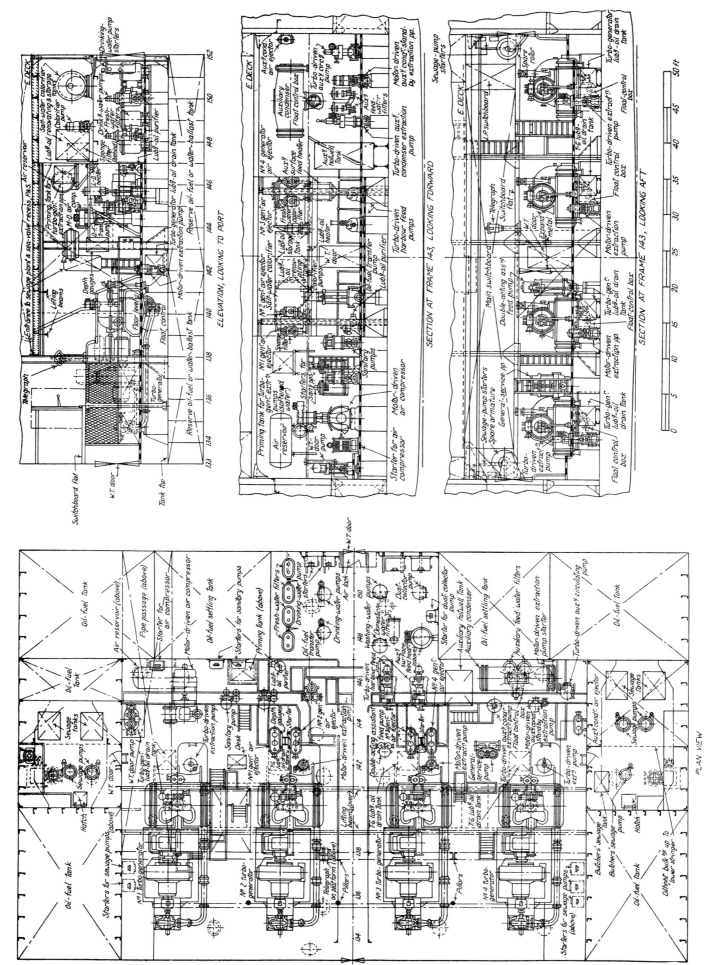

Fig. 2.—Arrangement of Machinery in Generator Room.

ment panels for the generators are mounted in the centre of the switchboard. In addition, there are linking arrangements at the central control position of the switchboard, so that the port and starboard sections can, if desired, be controlled in parallel. The two sections can be coupled through any of the nine ring-main circuits, which are fed from both stations but are normally open-circuited at the centre point. A 25-volt switchboard for the low-power services and earth-detecting panels are mounted as an extension of the main switchboard, the overall length of the combined assembly being approximately 54ft.

All the switchboard units, comprising one main and 30 auxiliary boards, have been supplied by Messrs. Whipp and Bourne, Ltd., of Castleton, Manchester. Black enamelled slate has been utilised for the main board, while Ebony Sindanyo panels are incorporated in the auxiliary boards, the last-mentioned composition being the product of Turners Asbestos Cement Co., Ltd., of Trafford Park, Manchester.

The control panels for the main generators are mounted at the ends of the main switchboard, two being at the port and two at the starboard side. Each generator is coupled to the board through a 4,500-amp. overload circuit-breaker, which is mechanically coupled to a 2,500-amp. non-automatic breaker for the equaliser pole. Both these breakers are hand-operated, while electrical control is adopted for the 4,500-amp. negative-pole overload and reverse-current circuit-breaker. This last-mentioned switch is so interlocked with the positive and equaliser pole circuits that it cannot be closed until these circuits are made. Mounted on each generator-control panel is a special instantaneous overload relay set to the same calibration as the main breakers, and hence this, being instantaneous in action, will operate before the breakers, which have an adjustable time-lag. This relay, on functioning, operates further relays to trip out certain feeder circuits in the event of overload on the generator.

The coupler unit, which, as previously mentioned, is located at the centre of the board, consists of a 5,000-amp. switch. The positive-pole circuit is closed by a hand-operated switch, and

the negative-pole circuit-breaker is electrically operated. This circuit cannot be closed until the correct sequence of switching has been carried out. The equipment of indicating and recording instruments is very complete.

Some hundreds of Crompton ammeters and voltmeters have been provided by Messrs. Crompton Parkinson, Ltd., of London. Of particular interest is the use, for the first time, of controller-type instruments with dials illuminated through glazed openings in the bases. A standard tubular lamp is mounted in the gear to which the instruments are fitted, or, where this is not convenient, to the inside of the hinged door of an accommodation box between the instrument and the controller or other gear.

The majority of the outgoing feeders are controlled by tandem-coupled overload and time-lag circuit-breakers, ranging from 100 to 1,200 amp. All circuits of less than 100 amp. capacity are controlled by tandem switches and fuses. The auxiliary switchboards are fitted throughout the vessel in all-steel compartments. They are fed direct from the main switchboard, and can be linked across, if necessary.

The electrical system is protected by Aeroflex LDF cartridge fuses, which have been manufactured by Messrs. Parmiter, Hope and Sugden, Ltd., of Longsight, Manchester. These fuses incorporate a fusible element of bi-metallic construction, in which a central pocket of low-melting temperature alloy is located between necks of reduced section in a copper strip. The result is that,

Fig. 3.—Generator Room.

on the lesser overloads, the low-melting point alloy is fused on account of the heat generated in the adjacent necks; so that the temperature rise of the fuse at full-load current, and the time-lag obtained during the lesser overloads, depend upon the melting point and the thermal capacity of the alloy. It is therefore impossible to have deterioration or overheating with these fuses, and a considerable time-lag is obtained on temporary overload conditions. In the case of severe short circuits, however, the narrow necks in the copper strip fuse so rapidly that the low-melting temperature alloy is not affected, and experiments have shown that the fuse

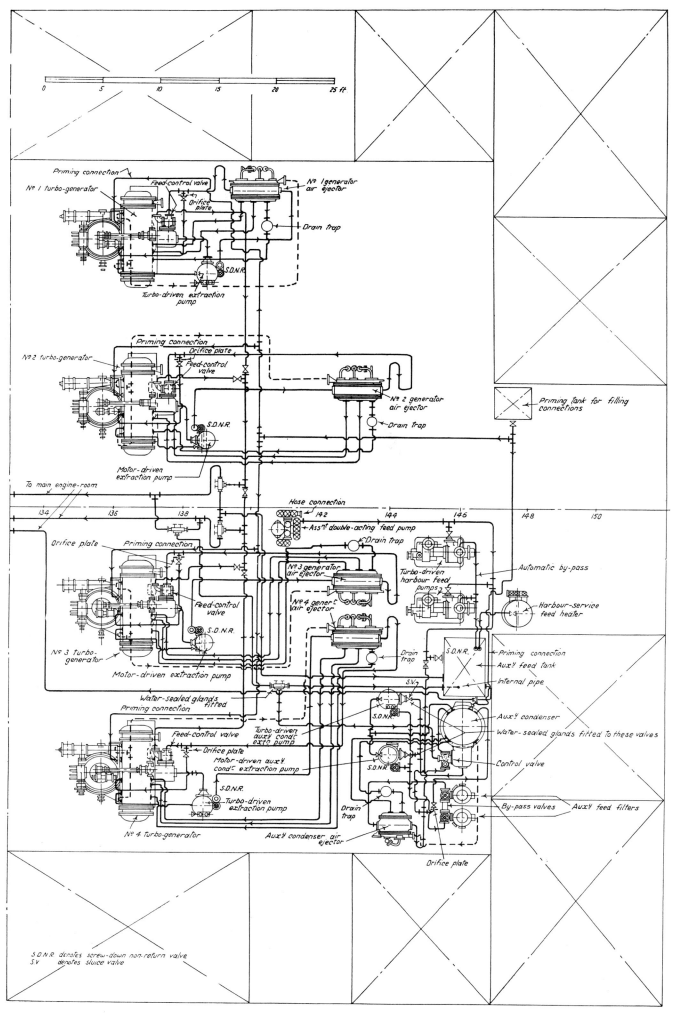

Fig. 4.—Arrangement of Closed-feed System in Generator Room.

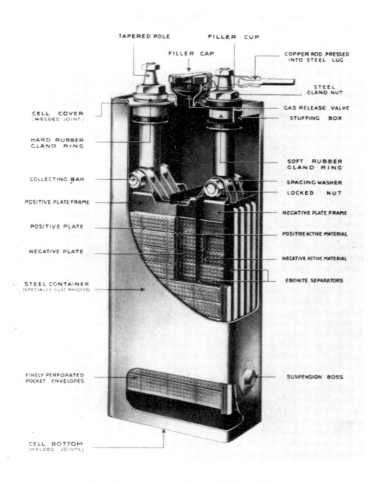

Fig. 5.—Sectional View of **NIFE** Cell.

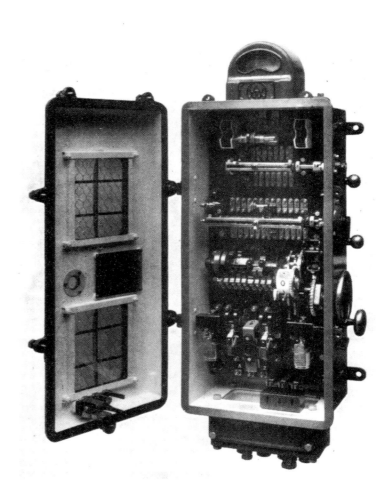

Fig. 7.—Starter for Fuel-oil Pressure Pumps.

Fig. 6.—Automatic Starter for Washing-water and Drinking-water Pumps.

Fig. 8.—Allen West Face-plate-Type Starter for Ventilation Motors.

Fig. 9.—Allen West Control Panel.

clears itself in a few thousandths of a second without any external flash.

The main feeders to the various auxiliary switchboards are rubber-insulated braided cables run on rack insulators, and all cables, except those in conduits, have a heavy fire-resisting braiding. A further safeguard is that all feeders supplying ventilating fans and heaters can be switched off from the bridge, thus ensuring that the heating and ventilating systems of any particular section can be shut down immediately in the event of a fire. Similarly, to avoid piercing watertight and fireproof bulkheads more than necessary, the various motors, lights, etc., are fed vertically upward and downward between fireproof bulkheads. The electric cables have been supplied by the British Insulated Cables, Ltd., of Prescot, Lancs., and Henley's Telegraph Works Co., Ltd., of London. Messrs. Henley's have supplied more than 400,000 yards of cables, ranging from single-core, V.I.R. insulated, taped, braided, and compounded, to ordinary flexible cords.

For emergency use, a self-contained Diesel-driven generator is located on *B* deck above the water level. This set has been supplied by Messrs. Ruston & Hornsby, Ltd., of Lincoln, and consists of a standard Ruston eight-cylinder Diesel auxiliary set developing 140 B.H.P. at 1,000 r.p.m. It drives a Sunderland-Forge 75-kW. generator, and the complete set is mounted on a combined base and cooled by means of a radiator manufactured by Serck Radiators, Ltd. The unit is arranged for electric starting. The engine is of the four-stroke cycle type and works on the Ruston fuel-injection system, in which fuel is injected by a fuel pump of the spill-valve type, and each cylinder has a separate plunger controlled by the governor. Lubrication is automatic, a forced-pressure system coming into service with the starting of the engine. The appropriate grade of Shell oil (supplied by Shell Mex & B.P., Ltd., of London) is used to lubricate the emergency generator.

Fig. 10.—Crabtree Silent-action Switch.

In addition to the emergency generator, there is a 220-volt battery capable of dealing with all the emergency lighting and sundry other services, including the micro-control of the passenger lifts, for a period of 30 minutes. This will ensure that, in an emergency involving the sudden shutting down of the main generators, sufficient light will be available throughout the ship for passengers and personnel to move about freely. This battery is of the NIFE nickel-cadmium alkaline type, supplied by Nife Batteries, Ltd., of Redditch, and consists of 200 cells having a capacity of 85 amp.-hours. A sectional view of a typical cell is reproduced in Fig. 5. The battery is capable of holding a full charge while standing idle for long periods, and gives an extremely heavy current in an emergency with very little drop in voltage. The total volume occupied by the battery is only 34 cu. ft., and its weight is under 3,000lb.

The low-voltage services are fed from two 25-volt motor generators in conjunction with a NIFE battery, and any failure of the generating sets causes the battery to take up the load automatically and supply the telephones, fire alarms, etc. This stand-by battery consists of 18 NIFE cells with a capacity of 70 amp.-hours.

The majority of the electric-motor starters for this vessel have been supplied by Messrs. Allen West & Co., Ltd., of Brighton. In the engine-room, Allen West control gear is fitted to the Laurence-Scott motors for the four 115/125-H.P. main circulating pumps, and to the six Laurence-Scott 15/25-H.P. motors for the forced-lubrication pumps. These starters are built up in open-panel form, making two five-panel boards, as shown in Fig. 9. They are mounted in two switchboard rooms, one on each side of the ship, away from the engine-room, and are controlled by a control unit mounted alongside each pump. The control unit embodies a field regulator (interlocked to prevent starting with a weak field), " stop " and " start " buttons, and a

moving-coil ammeter. Drum-type control pillars are provided for 12 pumps in the engine-room—ranging from the 30/50-H.P. ballast pumps to the 2/4-H.P. water-softening plant pumps— and all these controls are of the variable-speed pattern, speed variation being obtained by a hand-operated field regulator mounted in the control pillar.

As already mentioned, automatic starters are provided for the washing-water and drinking-water pumps. The float gear for these is of a special type, unaffected by the rolling of the ship, and Fig. 6 shows one of the automatic starters. The type of starter supplied for the Stothert & Pitt fuel-oil pressure pumps is illustrated in Fig. 7. This type of starter is provided with a vernier regulator, as well as the main regulator, giving a very fine graduation in speed. There is also a separate emergency " stop " push-button in the glass-fronted case. Messrs. Allen West & Co., Ltd., have also supplied starters for the engine-room ventilation motors. Key-operated starters of the face-plate pattern, provided with field regulators, are fitted to the smaller motors, while the larger starters are of the drum type. The face-plate type of starter is illustrated in Fig. 8.

A large number of electric switches, bell-pushes and switch sockets have been provided by Messrs. J. A. Crabtree & Co., Ltd., of Walsall. Among the products of the last-mentioned firm are more than 1,500 Lincoln 5-amp. surface switches, 600 ironclad, circular one-gang, semi-recessed switches, and large numbers of Jacelite flange-type socket-outlets. The ship's library, reading rooms and sleeping compartments are fitted throughout with Crabtree silent-action, quick make-and-break flush switches, as illustrated in Fig. 10.

"Mauretania" Departing from Pier 90 in New York.

PASSENGER AND CREW ACCOMMODATION.

INTRODUCTORY.

IN the three classes of accommodation provided in the *Mauretania, viz.,* cabin, tourist and third classes, public rooms of unusual size and spaciousness have been arranged in a manner which fully maintains the traditional high standard of accommodation of both the world-famous shipping lines which are now combined to form the Cunard White Star, Ltd. The public rooms of the cabin and tourist classes may be said to compare favourably in style and finish with those for the same classes in any other passenger liner ; while, in the case of the third class, the size, decoration and furnishing of the numerous apartments available for these passengers surpass those in any vessel afloat.

The architects to whom the shipbuilders entrusted the designing, detailing and supervising of the decoration and furnishing of the cabin, tourist and third-class public rooms and entrances throughout the ship, as well as of the special suite rooms, were Messrs. A. McInnes Gardner & Partners, of Glasgow.

In general, the number and purpose of the rooms are regulated by the class of passengers using the respective spaces. In the decoration, however, there is a consistency of style and a presence of well-balanced restraint which give evidence of a careful control of the design throughout the vessel, while permitting a variety and change of interest to be achieved in each room. The theme, in conception, has a basis in the traditional types of architectural interior treatments, although—by the process of eliminating unessential items, the use of new materials and rare veneers, the adoption of the effects which can now be obtained by reason of the progress in woodworking methods, and the development in the design of the steel structure in which the public rooms are contained—rooms which are modern in the best sense of the word have been produced.

The finely-figured panels and beautiful burrs which have been used make it apparent that no trouble has been spared in obtaining the choicest examples of woods. As mentioned later in this chapter, glass in a variety of forms plays a very prominent part throughout the accommodation, both as decorative features and in the form of vitreous tiling on the walls and decks. Marbles have also been adopted, as well as leather, Rexine and synthetically-faced boarding.

As in all modern liners, the illumination greatly enhances the decorative schemes. This illumination is detailed in a later section of this chapter, but it may be appropriate to mention here that the light fittings are designed on simple lines which harmonise with the different features of the rooms, and are carried out in silver-bronze and nickel-silver, and tinted obscured glasses.

The names of the artists who have contributed to the decoration of the *Mauretania* are given in the following note, together with particulars of the principal works of each artist :—

Miss Marion Dorn.—Adaptation of Zodiac figures and signs as designs for fabrics of loose covers for the furniture in the cabin-class lounge.

Miss Winifred Humphries.—Characters from circus life, on panels of white sycamore, in the children's playroom of the cabin-class accommodation.

Mrs. A. Pinder-Davis.—Walnut panel, inlaid with silver-metal foil, at the forward end of the tourist-class smoking room, as well as the inlaid silver metal on white sycamore depicting characters from children's stories in the tourist-class children's playroom.

Mr. C. Cameron Baillie.—Sculptured sycamore panel, 13ft. in length, depicting the bridging of the Western Ocean, which is placed in a position above the cold-buffet recess in the cabin-class dining saloon. The same artist has been responsible for a small panel in the cabin-class entrance on the sun deck depicting a classical subject relevant to the Sun, and for the green-bronze figures representing Air and Water which are arranged at the ends of the passageways at the sides of the cabin-class swimming pool.

Mr. A. H. Gerrard.—Panels of modern character, based on early Chinese, representing the Creation of Speed, which

are arranged in the grand hall. Other work of this artist includes the incised frieze, representing symbols of the Zodiac, round the base of the dome to the cabin-class lounge, and the design of the directional-sign panel on the wall of the corridor connecting the port and starboard verandahs on the sun deck.

Mr. Walter Gilbert.—Designs and models for the applied casting on a dull-bronze panel at the after end of the cabin-class smoking room.

Mr. William McDowell.—Pictorial chart panel recessed into the after end of the cabin-class entrance on *A* deck, adjacent to the main stairway.

Mr. Charles Pears, R.O.I.—English landscape on a large panel arranged in the main cabin-class entrance on the promenade deck.

Mr. Sigmund Pollitzer.—Design of the engraved and colour-filled mirror plate, representing ship models, in the cabin-class observation and cocktail lounge. This artist also designed a decorative panel which has been set against a background of black glass in a recess at the after end of the cabin-class swimming pool.

Mr. H. Davis Richter, R.O.I.—Recessed panel in the tourist-class dining saloon, featuring the Tower of London.

Mr. Barney Seale.—Design of three plaques, representing masks of Comedy, Drama and Tragedy, carved in soft modelling and arranged in the grand hall. The work of this artist is also represented by a green-bronze figure of a woman, typifying the North Atlantic, which is arranged at the forward end of the cabin-class lounge.

The different types and arrangements of suites and staterooms which are provided for the three classes of passengers may be seen from Table I., while a summary of the officers' and crew's accommodation is given in Table II.

A large number of the cabin-class public rooms and entrances in the *Mauretania*, as well as the stairways and special suite rooms, have been decorated and furnished by Messrs. Waring & Gillow (1932), Ltd., of London, who have also been similarly responsible for the entire tourist-class public rooms, entrances and stairways. A list of the apartments decorated and furnished by this firm is given in the two following paragraphs, while the detailed descriptions of the rooms will be found in subsequent sections of this chapter :—

Cabin-class Accommodation.—Restaurant, foyer and entrance on *B* deck ; observation and cocktail lounge on the promenade deck ; main entrance on the promenade deck forward, including shop and writing room ; smoking room on the promenade deck ; main stairway forward, from *B* deck to the sun deck ; embarkation hall on the main deck ; entrance forward on *A* deck ; entrance aft on the promenade deck ; entrance forward on the sun deck ; stairway and entrance aft, from *E* deck to the sun deck ; and four special suites, comprising eight rooms, on the main deck.

Tourist-class Accommodation.—Dining saloon on *B* deck ; lounge on the main deck ; smoking room on *A* deck ; cinema on the main deck ; children's playroom on the main deck ; gymnasium on *A* deck ; entrance and stairway from the main to *D* decks inclusive ; and entrance and stairway aft, from *A* to *C* decks inclusive.

A number of the important public rooms in the cabin-class accommodation have been decorated and furnished by Messrs. George Parnall & Co., Ltd., of London and Bristol. The rooms included in the work of this firm are listed in the following paragraph, while the detailed descriptions of the rooms are included in the appropriate sections of this chapter :—

Cabin-class Accommodation.—Grand hall, lounge, library, children's playroom, entrance amidships, gymnasium, and port and starboard verandahs.

CABIN-CLASS ACCOMMODATION.

The public rooms in the cabin-class accommodation include the restaurant on *B* deck, extending in height through the deck above, with every facility for immediate and excellent service and intimate supervision of cuisine. The other principal apartments situated on the promenade deck are the observation and cocktail lounge, writing room, grand hall and cinema, lounge and smoking room. Other rooms on this deck are the library, children's room and gymnasium ; with the double verandahs on the sun deck aft, overlooking the sports deck. A swimming pool and " treatment " rooms are on *E* deck.

Restaurant.—The restaurant (Fig. 1) measures about 80ft. long by 88ft. wide, and, by reason of the central raised roof measuring 48ft. by 56ft. which rises through the deck above, is of very fine proportions. Arrangements are made for seating passengers, in specially-designed upholstered arm-chairs covered in rich blue hide, at square and circular tables for two, four and six persons. To facilitate service, a plentiful supply of dumb-waiters is installed and fitted as integral parts of the decorative scheme. Many of these are of the hot-plate type, while eight combine in pairs to form the plinth to the central standard footlights. There is also a centre show-piece, which is complementary to the cold buffet at the after end. Built in the form of a long sideboard, the front of this buffet is veneered with choice burrs. The panelling to the walls and sides of the raised roof is of a mellowed richness, and the large areas forward and aft are in natural Tobasco mahogany of beautiful figure, divided into panels by a fine line of sycamore.

TABLE I.—SUMMARY OF PASSENGER-STATEROOM ACCOMMODATION OF THE CUNARD WHITE STAR ATLANTIC LINER " MAURETANIA."

	No. of Rooms.		No. of Passengers.			No. of Rooms.		No. of Passengers.	
CABIN CLASS.					**TOURIST CLASS—***Continued.*				
Sun Deck—					Rooms with w.c. :—				
Suites and rooms with bath and w.c. :—					Two beds and two upper berths	4		16	
One bed and Pullman	5		10		Two beds and one upper berth	16		48	
					One bed and one upper berth	14		28	
Rooms with shower and w.c. :—									
Two beds	7		14		Other rooms :—				
One bed and Pullman	9		18		Two beds and two upper berths	2		8	
One bed	5		5		One bed and one upper berth	8		16	
Rooms with w.c. :—						—	58	—	152
One bed	2		2		*" C " Deck*—				
	—	28	—	49	Rooms with shower and w.c. :—				
Main Deck—					Two beds and one upper berth	2		6	
Suites with bath and w.c., and convertible sitting room :—					One bed and one upper berth	5		10	
Two beds and sofa berth	8		12		Rooms with w.c. :—				
					Two beds and two upper berths	5		20	
Suites and rooms with bath and w.c. :—					Two beds and one upper berth	10		30	
Two beds and Pullman	8		24		One bed and one upper berth	13		26	
Two beds	51		102						
One bed and Pullman	10		20		Other rooms :—				
One bed	2		2		Two beds and two upper berths	1		4	
					Two beds and one upper berth	2		6	
Rooms with shower and w.c. :—					One bed and one upper berth	23		46	
Two beds and Pullman	2		6			—	61	—	148
Two beds	2		4		*" D " Deck*—				
One bed and Pullman	8		16		Rooms :—				
One bed	7		7		Two beds and one upper berth	6		18	
					One bed and one upper berth	36		72	
Other rooms :—						—	42	—	90
One bed and Pullman	1		2		Total number of tourist class		161		390
One bed	6		6						
	—	105	—	201	**THIRD CLASS.**				
" A " Deck—					*" B " Deck*—				
Suites and rooms with bath and w.c. :—					Rooms :—				
Two beds and sofa berth	36		108		Two beds and two upper berths	12		48	
Two beds and Pullman	4		12		One bed and one upper berth	57		114	
Two beds	10		20			—	69	—	162
One bed and Pullman	2		4		*" C " Deck*—				
					Rooms :—				
Rooms with shower and w.c. :—					Two beds and two upper berths	20		80	
Two beds and Pullman	6		18		One bed and one upper berth	58		116	
Two beds	9		18			—	78	—	196
One bed and Pullman	7		14		*" D " Deck*—				
One bed	2		2		Rooms :—				
					Two beds and two upper berths	11		44	
Rooms with w.c. :—					One bed and one upper berth	50		100	
Two beds	2		4			—	61	—	144
One bed and Pullman	8		16						
One bed	4		4						
					Total number of third class		208		502
Other rooms :—									
One bed and Pullman	6		12						
One bed	4		4		Grand totals		602		1,378
	—	100	—	236					
Total number of cabin-class		233		486					
TOURIST CLASS.									
" B " Deck—									
Rooms with shower and w.c. :—									
Two beds and one upper berth	8		24						
One bed and one upper berth	6		12						

Fig. 1.—Cabin-class Restaurant.

Fig. 2.—Cabin-class Observation Lounge and Cocktail Bar.

TABLE II.—SUMMARY OF OFFICERS' AND CREW'S ACCOMMODATION.

	No. of Cabins.	No. of Persons.
Sports Deck—		
Captain	2	1
Staff captain	1	1
Sun Deck—		
Deck officers	7	7
Wireless officers	3	3
Assistant pursers	3	6
Main Deck—		
Chief purser	1	1
Doctor	1	1
Nurses	2	2
Stewardesses	2	4
" A " Deck—		
Seamen	3	24
Look-outs	3	6
Quartermasters	3	6
Lamp-trimmer and yeoman	1	2
Boys	3	10
Masters-at-arms	4	7
Boatswain's mates	2	4
Carpenter	1	1
Plumber	1	1
Assistant plumbers	1	2
" B " Deck—		
Firemen	3	27
Greasers	8	25
Donkeyman	1	2
Storekeeper	1	1
Cinema attendant	1	1
Fire patrolmen	1	4
Refrigerating-machinery attendant	1	1
Tourist-class purser	1	1
Tourist-class chief steward	1	1
Laundry hands	4	7
Isolation-hospital attendants	2	4
" C " Deck—		
Interpreter	1	1
Leading stewards	19	38
Chief printer	1	1
Assistant printers	1	2
Cinema attendants	1	2
Dispenser	1	1
General-hospital attendants	1	2
Third-class purser	1	1
Leading stewards	11	16
Chief engineer	2	1
Staff engineer	1	1
Engineers	28	33
Stewardesses	7	16
Musicians	4	7
Baggage masters	1	2
" D " Deck—		
Stewards	33	292
Stewardesses	7	14
" E " Deck—		
Swimming-pool attendant	1	1
Grand totals	189	594

At the forward end this is flanked by covered pilasters in Pommele, which is repeated to various portions of a similar nature. Where fillings are of a horizontal nature, Niger cherry of a fairly straight figure is introduced and relieved by moulded work in toned sycamore. On the lower wings of the restaurant the panelling is in Tobasco mahogany, with moulded lines of sycamore, and the surrounds of the large window screens are in plane-tree burr, which is also used in some of the furniture. The trim is in solid mahogany, while all moulded work and contrasting relief are carried out in toned sycamore. The ceiling throughout is painted in a soft cream shade, and lowered soffits are panelled to correspond to their adjacent wall surfaces.

Among the decorative features introduced, the most striking one on entering the apartment is the 13-ft. long sculptured sycamore panel over the cold-buffet recess. This forms a tangible memorial to the ship's famous namesake and shows in relief the striking differences in form between the two vessels. The theme shows the bridging of the Western Ocean between

east and west, and in the background two greyhounds epitomise the speed and grace of the ships. To one hand Great Britain is represented by St. Paul's Cathedral and a flight of pigeons, and from this a bow carries across to America, represented by a group of famous skyscrapers. The work—bold in its conception and exceedingly well executed—has been carried out to the design of Mr. C. Cameron Baillie.

To amplify this continuance of a great tradition, eight glass panels have been utilised to give in brief a history of the two vessels; and to this end constellations of stars relative to the dates of the launch, trials and maiden voyage—and, in the case of the old *Mauretania*, her last voyage—have been represented in archaic form by means of sand-blast, acid and brilliant-cutting on clear and mirror plate. These panels are placed over dumb-waiter recesses at each side of the raised roof, and are in their chronological order, as follows:—

On the port side, the panels show the launching of the old *Mauretania* on the 20th September, 1906, represented by the symbol of the Scales; the beginning of the maiden voyage on the 16th November, 1907, by Sagittarius; the return from New York on the 30th November, 1907, by Pegasus; and the beginning of the last voyage on the 1st July, 1935, by the sign of Leo.

On the starboard side, the panels show the keel-laying of the new *Mauretania* on the 24th May, 1937, represented by the twins, Castor and Pollux; the launch on the 28th July, 1938, by Virgo; the maiden voyage, by Cancer the Crab; and the return from New York, by Leo the Lion.

The climax to this introduction of constellations into the decorative scheme is the large feature mirror glass at the forward end of the room. Approximately 12ft. 6in. by 7ft. 6in. wide, this mirror is divided into 15 panels, 10 of which are engraved and brilliant-cut with the signs of the major planets, four with comets and subsidiary units, and the central panel as a clock dial, representing the sun around which the planetary system revolves.

The symbols of the 10 planets shown are Ceres, Venus, Mars, Mercury, Earth, Jupiter, Neptune, Uranus, Saturn and Pluto, and they are shown in their correct relationship to the Sun. Below this mirror, a large *jardinière* is fitted, and, appropriately enough, Pluto is shown arising from the earthy contents. Throughout the room, plain tinted mirrors have been introduced. Metalwork is used extensively, and is exemplified in the very large screens to the window openings. These are in groups of three and five on each side, and, with the concealed illumination, give the effect of sunlight.

At the fore end, wide entrance gates screen the restaurant from the vestibules, and these are carried out in white-metal similar to the window screens and glazed in clear plate-glass. Six illuminated roundels are also introduced to the sides of the raised roof, and these are in metal formed in interesting patterns, the centre bosses repeating some of the symbols taken from the feature mirror.

The furniture, comprising tables and chairs, has been carried out in harmony with the decorations, and has been specially designed for this room, great care having been taken to ensure absolute comfort coupled with durability and strength. The tables are of pedestal and four-leg types, and the chairs are beautifully shaped in toned sycamore, the seats and backs being covered in blue hide. This gives the foundation for the colour motif to the room, and is used as a foil to the flooring of $\frac{1}{4}$-in. Korkoid, which is laid in a large panel design using alabaster-marble colour and two shades of brown marble, with contrasting borders of light blue, biscuit and brown. In the central raised portion, three shallow domes provide a happy combination of concealed and direct lighting, flanked by pendant fittings to each side. Amplifying this, four powerful flood-lights send their illumination upwards, and by themselves are sources of softly-graded light. To the sides of the dome, cornice lighting effects a compromise. The lower wings are lighted by elongated panels, which run across the room and divide the ceiling into squares of bright and evenly distributed light, these having, as a secondary source, the illuminated window screens already mentioned. Lighting effects are used to six of the glass decorative panels, as well as to the roundels in the dome sides.

Lastly, but not least important, is the ventilation by means of conditioned air, which is distributed throughout the room by louvred openings skilfully worked into the design and

Fig. 4.—Cabin-class Grand Hall.

Fig. 3.—Cabin-class Grand Hall.

exhausted through gratings disposed about the walls in unobtrusive positions. The temperature is controlled by ingenious devices to any pre-arranged degree to determine the utmost comfort for passengers.

Foyer and Entrance on " B " Deck.—The spacious cabin-class entrance on *B* deck serves as the foyer to the restaurant, as well as being a principal embarkation hall. Well situated for easy access to all parts of the cabin-class accommodation, this entrance hall is the termination of the main stairway and the two fast passenger lifts serving the forward portion of this accommodation.

The wide areas of panelling are carried out in finely figured Betula, with contrasting portions in way of the recesses and entrance doors in Paldao and Queensland walnut, relieved with toned sycamore. Double openings under a flat archway lead to the restaurant vestibules ; and, between these, a deep semi-elliptical recess veneered in burr elm features a thick plate-glass pylon, which is internally illuminated and set over an ebony plinth enclosed within a shaped *jardinière*. Each leaf of the pylon is cut to a shape suggestive of the growth of the magnolia tree, and this has served for the motif of enrichment in brilliant-cutting and deep engraving with which each section is decorated.

This striking and original feature is opposite the foot of the main stairway, which rises with a broad flight to a half-landing (dividing port and starboard) and leads through the *A*, main and promenade decks to the sun deck. The walls of the stairway are carried out in richly figured weathered sycamore and Queensland walnut, the latter being repeated to the low balustrade, which is surmounted by a very fine wrought and cast railing of silver and bronze metal, ending in shaped and carved newel posts of unique and imposing appearance. These posts are set on the wide sweep of the lower curtail steps, which finish the lower flight. The stair is flanked by the lift doors, carried out in silver metal and set above small reception platforms, which are protected by simple yet elegant balusters. The ceiling is perfectly simple and straightforward, and is painted with lowered soffits carried out in veneers matching the walls; while on the higher panels, circular lighting fittings are placed which have been specially considered for the space, one being remarkable for its size and well-balanced design. Special lighting of a concealed nature is used for the feature recess, giving full decorative value to the work and skill which have been extended to the glasswork. Several comfortable tub easy chairs in walnut and in blue and fawn hide, accompanied by low circular tables, comprise the furnishings ; and these, with the specially designed notice-boards and directional signs, complete the entrance hall.

Observation Lounge and Cocktail Bar.—The cocktail bar is situated at the fore end of the promenade deck, and doubtless will be used as an observation lounge, its well-favoured position and wide sweep of windows, positioned in groups of three and four across the bridge front and to the port and starboard sides, assisting effectively in this object. To facilitate comfort, a low platform is built into both sides, which raises the floor about 11in. above normal. The plan of the cocktail bar or lounge is semi-elliptical, and a photograph is reproduced in Fig. 2.

The window groups are framed with surrounds and mullions of blistered maple ; while the panelling is laid in horizontal fashion stepped out slightly from floor to ceiling, and is veneered in a rare figured olive ash contrasting with the cross-banded casings and pillars, which are carried out in Queensland walnut. Doorways are arranged, one on each side, clear of the platforms at the after end, and are fitted with silver-bronze doors which

were cast in one piece in the round. They have each a decorative grille in low relief, representing the fruits of the earth, and are pierced and chased on the front. These doors are the work of Messrs. H. H. Martyn & Co., Ltd., of Cheltenham. A low flight of steps gives access to the platforms, which are enclosed by a low balustrade terminating at each end on a pillar casing. The balustrade has a carved open-work filling carried out in rosewood, and enriched with silver-metal beading and solid sycamore imposts, all supporting a flat rail which is also in rosewood.

The lower solid part of the balustrade is in cross-band walnut, which is repeated to the lower part of the bar front above a stepped plinth of white-metal and ebony, the last-mentioned also forming an integral part of the bases to the bar stools. A decorative band of fine burr elm is carried across under the top, which is edged with white-metal moulding worked in conjunction with a substantial elbow rail set on cast decorative brackets. The top is laid with dull-polished slabs of golden onyx ; and, on the service side, complete equipment is arranged in a compact and efficient way, with a working dresser top carried out completely in Staybrite. Above the dresser, and framed on three sides by recessed and glazed illuminated panels, a muffled mirror plate, designed by Mr. Sigmund Pollitzer, has been inset and engraved, and colour-filled with a free and happy rendering of bottle ship-models showing types which range from the Viking ship to the first Atlantic steamship. The recess itself is surrounded by a stepped and cross-banded architrave enriched with metal beading—all culminating in a central inverted shell which carries a floodlight illuminating the elliptical dome already mentioned. The ceiling follows the line of the front in wide curved sweeps of stepped planes, and the central suspended member is bordered by double lines of fluorescent-tube lighting of soft coloured shades producing a rich golden glow. This is supplemented by large pendant fittings of decorative types and wall brackets, which carry the lighting to all parts of the cocktail lounge and give a brilliantly lighted and cheerful aspect to the room. The chair coverings of bright green and coral are reproduced in the curtain fabrics. The tables, too, contribute their share to this colourful space

Fig. 5.—Strohmenger Grand Piano in Cabin-class Lounge.

by having inlaid tops of Formica, which again pick out the prominent colour tones. A special circular design of $\frac{1}{4}$-in. Korkoid, adapted to the shape of the room, is laid in light-marble and terra-cotta marble colours, with contrasting borders and bands of biscuit, scarlet, chocolate and cinnamon.

Main Entrance—Promenade Deck.—Of good and well-proportioned shape, the entrance on the promenade deck centralises varied activities, and provides free access by the two lifts serving the lower decks, *i.e.*, forward to the observation and cocktail lounge, and aft to the grand hall and cinema.

On the port side, a large annexe is fitted as the shopping centre, complete with a shop and show and display cases. On the starboard side there is a writing room. The panelling throughout is in Betula, relieved by Paldao and Australian walnut, and elm burr and toned sycamore are introduced to special features.

A notable contribution to the artistic work on board is the large panel by Mr. Charles Pears, R.O.I., showing a pleasant landscape, which could well be named " Turrets of England."

The ceilings are painted, and have lowered soffits in veneer. The lighting generally is from fittings specially arranged for the space and function of illuminating units. An exception has been made in the writing room, where the general lighting is diffused from a concealed trough and reliance for direct light

Fig. 6.—Cabin-class Lounge.

Fig. 7.—Cabin-class Lounge.

Fig. 8.—Cabin-class Smoking Room.

Fig. 9.—Cabin-class Gymnasium.

made dependent on the individual lamps to each writing desk. Tub chairs are arranged informally about the entrance, and these, together with the writing chairs, are all covered in hide of a colour harmonising with their setting. Substantial writing desks are provided on the starboard side. This space has a carpeted floor and rich coloured curtains to the group of windows, all being carried out in a scheme of deep wine, fawn and brown. Elsewhere, the floors are in Korkoid of appropriate design.

Grand Hall, Cinema and Ballroom.—The most important room on the promenade deck is the grand hall (Figs. 3 and 4), which is about 60ft. in length and 64ft. wide, and has a raised central roof 18ft. high, supported by four columns in beautifully designed casings. In the design and layout of the room, the triple functions of lounge, cinema and ballroom have been borne in mind, and with little adjustment any of these activities can very quickly be catered for. At one end of the room an almost full-size proscenium (Fig. 3) is the predominant feature, and is fitted with a permanent cinema screen and complete "talkie" apparatus. Approximately 250 passengers may be seated in this cinema theatre. Draw curtains in cloth of gold, actuated by an electric motor, come into action when cinema performances are being given; but normally the proscenium is enclosed by a five-part decorative lacquer screen, beautifully carried out in gold, vermilion and pale green on a black background.

Relief and incised work is used to give emphasis to other work which is of modern character based on early Chinese, and which depicts several herds of antelopes at various stages of development, and ultimately racing off into the misty forest wilderness of the background. The motif might well represent the "Creation of Speed," and has been designed and carried out by Mr. A. H. Gerrard.

Opposite the proscenium, at the forward end of the room, there is a semi-elliptical recess decorated with vertically-shaped panelling veneered in fine ash burr of great beauty. To the centre of this recess a radiant electric fire, with a silver-bronze grille, is set into a surround of onyx and black and gold marbles. The marble is itself set in a surround of finely-shaped ash-burr panels with a sycamore-veneered coved soffit, over

Fig. 10.—Plaque in Cast Nickel-silver at the After End of the Cabin-class Smoking Room.

which is featured an indirectly-lighted tinted mirror. The woods used in the upper part of the central dome and in the proscenium are teak and finely figured peroba veneers, while the frieze is carried out in ash burr.

Relief is obtained by the introduction of three plaques showing masks of Comedy, Drama and Tragedy, designed by Mr. Barney Seale, and carved in soft modelling.

The sides of the room are panelled in figured peroba; while recessed openings frame and surround the windows, this latter work being carried out in sycamore and ash burr. The windows have double sashes on account of the air-conditioning system used in this room, and are of large dimensions, giving the maximum daylight. Illuminated niches are fitted between each window group, and there are moulded and shaped *jardinières* carried on brackets at the foot of each window. At each end of the grand hall there are two sets of double entrance doors and side screens, which have coffered panels, with sycamore and ash-burr surrounds and inlays of hollywood and peroba in floral and other motifs. These motifs are repeated in the glass panels of the doors, which are also mounted with silver-metal beading and elaborate handles. The ceilings are of a simple character and painted a soft cream, with lowered soffits veneered in the same manner as the wall panelling. To the raised roof of the dome a broad-shaped centre panel is arranged above the cornice, which has concealed lighting; and to each side, under this, a continuous light fitting is utilised to throw illumination downwards.

Supplementing the indirect lighting, four decorative bracket bowls are fitted to the pillars. The lighting at the sides is from continuous fittings which form decorative wall brackets.

The floor is partially covered in ¼-in. Korkoid in a large panel design, the main shades being light-coloured and sienna marbles, with borders of cinnamon, meadow-green and biscuit. There is a central area of parquetry for use when dancing is in progress. The whole floor, however, is covered by large and luxurious carpets of modern design in shades of green, beige and fawn. The upholstery materials are in rich fabrics and of special selection, giving the colour note to the room, and range from russet, beige and fawn to the deep rich green in the crushed-velvet of the window curtains. Card and coffee tables in peroba and ash are arranged in conjunction with the seating and side tables; writing desks and other occasional pieces of furniture being provided as necessary. Settees and easy chairs of a particularly comfortable pattern have also been installed. For the use of passengers, and for the orchestra while dancing is in progress, there is a Steinway grand piano at the after end. The case of the piano is in fine ash burr and peroba, and is in complete harmony with the furnishing and decorative scheme of the grand hall. This instrument has been specially designed and constructed for the *Mauretania* by Messrs. Steinway & Sons, of London.

Lounge.—The cabin-class lounge (Figs. 6 and 7), which is situated about amidships, is approximately 54ft. square, and has a central raised roof, about 18ft. square, fitted with a circular dome, from which the basis of the design has been evolved. The radiating ceiling is stepped downwards and outwards in a series of planes, which terminate at the sides with a veneered soffit and features planned to the arc of the circle. The panelling is in a rare type of Primavera, which has an interesting figure in a pinkish colour, and the walls are divided by horizontal V-cut joint lines. As a contrast, Paldao is used in the entrance doors. Four wide groups of windows are framed together within surrounds of moulded sycamore. Between each two groups of windows, double doors give access to the promenade deck, the doors themselves being faced with elm burr and sycamore and mounted with silver metal. The column casings are in elm burr and sycamore, with enrichments of silver-bronze metal.

A recess at the forward end, planned on the arc of the circle, has shaped and stepped ingoings in fine ash burr, and conceals vertical panel lighting. Similar panels return to a central niche, which is illuminated to throw into high relief the symbolical green-bronze figure which is set over the radiant electric-fire surround. The figure is of a woman with severely classical features—almost angry in effect—typifying the North Atlantic. Held aloft by the figure is an idealised model of the ship, while wind-swept drapery wreathes the body, and sea-birds flutter around the unruly hair. The work of Mr. Barney Seale, the figure is both striking and effective in its execution, and may be seen in the photograph reproduced in Fig. 6.

A low mantelpiece of modern conception in elm burr and Paldao encloses a surround of black and gold marble, and there is a recessed electric fire enclosed within a decorative grille. Opposite this, at the after end, a large tinted and brilliant-cut mirror is fitted with a plinth formed as a *jardinière*.

The ceiling is painted a pale pastel blue, culminating in a frieze which encircles the base of the dome. The frieze—which, with the dome, is carried out in plaster—has incised decoration to illustrate the symbols of the Zodiac, and is the work of Mr. A. H. Gerrard. The incised frieze may be seen in Fig. 7.

The central crown of the dome is fitted with a flat laylight

Fig. 11.—Cabin-class Library.

Fig. 12.—Cabin-class Verandah, Port Side.

Fig. 13.—Cabin-class Verandah, Port Side.

Fig. 14.—Swimming Pool.

having a central hemisphere of obscure glass. The whole is brilliantly lighted, and, to ensure that the diffusion is complete over the raised surface, concealed lighting is provided above the decorated cornice. For general lighting purposes, flat laylight fittings of segmental shape are arranged to the marginal planes, and are supplemented by wall brackets and decorative standard lamps.

There are informal groups of extremely comfortable settees, easy and tub-shaped easy chairs, tables and cabinets, which are all of a light modern type in keeping with the decorations. A few groups are arranged for card-playing. The centre of the floor is of wood parquetry, laid in an interesting pattern, for dancing, and is directly under the central raised roof with its brilliant illumination.

The fabrics employed blend exceedingly well with the background, being in tones of pale pastel blue, brown, cream and beige, with a stronger colour note in the loose covers provided for occasional service for the larger seats and settees. The fabric for the loose covers was designed by Miss Marion Dorn, and is an interesting example of her work, showing an adaptation of the figures and signs of the Zodiac to a covering material.

Among other fabrics worthy of note are the window curtains, which are a fine example of the abstract in design ; and the shades of blue and brown, blending both with the walls and the ceiling, give the key to the colour scheme.

A fine piano of the semicircular grand type has a prominent position at the after end of the room. The casework of this instrument, as well as that of the pianos in the tourist and third-class lounges, has been specially designed for the *Mauretania* by Messrs. A. McInnes Gardner & Partners. The piano in the cabin-class lounge is in a strikingly attractive case of burr elm, with cross-bandings and a plinth of Paldao. This instrument, which is shown in Fig. 5, has been constructed by Messrs. John Strohmenger & Sons (1938), Ltd., of London.

Carpets of heavy pile cover a large area of the floor, as well as the dancing space, and tone with the scheme, having motifs in colours similar in character to those shown in the fabrics. The floor is laid with ¼-in. Korkoid in a large panel design embodying alabaster-marble, light-walnut marble, and light-grey marble colours, with borders of light blue, cinnamon and biscuit.

Smoking Room.—Situated at the extreme after end of the promenade deck, the cabin-class smoking room (Fig. 8) measures approximately 54ft. square, and is planned to give a feeling of retirement and unobtrusiveness. The basis of the design is almost Elizabethan in tradition, yet each and every detail in the room is entirely modern in character. The square beams and pillars to the wings of the room are cross-banded in Australian walnut, while the large wall panels are carried out in finely figured Australian maple. A moulded trim of solid sycamore is introduced at about dado height, and is carried around the room, introducing lighter effects to the pilaster panels. These panels are in Mazur birch, framed in hardwood to match, and give interesting relief to the richer and darker walnut and maple.

The central ceiling panel of this room is carried out in a quite different manner, and gives the illusion of a somewhat higher ceiling ; the lower margins and bordering moulding, of heavy upstanding section, being shaped to an almost traditional plan.

An outstanding feature is the large panelled fireplace surround in polished and unpolished Quarzite, which measures some 14ft. wide by 7ft. 6in. high, the background being unpolished with beautiful veining. The actual surround, of moulded and polished Quarzite, is modern in style, and encloses an opening with a raised hearth of Hoptonwood marble, on which is set a modern dog grate in Staybrite. For bordering the marble work, squared panelling veneered in cherry burr is used. At the after end of the room, the squared cherry-burr panelling again appears. A long buffet is placed in the centre, and is fitted with a hot-plate and cupboards.

Over the buffet, a panel in dull bronze (Fig. 10) is featured. In the centre of this panel there is an applied casting in nickel-silver metal representing those illustrious Elizabethan knights Raleigh, Drake and Humphries discussing some projected adventure by the fireside in a house of the period, and the whole worked into a strapwork formation reminiscent of the period. Small roundels are fixed at the four corners of this plaque, and depict in bas-relief the phœnix (symbolical of the new ship rising from the old), migratory birds (representing ocean passage) and a Chinese unicorn (symbolical of the meeting of wise men). This

work has been carried out to the designs and models prepared by Mr. Walter Gilbert, and has been executed by Messrs. H. H. Martyn & Co., Ltd., of Cheltenham, who also have supplied the stainless-steel fireplace and surround.

Of suitable and substantial character, the furnishings include circular tables for six or more, comfortable settees, and deep, luxurious easy chairs.

The coverings, in brick red and fawn hide, contrast with the rich tapestry and needlework embroidery on a nigger-brown background. Floral motifs in needlework are also introduced in the heavy curtains of plain tan-coloured material, and the predominant colours are again picked up in the large carpet covering the central portion of the floor, which is of a simple panelled design in colourings to suit. The floor covering consists of ¼-in. Korkoid in a large tile design, using an alabaster-marble colour, with other shades of brown marble, and with borders of brown, biscuit and red.

Special lighting suitable for the smoking room has been introduced.

Library.—In the library (Fig. 11), also on the promenade deck, the decoration is subsidiary to the bookcases, which occupy more than half the wall space and give accommodation for over 1,400 volumes. The books are enclosed within hinged and sliding bronze-framed doors, with bronze grilles in the panels instead of glass. The cupboards and surrounds are in finely figured Queensland maple, with cross-bandings of Sapeli. The entrance door, which is flanked by bookcases, is in cherry burr and has a trim of sycamore ; while opposite, at the after end, a recessed cupboard, with a projecting cabinet underneath, forms a feature of interest and at the same time conceals an altar fitment. To the outboard side, a group of windows is surrounded by cross-banded architraves and fitted with inner screens of bronze metal and glazed with sand-blasted tinted glass. The ceiling is of unusual form in that it carries concealed lighting coves down the centre, with directed light towards the side bookcases. This is also supplemented by a centre light of imposing appearance and by wall brackets. Comfortable tub chairs are arranged around an octagonal centre table of unusual design, and the furniture is carried out in cherry burr, sapeli and sycamore veneers. The chairs are covered in blue and fawn hides, contrasting well with the beige-coloured carpet, which is carried out in a new process giving an effect of relief.

The floor is covered with ¼-in. Korkoid in a simple panel design, using beige, biscuit and royal-blue colours. Rich blue-velvet curtains, piped in pale fawn, complete and finish a most dignified and restful room.

Children's Playroom.—The playroom is situated on the promenade deck in a position corresponding to that of the library, but on the port side of the ship. Above a low dado the walls and ceiling are panelled in white and weathered sycamore, while the dado and entrance doors are covered in a bright jade-green leather.

On the larger panels of white sycamore, Miss Winifred Humphries has carried out highly coloured characters from circus-life, which are both amusing and entertaining.

The small-scale chairs and tables are in keeping with the decoration, and the curtains, of self-coloured material, are embroidered with coloured motifs harmonising with the painted decoration.

The usual toys and games are provided, and include a blackboard and pedal-car. The floor covering, of ¼-in. Korkoid, in simple panel effects with special motifs, itself makes an attractive playground.

Gymnasium.—The gymnasium (Fig. 9), which is entered from the after entrance hall on the promenade deck, is panelled in light and brown oak in a straightforward and utilitarian manner. The large windows provide maximum daylight and fresh air, as required, and these can also be screened by sliding louvred jalousies. Flat laylights give artificial lighting. The floor covering, of ¼-in. Korkoid, is a tile effect of alabaster-marble colour, with dark and light-blue and cinnamon borders.

The apparatus provided includes cycles, horse and camel machines, rowing and vibratory machines, punch ball, wall bars, etc.

Swimming Pool.—The swimming pool for cabin-class passengers is situated aft on *E* deck. There is direct access from the entrance hall, being served by a lift and stairway from the decks above, and by intercommunicating corridors from the tourist-class accommodation.

This swimming pool, which, with its surrounds, has been carried out by Messrs. Purdy & Millard, of Belfast, is about 24ft. by 17ft. The pool, which is shown in Fig. 14, is lined with pale-cream and jade-green glazed briquettes, with green directional lines. An anti-surge ledge, with vermilion nosing, projects under-water at each end, while moulded hand-grips and troughs are arranged on all sides. Depth numerals in green are introduced in suitable positions. The ladders into the water are in silver-bronze, and have teak treads with non-slip rubber insets.

The surround is covered in non-slip Quarzite marble tiling of a soft golden-yellow colour. The same material is used for the low solid balustrade which encloses three sides, and which is surmounted by a handrail in non-inflammable jade-green plastic, supported on silver-bronze pedestals. Duodecahedron columns, giving a colonnade effect to each side, rise from the surround and are also carried out in Quarzite.

The walls and floor-space outside the balustrade are lined with Vitrolite-glass floor tiles, which have been manufactured by Messrs. Pilkington Brothers & Co., Ltd., of St. Helens, the colour adopted being an ivory shade, with horizontal bands and motifs of modern design in green and grey, and relieved with silvered and tinted glass tiles. Green beading divides the walls into attractive panels.

To the centre of the after end, above a low platform, a recess has been arranged, which is flanked by large panels of green agate Vitrolite, framed in teak and silver-bronze. In the recess, against a background of black glass, a decorative panel has been set in a silver-bronze frame, and shows in bright relief submarine subjects cleverly worked on thick plate-glass and illuminated through the edges. The work has been carried out to the design of Mr. Sigmund Pollitzer.

At the end of the passageways on each side, and flanking the feature to which reference has just been made, half-round niches are framed in the vitreous tiling, and in these are placed green-bronze figures of great beauty symbolising Air and Water. These are the work of Mr. C. Cameron Baillie. At the forward end, a drinking-water fountain in ivory, green and grey has been built against a black-glass background flanked by green onyx.

The entrance screen doors, in silver-bronze, are to the starboard side of the fountain, and to the port side a recess leads to the ladies' dressing boxes, those for gentlemen being positioned aft. An attendant's office and drying room are situated on the starboard side, a window with silver-bronze frame giving a clear view over the pool. The remaining doors are in weathered teak, with silver-bronze fittings. The chairs, tables and other furniture are in weathered teak to harmonise with the general surroundings. Directional signs in green are provided.

The central suspended ceiling and marginal panels are carried out in a highly finished white enamel, while in the edges the cornice type of light fittings are recessed. These are carried out in silver-bronze, with obscure toughened plate-glass, and all arranged to give diffused lighting over the whole space. Special lighting is arranged at the features on the centre-line forward and aft.

The cubicles which form the dressing-room accommodation are framed in weathered teak and have partitions surfaced with Bakelite in a delicate shade of green, this latter material having been manufactured by Bakelite, Ltd., of London. The floor in these spaces is of Quarzite with a terrazzo coved skirting. The cubicles are adequately ventilated, and are each equipped with a contact light, mirror, tray, seat and sparred grating. Door and other fittings are in silver-bronze.

Adjoining the swimming pool are rooms for electrical and massage treatment, the walls of these rooms being lined with Bakelite panelled in matt-finish silver-bronze, while the floors are covered with Quarzite tiling. All the doors are of the flush type and of the same material as the walls, while the framing is of silver-bronze. The electric lights are of the shallow-bowl type, and silver-bronze is also used for the framing for the bowls.

Sun-deck Verandahs.—The last of the cabin-class public rooms are on the sun deck, and are accessible from the sports deck and from the promenade deck by the after cabin-class stairway. These rooms, designated verandahs (Figs. 12 and 13), are very similar in general appearance and are suitably arranged as useful adjuncts to the open-air sports deck as games rooms. The decoration is of simple design, and consists of silver and

pastel-green jaspé Mural Rexine, with a smooth-finish pastel type for panelling the small sections. Rexine is a well-known and widely-employed product of I.C.I. (Rexine), Ltd., of Hyde, Cheshire. Teakwood is used throughout, with sycamore for the casings and surrounds to the groups of large windows, port and starboard. The doors are veneered in elm burr. On the wall of the corridor which connects the two rooms a large panel of plain green has been decorated with applied half-round silver-metal beading. The design of this panel is in the nature of a large directional sign giving the deck name, the port and starboard verandahs, and the position of the aquarium built into the bulkhead on the port side, and directs one to the passageway leading forward on the starboard side. This work has been ingeniously conceived, and has been carried out to the design of Mr. A. H. Gerrard. Café furniture in cane is used, and the bright coverings in printed linen promote the cheerful air of these verandahs.

The floor covering is of ¼-in. Korkoid in a panel design, the predominant colours being duck-egg marble, with borders of cinnamon, pea-green, black and biscuit.

In the after end of the verandahs and the communicating corridor between the port and starboard rooms, Esavian screens have been fitted, two being 9ft. 6in. in length and the third 13ft. 6in., while all three screens are 6ft. 0in. in height. The 13ft. 6in. screen is fitted in way of the corridor, and is arranged with centre leaves which may be opened as casements and which are fitted with flush handles. These screens, which are shown in the open and closed positions in Figs. 15 and 16, have been manufactured by the Educational Supply Association, Ltd., of London. The top and bottom fittings, tracks and handles are all made in solid manganese bronze in order to resist deterioration by the action of the sea-air, the exposed parts being polished and finished in antique B.M.A. colour. The bottom rollers are fitted with waterproof bearings; and the top guide-wheels are provided with vulcanised-rubber tyres to minimise noise while the screens are being operated, and also any disturbance which might arise from vibration.

Stairways and Entrances.—Throughout the cabin-class accommodation, the stairway and entrance-hall service is very complete, and provides easy access between all the stateroom decks and public rooms. The principal stairway is situated forward and rises from *B* deck through the *A*, main and promenade decks to the sun deck. The panelling, in beautifully figured weathered sycamore, is relieved by Australian-walnut cross-band surrounds to the large feature mirrors on each half-landing. A balustrade, also in walnut, is surmounted by a finely-wrought balustrade in metal having a silver and pale-bronze colour, and fitted with a continuous solid walnut handrail.

Flanking the stairway on each side, fast passenger lifts serve each deck, the cars of which are carried out in a manner suitable to the entrance halls, while the doors, of synchronised sliding type, are in silver metal.

Among the features of note in the entrances adjacent to the main stairway is a panel by Mr. William McDowell, which is an interesting variant of the pictorial chart, and, by reason of its harmonious colourings and clever drawing, excites attention. This panel is recessed at the after end of the entrance on *A* deck. In the main-deck entrance, the bureau occupies a central position; while the office and consulting rooms of the purser and doctor are also adjacent. Wireless-telephone kiosks are placed port and starboard, aft of the wide embarkation doors.

The last of the entrances is that on the sun deck, which has been made particularly attractive by the inclusion of a small panel, by Mr. C. Cameron Baillie, depicting a classical subject relevant to the sun and, naturally, the sun deck. This panel is placed over a long fitted sofa seat covered in rich-blue hide.

The foyer and entrance on *B* deck have already been dealt with in an earlier section of this chapter.

Staterooms.—As already indicated, accommodation for **486** cabin-class passengers is provided in **233** staterooms situated on the sun, main and *A* decks.

An examination of these staterooms immediately reveals an elegance of treatment and workmanship. The general scheme of decoration depends mainly on differences of colour and textures in woods and fabrics, and, both from the point of view of comfort and refinement, they may be confidently described as being among the finest ranges of staterooms in any ship afloat.

In addition to the four special suites on the main deck, of which one of the bedrooms is illustrated in Fig. 17, there are single and two-berth rooms, an unusually large number being

Fig. 15.—Esavian Screens in Verandahs—Open Position.

Fig. 16.—Esavian Screens in Verandahs—Closed Position.

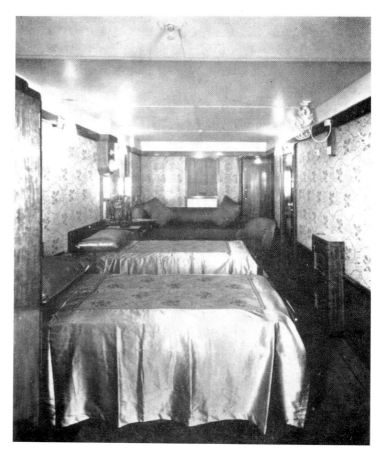

Fig. 18.—Cabin-class Room on " A " Deck.

Fig. 17.—Cabin-class Special Suite Bedroom.

Fig. 19.—Washbasin Recess in Cabin-class Stateroom No. A62 on "A" Deck.

Fig. 20.—Tourist-class Dining Saloon.

Fig. 21.—Tourist-class Smoking Room.

" outboard " rooms, with natural light and ventilation from the ship's side.

While some passengers may prefer those rooms the walls of which have been panelled in birch (which, incidentally, is a most difficult wood to employ) or sycamore " weathered " to a delicate creamy brown, others will undoubtedly delight in those rooms where fabrics have been used as wall coverings. These fabrics will undoubtedly excite much admiration. Dignified in their conception, they yet contrive to give each room a warm, informal and homelike atmosphere.

Some of the room walls have been covered in a peach-coloured " antique " satin, overprinted with a leaf design in nigger brown and white. A particularly interesting leaf design has been selected for another series of rooms, to achieve which three distinct types of weave have been necessary. The beige background, effected in honeycomb weave, gives the effect of the bark of a tree. Running through this honeycomb weave is another weave which provides the branches, while a third weave has been used in the leaf figure, even to the " veins " across each leaf. One of these rooms is illustrated in Fig. 18.

Then there are rooms in which a cream quilted chintz has been used, and others where a blue and fawn quilted brocade has been employed. In several rooms, self-coloured fabrics in two shades of cream provide a cool effect ; while in those cases where panelling or fabrics would have proved obtrusive, the walls have been enamelled in

Fig. 22.—Tourist-class Lounge.

delicate pastel shades of green, rich cream and beige.

In the washbasin recesses, Mural Rexine with a green and brown plastic design has been used for the wall covering, the pleasing effect of which may be seen in Fig. 19.

Carpets in two-tone effects of green, soft pinks and fawns, according to the decorative scheme of each room, have been selected for the floor coverings.

The furniture in each room has been chosen to harmonise with the decorative schemes. In this way, such woods as Bubinga (African rosewood), quilted maple (which provides a silk-like sheen), Betula (the heart of Canadian birch) and cherry

have been used for the bedsteads, dressing tables, bedside tables, wardrobes and other stateroom fittings.

Special attention has been paid to the all-important features of temperature, ventilation and lighting. Each passenger has control of the temperature and ventilation of his stateroom, which has been achieved by installing the newest type of Winsor ventilating and heating systems. Ducts providing separate supplies of warm, medium and cold air are led throughout the accommodation, as described at length elsewhere.

The electrical equipment and lighting of the various state-rooms include architectural strip lighting with bracket fittings for the wall lights, while separate lighting is employed for the dressing tables and reading lamps. Other electric fittings include plugs for heating curling irons, and electric fires to supplement the warm-air heating, when desired.

A striking feature which is noticeable throughout all the stateroom accommodation is the almost complete absence of visible metalwork. Roanoid has been used for the door handles coat-hooks, etc. This material, which harmonises with the colour schemes, is warm to the touch, and remains clean indefinitely. All the doors are flush with the walls, without mouldings or beadings of any description, and the few metal articles considered essential are of a non-tarnishable material.

TOURIST-CLASS ACCOMMODATION.

New standards in the comfort and facilities provided for tourist-class passengers were undoubtedly formed when the new *Mauretania* began her maiden voyage from Liverpool and Cobh to New York on the 17th June, 1939.

No fewer than five public rooms have been provided for passengers of the tourist class. Extending over three decks, they comprise a lounge, smoking room, dining saloon, cinema, and children's playroom.

Tourist-class passengers have also every facility for exercise in their well-equipped gymnasium on *A* deck aft, in the large interior swimming pool, which is reserved for their exclusive use during certain periods each day, and on the gracefully-terraced and entirely unobstructed decks for games and promenading.

Dining Saloon.—Situated on *B* deck, the tourist-class dining saloon, a photograph of which is reproduced in Fig. 20, occupies the width of the ship and is approximately 60ft. long. This room is simply panelled in finely figured weathered sycamore, contrasted with bandings of Queensland walnut, while recesses are formed by mouldings and panelling of beautiful white sycamore. The windows are screened by horizontal, obscurely-glazed sashes of white-metal. Double entrance doors of similar design and material flank the well-designed sideboard, which is centred at the after end. Above the sideboard there is a long brilliant-cut and acid-bitten tinted mirror glass, which forms a background to the clock incorporated in its design.

Opposite, a cold buffet of similar design to the sideboard has as a feature a recessed panel decorated by Mr. H. Davis

above the long low chimneypiece, this latter being of very modern design and enclosing a surround of Hoptonwood stone and a radiant electric fire.

At the forward end of this apartment is another walnut panel, inlaid with silver-metal foil in a design embodying the grape vine, tobacco and similar plant forms, as well as church-warden pipes and other items of interest to smokers. This work has been carried out by Mrs. A. Pinder-Davis.

A recessed cocktail bar is fitted to port at the after end of the smoking room. In complete harmony with the larger part of the room, this cocktail bar has yet a distinctive character of its own. The high bar, carried out in burr and straight figured veneer, is mounted with silver-metal foot and elbow rails. The fitment stools and recessed sofa seat are all covered in blue-green hide. Complete service arrangements are installed, as would naturally be expected, and over the dresser at the rear a wide

Fig. 23.—Tourist-class Cinema.

Richter, R.O.I., who has chosen the Tower of London as his subject.

A painted ceiling of shallow coffer formation permits each square to have centred in it a lighting fitting, and these are supplemented by wall brackets on the pillar casings.

Seating is provided at tables for two, four or six persons, arranged with ample clearance for service from the vestibules at the forward end. The armchairs, of good and strong design, have deep sprung seats covered in claret-coloured hide. The floor covering is in a large panel design of ¼-in. Korkoid, in colours of light-grey marble and two shades of brown marble, with borders of drab and claret colours.

Smoking Room.—On *A* deck aft, the smoking room (Fig. 21) is of simple character, plainly carried out in finely figured chestnut. The main features are perhaps the leather-covered panels, of deep blue-green at central positions, and worked with tooled and silver-studded motifs. Walnut and walnut burr are used for bandings and special panels. Of particular interest is the panel

muffled plate-glass mirror is worked with motifs similar to those on the leather panels.

The ceilings throughout this room are painted with margins veneered in similar style to the walls, and are of simple section and fitted with shallow electric-light units.

The walnut furniture is positioned in suitable groups, and combines all the functions of the smoking room with the necessary comforts represented by the deep-seated settees and easy chairs.

The coverings are in hide of blue-green, fawn and brown shades, and tapestry in suitable colourings and pattern is also used for curtains. A rich Oriental carpet, which picks up these colourings, is placed near the radiant fire. The flooring, of ¼-in. Korkoid, is laid in a large tile design having main colours of light marbles, and with green and brown borders.

Lounge.—The lounge for tourist-class passengers is on the port side of the main deck, and a photograph of this room is reproduced in Fig. 22. Simply decorated, the chief features are the recessed ingoings to the window groups flanked by reed-

Fig. 24.—Tourist-class Children's Playroom.

moulded pilasters, and the recessed panels of ash burr divided into squares by fine lines of peroba. Peroba is used for all general panelling, with teakwood to match for the solid trim. For contrast, there is fine white sycamore for the moulded architraves, carved frieze over the doorway, and wide bookcase fitment on the inboard wall.

The ceilings are of interesting shape, and have central raised panels with half-round ends, permitting the introduction of semi-recessed units to the edges. In the centre, large fittings of imposing design are placed at suitable intervals, and give complete and brilliant illumination. This illumination is supplemented by bracket wall lamps and the lighted panels already mentioned.

Two pillar casings and four corner pilasters are arranged with panel lighting, and have decorative motifs in ceramic enamel and sand-blast. These motifs represent music, dancing, writing, leisure, reading and sport, all of which are catered for in this room.

The furniture is in figured teakwood and ash burr, with coverings in beige and pale-green tapestry materials. The curtain hangings are of specially woven material having a tufted pattern worked into them, this matching the general design motif. Large carpets of two shades of green cover the Korkoid and wood mosaic floors, all of which are in complete harmony with the furnishings and decorative scheme of the lounge. The Korkoid is ⅛in. in thickness and is in a large panel design, the colour employed being maize marble, with borders of meadow-green, beige and cream.

An attractive feature in this room is a beautiful grand piano of the semicircular type, constructed by Messrs. John Strohmenger & Sons (1938), Ltd. This instrument is in ash burr, with bandings and enrichment of quartered peroba.

Cinema.—Occupying a similar position to starboard to that of the tourist-class lounge on the port side, the tourist-class cinema is ideally planned for its purpose. Provision is made for about 125 persons, in seating graded in height from back to front. A photograph of this room is reproduced in Fig. 23.

The walls are panelled in Mural Rexine with a green and stone watered effect. The covering has been hung horizontally. Broad flat pilasters, which are continued across the ceiling, are carried out in Indian silver greywood, and divide the wall space into shallow bays.

The screen is surrounded by a proscenium in greywood and sycamore, with cross-bands in Macassar ebony. Curtains in rich fabric, decorated with wool tufted motifs, cover the opening.

Solid emergency exit doors, and windows with hinged shutters, are positioned on the outboard wall.

Comfortable tip-up armchairs are arranged in rows of six and seven, and these are covered in a rose corded tapestry of substantial weave, which gives a colourful aspect to the cinema.

The floor covering, which is ¼-in. Korkoid, is in a large panel design of orange-marble and sienna-marble effects, with borders of cream and dark brown. Unobtrusive lighting fittings are fixed to the ceiling panels, and are supplemented by flat amber-coloured pilot lights at suitable intervals.

Children's Playroom.—The playroom for the children of tourist-class passengers is on the starboard side of the entrance for this class on the main deck, and is illustrated in Fig. 24. Moulded surrounds in sycamore frame the window openings, and are repeated to the after elevations, where the infilling consists of inlaid silver metal on white sycamore, showing characters from "Alice in Wonderland" and "Brer Rabbit" stories. These amusing panels are the work of Mrs. A. Pinder-Davis, and are carried out in bleached silky oak from Tasmania. Relief is given by Zebrano cross-banding and solid trim in sycamore, while a low dado in bright-orange Bakelite is also introduced.

A toy locker, blackboard and pedal-car have been installed, and these, with the brightly coloured inlaid floor, complete the permanent decorations. The floor covering, of ¼-in. Korkoid, is laid in simple panel effects with special motifs.

Furniture, comprising cane tub-chairs and colour-enamelled tables of sizes suitable for children, is arranged in groups; while the coverings and curtains, of printed linen in appropriate designs, have been selected to harmonise with the scheme.

Gymnasium.—On *A* deck aft, the tourist-class gymnasium is accessible from the entrance hall at the head of a stairway which serves *B* and *C* decks. This room is simply panelled in light oak, and is completely equipped with the usual apparatus.

Fig. 25.—Tourist-class Stateroom.

Fig. 26.—Third-class Dining Saloon.

Fig. 27.—Third-class Smoking Room.

The floor covering is of ¼-in. Korkoid, and is in a panel design of alabaster, light-grey and sienna-marble colours, with borders of light and dark blues, cinnamon and biscuit.

Entrances and Stairway.—The main stairway in the tourist-class accommodation, which rises from *D* deck and serves the *C*, *B*, *A* and main decks, is arranged on three sides of a central enclosed lift trunk. The panelling is of a rich reddish brown, and is carried out in Nigerian cherrywood, relieved by Sapeli cross-bandings and sycamore beading. Mahogany is used for all solid trim and for the stormrails. The lift shaft is panelled in similar fashion, and there are two-part automatic sliding doors in fine cherry burr for access to or exit from the car on each deck.

Among the entrance halls, that on the main deck is the most important. In addition to giving access to the lounge, cinema and children's room, as well as to the covered weather deck, this particular entrance hall is provided with a large general shop and showcases. The shop is on the port side, and

ing, of low height, is surmounted by a cast railing in white-metal, silver-finished, of simple yet pleasing design.

Staterooms.—Delightful modern fabrics and curtains have been chosen for the staterooms, all of which are supplied with hot and cold running water, bedside lights, large windows and mirrors, comfortable chairs, dressing chests, and unusually spacious wardrobes. A typical tourist-class stateroom is shown in Fig. 25.

The staterooms of this class are particularly well ventilated by a system which can be controlled by the passengers. Another interesting innovation is the numerous intercommunicating rooms, so that families may travel together ; while there are also unusually large numbers of " outside " and two-berth rooms.

THIRD-CLASS ACCOMMODATION.

Third-class accommodation, on a scale which, it is claimed, has never previously been attempted in an Atlantic liner, is one of the special features of the new *Mauretania*.

Fig. 28.—Third-class Lounge.

has a wide range of cases carried out in white-metal for displaying goods. Showcases are also arranged in the centre of the entrance hall, these being enclosed with panelling.

The principal feature of *A* deck is the inquiry bureau, which is placed centrally at the after end opposite the stairway, and has a fine front carried out in cherry burr and Sapeli. There is also a wireless-telephone kiosk, as well as the corridors to the smoking room and staterooms. *B*-deck entrance serves the dining saloon forward and the staterooms aft, while *C* and *D*-deck entrances are in the accommodation. Each has been carried out in simple panelling of good proportions and veneered in Nigerian cherry with bandings of Sapeli ; while each has also some individual feature which gives added interest, such as mirror panels or specially selected examples of fine cherry burr relieved with moulded sycamore.

The after stairway and entrances from *A* to *C* decks are carried out in a similar combination of woods ; and the balustrad-

Extending over three decks, the public rooms comprise a lounge and a cinema theatre on *A* deck, a smoking room on *B* deck, and a special room for children on *C* deck. The dining saloon, also situated on *C* deck, is a fine, spacious apartment furnished with tables for parties of two, four and six persons.

Perhaps, in many ways, the most outstanding innovation, so far as the third-class accommodation is concerned, is the provision of a special deck-games area on the sports deck of the vessel. Located just aft of the bridge, this deck-games area is exceptionally spacious, access being by means of a special elevator service.

Dining Saloon.—Planned to approximately the shape of the letter L, the third-class dining saloon (Fig. 26) has groups of sidelights arranged in the ship's side, framed together by surrounds of light oak, and divided into bays by casings of the same wood. The inner walls repeat the surround motif, but the window cases are replaced by tinted mirror plates. The

Fig. 30.—Third-class Entrance on Main Deck Forward.

Fig. 32.—Cabin-class Sports Deck, with Third-class Sports Deck beyond.

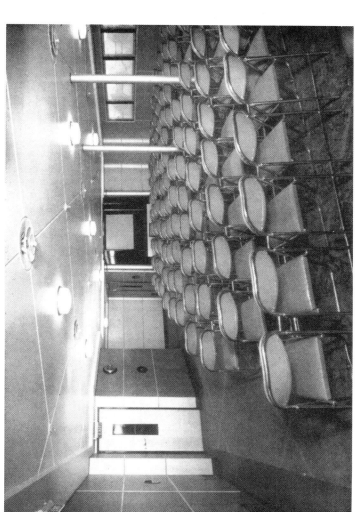

Fig. 29.—Third-class Cinema.

Fig 31.—A Third-class Stateroom.

general scheme consists of a low dado of this light oak, banded with dark-brown oak, and above this the walls are painted a light-beige shade. Forward, there are two sets of double glazed entrance doors, and there are ample arrangements for expeditious service from the kitchen, which is aft of the dining saloon. The ceiling is treated perfectly simply, being divided into squares by a shallow channelled line and painted to tone with the walls. Shallow light fittings are placed in alternate squares, and in the bays at the sides flush laylights are used. The armchairs, in light oak with seats covered in tangerine-coloured hide, are placed at tables for two, four and six persons. The tables have extensions making them suitable for eight and 12 persons, when necessary. There are curtains to the window surrounds and to the inboard windows to complete the scheme, and these pick up the tangerine of the chair coverings and the colours introduced in the design of the floor covering. This consists of $\frac{1}{4}$-in. Korkoid, laid in a large panel effect, with a main colour of light-brown marble, and with contrasting borders of dark-brown marble, red, biscuit and beige.

Smoking Room.—Situated on *B* deck, and lighted by groups of sidelights, the third-class smoking room (Fig. 27) has been treated in a simple manner in a combination of Rexine and Australian walnut. The windows are grouped and enclosed with moulded sycamore framing. The walls are covered in brown antique-leather Rexine as dadoes, and divided into bays by webs and low portions of walnut. Higher sections of the walls are in a two-colour leather effect with a stone base. This brown wall treatment is divided into squares by half-round beading and terminates in way of the bar service window forward, which has a permanent screenwork of brown Rexine and white-metal. The after walls have a low dado and broad flat pilasters of walnut, while the wide panels between are covered in the two-coloured leather-effect Rexine, each panel carrying a wall bracket light for decorative effect. There are double entrance doors in walnut, and a recessed dartboard is placed on the foremost wall. The furniture is in walnut and sycamore, the tub chairs, settees and easy chairs being covered in a rich-blue hide. The card armchairs are covered in tapestry, which combines the rich blue with fawns, yellows and a touch of red. The scheme is completed by the floor covering of $\frac{1}{4}$-in. Korkoid in a large tile design of blue and light-grey marbles, with borders of biscuit, cinnamon and light blue.

Lounge.—A dado effect has also been introduced in the third-class lounge (Fig. 28), where the low surbase is in Indian silver greywood, which, in way of the bookcase features forward and aft and the double entrance doors, is carried right up to the ceiling. In grouping the sidelights, sycamore has been used as a foil to the curtains, and elsewhere as moulded trim to the doors. Bandings of Macassar ebony have been employed for the door and bookcase surrounds. An interesting innovation is the writing recess, where three writing desks have been fitted, complete with all the essential equipment, and provided with wall bracket lights. The remaining portions of the walls above the dado are painted blush pink, and harmonise with the striking curtain and seat-covering materials, in pink and grey against backgrounds of nigger brown. The furniture, in sycamore and teak, is of simple character and in perfect accord with the style of the room. The $\frac{1}{4}$-in. Korkoid on the floor is in a panel design embodying colours of alabaster and coral marbles, with borders of chocolate, rose pink and drab.

A grand piano of the semicircular type, having a case in toned curl sycamore, with supports of straight sycamore and bandings of Indian greywood, has been constructed and supplied for this room by Messrs. John Strohmenger & Sons (1938), Ltd.

Cinema.—On the port side of the ship, and similar in shape to the lounge, the third-class cinema and games room (Fig. 29) is laid out in simple manner. The walls are covered for the full height in pale monastral-blue Mural Rexine with smooth finish, divided horizontally by bright-blue enamelled beading. The latter colour is used for the sidelight surrounds, relieved by jet black. This combination is also introduced in the proscenium surround and entrance doors. The painted ceiling is set out in diagonal squares. The $\frac{1}{4}$-in. Korkoid floor covering is in a tile design of blue-marble colour, with borders of biscuit and dark blue. Tubular-steel chairs, with seats in orange hide, are arranged in rows. These chairs are easily portable, and can be stacked to clear the room for games.

Children's Room.—A room has been provided on *C* deck forward in a position adjoining the third-class embarkation hall. The walls are covered with Mural Rexine in a farmyard designs, pigs, cows and rabbits being represented in brown and orange shades on cinnamon. The floor covering is of $\frac{1}{4}$-in. Korkoid and is laid in simple panel effects with special motifs.

Entrances and Stairways.—The panelling of the third-class entrances and stairways, both full height and as a low dado, is carried out in flame-figured birch, in contrast with mahogany, excepting on *C* deck, where full-height panelling of Niger cherry is used. Above the dado portion, the walls are covered in a particularly effective pale monastral Mural Rexine with pin-point effect, while the ceilings throughout are painted cream. In addition to giving access to the various public rooms and their use as embarkation centres, various services are catered for in the entrances, as exemplified by the inquiry bureau on *C* deck and the shop on the main deck. Feature panels of veneer and brilliant-cut mirrors enliven the more extensive stretches of wall panelling. The stairs, in straight flights of four, are exceedingly easy-going, and have been arranged to afford the greatest number of passengers rapid access to the public rooms and various deck spaces at their disposal. The third-class entrance on the main deck forward is illustrated in Fig. 30.

Staterooms.—Outstanding among the features of the third-class accommodation are the staterooms, all of which are supplied with hot and cold running water, berths with bedside lights, curtained windows, comfortable chairs, dressing chests and spacious wardrobes. The rooms are also particularly well ventilated by a system which can be controlled at the passengers' will. One of the staterooms is illustrated in Fig. 31.

DECK COVERINGS.

All the open decks in the ship, including the promenades and sports decks, are sheathed with teak. A photograph of the sports decks is reproduced in Fig. 32. Incidentally, a large quantity of the timber used in the construction of the *Mauretania* has been supplied by Mr. Richard H. Keeping, of London.

In all public rooms, entrances and corridors, the Korkoid flooring has been laid over an underlay of Aranbee plastic deck composition, supplied by Messrs. Rowan & Boden, Ltd., of Glasgow.

The contract for the extensive floor coverings in the *Mauretania* has been fulfilled by Korkoid Decorative Floors, of Glasgow, and comprised large quantities of their Korkoid and Korkoleum deck coverings. The floors in all the cabin, tourist, and third-class staterooms have been laid with Korkoleum flooring of $\frac{1}{8}$in. thickness of a special beige-marble colour, with borders of plain beige. The officers' and engineers' cabins and the crew's accommodation also have floors laid with this material, of the same thickness, and in various shades to tone with the different schemes of decoration. In all the hospitals, $\frac{1}{8}$-in. Korkoleum floor covering in a special shade of blue marble has been laid.

The remaining areas of floors throughout the accommodation of the vessel have been laid with $\frac{1}{4}$-in. Korkoid. The different designs and colours adopted are detailed in the previous descriptions of the respective rooms, while the schemes of $\frac{1}{4}$-in. Korkoid in the remaining parts of the passenger accommodation are described in the following notes :—

The entrances for all three classes of passengers are laid in large panel and tiling designs embodying colours of alabaster, blue, sienna and light-grey marbles, while the stairway treads are in similar designs to the corresponding entrances. The cabin and tourist-class corridors are in tile designs, which include the same colours as the entrances, while the third-class corridors are similar except for the adoption of a simplified design. The cabin-class bureau and the tourist and third-class shops are laid in modern designs using colours which match those used in the entrances.

The cabin-class bathrooms and lavatories are paved with vitreous-glass cube mosaic in various designs, and with borders and coves of terrazzo round the bulkheads. Messrs. Diespeker and Co., Ltd., of London, have been responsible for these pavings and for the Diespeker special *in situ* non-slip terrazzo, with the associated coves, gutterways and borders which have been laid in the third-class bathrooms and lavatories, and the crew's shower-rooms, washplaces and lavatories. The floors of the kitchens and the dependent domestic spaces are covered with Diespeker pre-cast non-slip terrazzo tile paving. Other work

Fig. 33.—One of the Utley 18-in. Sidelights.

of Messrs. Diespeker in the kitchens includes the fire-brick bases beneath the ranges and the enamelled-brick edges to the bases.

It is of interest to note that all the pavings detailed in the preceding paragraph are laid on a foundation of Bentata, a material devised by Messrs. Diespeker after exhaustive theoretical and practical tests over a long period. The material, which is a form of concrete bottoming half the weight of ordinary fine concrete, with a greatly increased resistance to compression, was first used in the *Queen Mary* and is also being adopted in the *Queen Elizabeth*. It is claimed that Bentata has an elasticity factor which enables the material to withstand the strains set up in the deck plating of a vessel.

Special flooring of Bituladeck composition, manufactured by Bitulac, Ltd., of Newcastle-on-Tyne, has been laid in the vegetable, provision, fruit, spirit, beer, wine and tobacco rooms on *D* and *E* decks.

Windows and Sidelights.

The windows for all the public rooms have been supplied by Messrs. Thomas Utley (Rainhill), Ltd., of Rainhill, Liverpool, this contract entailing the provision of about 300 windows. In the principal rooms the windows measure 4ft. 8in. in height by 2ft. 1in., and are arranged so that the top panel slides down over the lower panel.

In the staterooms on each side of the sun deck, hinged windows, 24in. by 18in. in dimensions, are fitted ; while in the wheelhouse vertically-sliding and fixed windows are arranged. These three types of windows have also been supplied by Messrs. Utley. In addition, the 27 large windows in the screen across the fore end of the promenade deck, which are fitted with sliding deadlights, have been provided by these manufacturers.

The cabin-class promenading spaces at the sides of the promenade deck are enclosed for the whole length of the public rooms on that deck by side screens fitted with vertically-sliding windows, which have been supplied by the Carron Company, of Carron, Falkirk.

Below the promenade-deck level, sidelights have been fitted, these having been manufactured by Messrs. Thomas Utley (Rainhill), Ltd., and comprise about 800 circular sidelights of the makers' bevelled-lug type. In the compartments on the lower decks, 10-in., 12-in. and 14-in. diameter sidelights have been adopted, while those in the rooms on the main deck are 18in. in diameter. An illustration of one of these last-mentioned sidelights is given in Fig. 33.

Miscellaneous Furnishing Materials and Fittings.

Plywood has been employed to a large extent for divisional and boundary bulkheads and ship-side lining in the accommodation of the *Mauretania*. The whole of the plywood, including the plywood-asbestos bulkheading and the Plymax metal-faced plywood, has been supplied by Messrs. L. Keizer & Co., Ltd., of Liverpool, etc.

It is interesting to note that all the wood grounds in the public rooms and passenger accommodation, and the back of all panelling throughout the ship, have been treated with Porcella fire-resisting paint, supplied by Porcella Products, Ltd., of London.

In the manufacture of most of the wood panels for which Messrs. Cammell, Laird & Co., Ltd., have been responsible, Casco heat-reactive glue has been employed. This glue, in addition to being heat-proof, is also waterproof, and has the further advantage of being absolutely stainless, so that no discolouring of the veneers of the panels is possible. Casco glue is the product of Messrs. Leicester, Lovell & Co., Ltd., of London.

Some 1,600 flush-surface wood doors in the accommodation for passengers and for the ship's personnel have been made and supplied by Messrs. Adams & Co. (London), Ltd., of London. These doors are veneered with various woods, such as figured African mahogany, figured African cherry mahogany, Bubinga and Nigerian striped Sapeli mahogany, etc.

A good example of the many and varied uses of Lloyd boards—the products of Lloyd Boards, Ltd., of London—is their adoption for the decorative panels which make up the sliding cover for the cinema screen in the grand hall. These panels are about 9ft. high, and, as stated in the introductory note to this chapter, were carved by Mr. A. H. Gerrard, an artist of the Slade School. The design, symbolising the Birth of Speed, was lightly scratched on the surface of the $\frac{3}{16}$-in. Lloyd super-hard board and then carved to a depth of $\frac{1}{8}$in. The design was then " built up " with successive coats of Chinese lacquer, bringing the artist's work into attractive and colourful relief. A photograph of the screen, showing the good effect obtained by this process, is reproduced in Fig. 34.

Among the modern materials used in the interior treatment of the *Mauretania*, Bakelite veneers have been extensively employed. This material, manufactured by Bakelite, Ltd., of London, is obtainable in many attractive colours and effects, and has qualities of heat and moisture resistance, light weight and anti-corrosion which make it particularly suitable for marine use.

In many of the public rooms, including the grand hall, cabin-class lounge and the third-class lounge and smoking room, all the tables and coffee stools are surfaced with Bakelite veneers.

The new fabric-faced material perfected by Bakelite, Ltd., only within recent months, has been used on tables and counter tops in the sun-deck verandahs. A photograph of a serving

Fig. 34.—Lloyd-board Screen enclosing Proscenium in Grand Hall.

Fig. 35.—Cabin-class Serving Table, with Bakelite Fabric Top.

table in one of the verandahs, showing the Bakelite fabric top, is reproduced in Fig. 35. All the appearance of a gaily-coloured cloth, without the attendant disadvantages, is given by this material, which consists of fabric incorporated in the process of manufacture as an integral part of the Bakelite sheet. Other furnishings surfaced with these veneers include the tops and shelves of dumb waiters and dressing tables, while portions of the third-class dining saloon, corridors, etc., are similarly treated.

Many of the tables throughout the vessel are covered with a special blisterproof grade of Bakelite, which will withstand, without blemishes, direct contact with burning cigarettes.

The clean appearance of partitions, walls and doors surfaced with Bakelite may be seen from Figs. 36 and 37, which show respectively the partitions of the dressing-room cubicles for passengers using the cabin-class swimming pool, and the bulkheads and doors of one of the treatment rooms adjoining the pool.

The stateroom fittings are in moulded Roanoid, of which the decorative appearance, strength and permanence of colour and polish combine to make it eminently suitable for the purpose. The comprehensive range of fittings supplied in this material by Roanoid, Ltd., of Glasgow, includes door furniture, wardrobe fasteners and hooks, hat and coat hooks, cupboard catches, mortice slip-bolts, berth grips, curtain rods and fittings, and electric-light fittings, as well as washbasin fittings, such as tumbler and bottle-holders, toilet shelves, etc. In addition, this firm have supplied their Formica material for use as bathroom-wall linings, and, in a special blisterproof quality, as veneering for furniture.

Among the most pleasing features in the interior decoration of the *Mauretania*, to which brief reference has already been made, are the beautiful examples of mirror and pictured glass-work. A particularly distinctive item is the planet mirror, which, as mentioned previously, is arranged at the forward end of the cabin-class restaurant. Carried out in $\frac{1}{4}$-in. peach mirror-plate, with bevelled and polished edges, it includes a clock dial worked in brilliant-cutting, stone-cutting and acid embossing. The surrounding plates are decorated in a similar manner to the clock dial, with designs also in brilliant-cutting, stone-cutting and acid work, and bear references to the mythical characters connected with the 10 most important planets in the Solar System, as detailed in the description of the restaurant.

The four corner plates depict comets, while brilliant-cutting has been employed to denote the orbits of the planets round the sun, the last-named being represented by the clock dial,

Other examples of decorative glasswork in the cabin-class restaurant include the glass pictures over the dumb-waiter recesses referring to outstanding dates in the histories of the old and new *Mauretanias*. The designs are of mythical figures and animals, and comprise Saggitarius, Pegasus, Leo, Virgo, Cancer, Leo (in another form), the twins Castor and Pollux, and the symbol of the Scales. With the exception of the two last-mentioned designs, which are worked on peach plate mirrors, the glass used for this work is $\frac{1}{2}$-in. polished plate. The designs for all eight panels are worked in brilliant-cutting, sand-blast and acid work on backgrounds showing stars, comets and the nebulæ winding through space.

The windows in the cabin-class restaurant are in peach plate, and are worked with motifs in keeping with the character of the rest of the glass decoration.

The whole of the glasswork detailed in the preceding paragraphs has been carried out by the London Sand Blast Decorative Glass Works, Ltd., of London ; while they have also been responsible for the decorative feature in 1-in. plate-glass, incorporating a design based on the magnolia tree in flower, arranged in the cabin-class foyer and entrance on *B* deck. Other work carried out by this firm includes six illuminated pilaster panels which are treated with sand-blast and ceramic enamelling, and which are mentioned elsewhere in the description of the tourist-class lounge.

Messrs. L. Keizer & Co., Ltd., of Liverpool, etc., have provided their Elcoplated mirrors for the *Mauretania*.

An interesting detail in connection with the public rooms is the application of Dunlopillo cushioning to the edges of the swing doors. Nearly 100 lineal feet of Dunlopillo door edging has been fitted in this way, and by this means draught-proof doors have been obtained, which at the same time obviate injury in the event of a person's fingers being caught between the edges.

Old Bleach Furnishings, Ltd., of Randalstown (Northern Ireland) and London, have been responsible for a quantity of the furnishings in the public rooms, comprising table covers in the the tourist-class dining saloon, and chair covers in the cabin-

Fig. 36.—Cabin-class Swimming-pool Cubicle Partitions.

class lounge. The last-mentioned are in hand-painted worsted-wool, linen and Rayon fabric. Loose covers have also been supplied for some of the furniture, and consist of hand-blocked printed linen containing all the signs and symbols of the Zodiac. The same firm have also supplied suitable hand-embroidered curtains for the children's playroom, as well as loose covers for the tourist-class lounge.

The Cunard White Star Line specified that the curtains and chair covers in certain rooms were to be of fabrics supplied by Morton Sundour Fabrics, Ltd., of London ; and of the 14 Sundour and Edinburgh Weavers' cloths which were employed, six were specially designed and woven. The fabrics have been used for curtains in the cabin-class observation lounge and writing room, the tourist-class lounge and smoking room, and the third-class cinema ; while they have also been adopted for curtains and chair covers in certain of the staterooms.

Somnus sleep equipment is used extensively in the *Mauretania*, the Somnus Inta bedstead fittings of Messrs. William Rhodes, Ltd., of Nottingham, etc., having been fitted throughout the ship. About 200 of the cabin-class beds are provided with Somnus flexible upholstered base mattresses and overlays, while there is similar equipment in half the cabin-class Pullman berths. Each of the tourist-class beds is supplied with a Somnus marine spring base, and about 200 of the overlay mattresses for these beds have also been provided by Messrs. Rhodes. The whole of the third-class beds are fitted with Somnus marine bases, having pocketed spring overlays of the same make. Similar equipment is also provided for the beds in the hospital wards. The beds for the officers and other members of the ship's staff have Somnus marine bases and overlays, while a further 513 marine spring bases have been supplied for the crew's quarters.

On the port side of the vessel, the entire passenger accommoda-

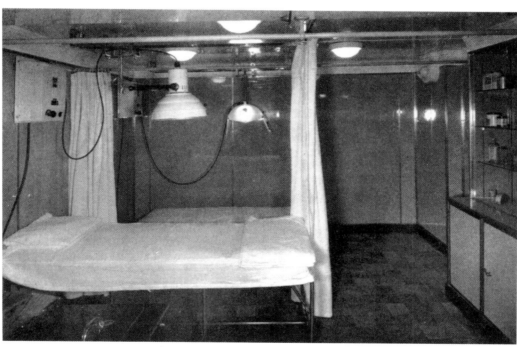

Fig. 37.—One of the Treatment Rooms adjoining the Swimming Pool.

tion is equipped with Vi-Spring mattresses, which are the speciality of Vi-Spring Products, Ltd., of London. In the cabin-class rooms, Vi-Spring mattresses with Vitoflex supports are provided, while the whole of the tourist-class berths are furnished with Vi-Spring mattresses.

Lan-Air-Cel blankets, made by Messrs. McCallum and Craigie, Ltd., of Glasgow, have been supplied for the *Mauretania*. The "covered-cell" weave of these blankets is claimed to obviate stuffiness, thus making for refreshing sleep.

The tables in the third-class dining saloon are fitted with an extruded aluminium section surround embodying a rubber insert, which simultaneously prevents table-ware slipping off the tables and protects the edges of the tables against damage by contact with other furniture. This table surround has been made and supplied by Metal Mouldings, Ltd., of London, to whom large quantities of decorative moulding in aluminium have been provided by the Northern Aluminium Co., Ltd., of London, etc.

In addition to the items referred to in the descriptions of the cabin-class observation lounge and smoking room, Messrs. H. H. Martyn & Co., Ltd., of Cheltenham, have been responsible for window-screen roundels and entrance-door screens in the cabin-class restaurant, and for the silver-bronze window screens and two complete sets of double doors in the tourist-class dining saloon.

Nickel-silver appears extensively in the interior decoration of the *Mauretania*, the uses to which this material has been put including hand-rails and balustrading, decorative doors and surrounds, window frames, lighting frames, etc., in addition to the numerous instances detailed in other chapters.

The decorative materials in the *Mauretania* include Delta No. 2 silver-bronze and Delta bronze No. IV., manufactured by the Delta Metal Co., Ltd., of London and Birmingham.

One of the most interesting of the minor fittings in the passenger accommodation is the type of deck fastening used for the furniture. In the dining saloons, some 800 Bowman patent deck fastenings are employed for the purpose of anchoring the chairs. This fitting has been designed by Mr. S. Bowman, of London, and those on board the *Mauretania* have been manufactured by Messrs. Comyn Ching & Co. (London), Ltd. This type of fastening comprises an eyebolt which acts against a spring in a suitable casing, and a socket attached to the deck, into which the eyebolt is inserted and locked by the simple process of turning through 90 deg. The spring in the fastening takes no load from the chair, while the system of attachment offers many advantages over the ordinary screwed connection for such fittings.

A contract for extensive wire-screening work on board the *Mauretania* has been fulfilled by Messrs. Thomas Locker and Co., Ltd., of Warrington. The type of screens which are arranged round the sports decks may be seen in the photograph of the sports decks reproduced in Fig. 32.

ILLUMINATION.

Details of the lighting arrangements and the enhancement of the decorative schemes by the many attractive forms of illumination have been referred to previously in the descriptions of the various rooms. It seems appropriate, however, to give in a separate section a summarised account of the most interesting features.

The lighting fittings have been supplied by three leading firms in the electrical world, *viz.*, the General Electric Co., Ltd., of London, the British Thomson-Houston Co., Ltd., of Rugby, and Messrs. Osler & Faraday, Ltd., of London. It may also be mentioned, in this connection, that extruded bronze and nickel-silver sections, manufactured by Messrs. McKechnie Brothers, Ltd., of Birmingham, have been used extensively in this work and for other internal fittings.

The G.E.C. Lighting.—The General Electric Co., Ltd., have worked in collaboration with the architects, Messrs. A. McInnes Gardner & Partners, of Glasgow, in designing the lighting equipment which they have supplied for the cabin-class restaurant, observation lounge and cocktail bar, lounge, verandahs and swimming pool, and the tourist-class smoking room, lounge, cinema and children's playroom. The metalwork throughout is of silver-bronze, with glasswork of various types to harmonise with the decorative schemes of the rooms.

Examples of the G.E.C. lighting fittings may be seen in the photographs reproduced in Figs. 1, 2, 6, 7, 12, 13, 14, 21, 22, 23 and 24.

On the ceiling of the raised roof of the cabin-class restaurant, three bowl-type fittings 3ft. diameter and of semi-indirect type are arranged as central features in three shallow domes of 9ft. 6in. diameter. Each bowl houses one 200-Watt and eight 25-Watt lamps. At the edge of each dome, architectural Striplite lamps are arranged, while abreast the circular fittings are four 24-in. square fixtures which form direct and indirect-lighting units to square recessed panels. Four standard lamps of 3-ft. height are arranged on the dumb-waiters, providing indirect lighting from Gecoray reflectors and 500-Watt Class-B projector lamps concealed in the metal bowls. The shafts of the standards have glass cylinders superimposed on inner cylinders finished ebony black. These cylinders are edge-lighted from concealed architectural Striplite lamps. At the sides of the raised roof are three circular decorative motifs, indirectly lighted, and below these are two special rounded-section frieze lights, each approximately 43ft. long and housing architectural Striplite lamps. The lighting of the outboard areas, where the ceiling is at the normal height, is by 26 beam-type fittings, each approximately 9ft. long, also illuminated by architectural Striplite lamps. The window lighting is by 28 special Gecoray reflector fittings, and various other types of fittings are employed in the vestibules, service lobbies, etc. The glassware in this space is mainly of pink-flashed opal, excepting in the case of certain fittings, where ¼-in. white plate-glass is used.

The cabin-class observation lounge and cocktail bar is lighted by a combination of Osira fluorescent tubing and decorative fittings with standard tungsten lamps. The Osira fluorescent-tube installation comprises two rows of double tubing semi-recessed into the ceiling, radiating from the after bulkhead on the port side, forming a semicircular design around the bar, and terminating at similar points on the starboard side. Each run of double tubing consists of gold and pale-blue tubes. There is a total of 300ft. of tubing in the observation lounge, and this is operated from eight transformers. The alternating current for the transformers is obtained from a 2·4-kVA. rotary converter, which is remote-controlled by a push-button switch. The decorative fittings consist of three combined direct and indirect lighting units, 3ft. diameter, four 4-light wall lights, five enclosed-type wall lights fitted at cornice level, and panel units fitted over and at the sides of the bar. There is also a special reflector unit concealed in the decorative shell feature over the bar. The glassware in this space is in pink-flashed opal.

The central lighting feature of the cabin-class lounge is a circular laylight fitted in the centre of the dome, which is 16ft. high and approximately 17ft. diameter. The fitting is approximately 7ft. diameter and illuminated by eight special dispersive-type reflectors housing 100-Watt lamps, and with a 300-Watt lamp in a centre 20-in. diameter bowl. Below this, and at the sides of the dome, is a cornice for indirect lighting, equipped with special mirror-lined cornice reflector and architectural Striplite lamps. The main lighting for the low-level ceiling, which is 9ft. high, consists of 10 shallow panel fittings, 5ft. by 1ft. 6in. These are shaped specially and placed in line forming a circle, the focal point of which is the 7-ft. diameter dome fitting already mentioned. These 10 fittings are each equipped with eight 40-Watt lamps. The extreme outboard areas are lighted by four circular ceiling fittings, 17in. diameter, and four indirect lighting brackets, the last housing Gecoray reflectors and 250-Watt Class-B projector lamps. Around the walls are a number of horizontal wall fittings, 2ft. 6in. long, with architectural Striplite lamps. Supplementary and mainly decorative lighting is provided by four floor lamps and strip panel lights and reflectors at the forward end of the room, the reflectors being used for the purposes of illuminating a figure in a niche over the fireplace. The glassware used in the fittings in this room is a new flashed opal known as " Chamois."

The cabin-class port and starboard verandahs are equipped with a total of 12 ceiling lights, approximately 17in. diameter. They are glazed with champagne-flashed opal-glass bowls, superlux finish, and each fitting has three 60-Watt lamps. In the passageway connecting the verandahs are three panel fittings built into the cornice, each housing three 40-Watt lamps.

There are six cornice lighting fittings in the cabin-class swimming pool, approximately 6ft. by 1ft. 3in., each with a total of 360 Watts of architectural lamps. They are glazed with ¼-in. plate-glass (sand-blasted), and provide the lighting over the actual pool. Supplementing these at the fore and after ends of the pool are two flush fittings, approximately 3ft. by 1ft. 3in. and having 160 Watts of architectural lamp lighting. At the extreme outboard areas are 10 cornice-type fittings, approximately 1ft. 6in. by 9in., with three 40-Watt

lamps. At the extreme forward end is a flush-panel light, semicircular in form and approximately 3ft. by 1ft. 9in. This fitting houses one 100-Watt lamp and two curved 60-Watt architectural lamps. To complete the lighting of this space, two architectural lamp reflector fittings are employed to light a decorative glass panel at the after end.

The tourist-class smoking room is illuminated by three shallow ceiling fittings, 3ft. diameter, housing eleven 40-Watt lamps. These constitute the central lighting features of this space. They are glazed with a combination of Chamois flashed-opal and sand-blasted Stippolite glass. General lighting in the outboard and fore and after areas is by 21 ceiling fittings, 16in. diameter, with specially moulded champagne-flashed opal bowls, each with three 60-Watt lamps, and also 12 tubular brackets. There is a large panel fitting over the bar housing fourteen 40-Watt lamps and architectural strip-lighting to the bar display.

The main source of illumination in the tourist-class lounge is from five ceiling fittings, 4ft. diameter, glazed with Chamois flashed opal and white sand-blasted Stippolite glass, and also relieved with amber-glass rods. The total rating of each fitting is approximately 880 Watts. There are also six vertical flush wall-panel lights ; these are 4ft. 6in. by 1ft., and two are shaped to fit circular columns. Twelve built-in cornice fittings, 2ft. long by 1ft. wide, and four wall lights taking architectural Striplite lamps complete the scheme.

The tourist-class cinema is illuminated by 10 ceiling fittings, 16in. diameter, with special champagne-flashed opal-glass bowls and three 60-Watt lamps which form the general lighting equipment of this room, together with four pilot lights, which, as in the case of the usual cinema, are recessed into the ceiling.

The tourist-class children's playroom has six small ceiling fittings, approximately 16in. diameter, with three 40-Watt lamps providing the necessary lighting. They are glazed with champagne-flashed opal bowls.

The G.E.C. have also supplied a large number of Roanoid lighting fittings and shades for the various staterooms—over 100 special Utility-type promenade-deck fittings, and 40 cargo lanterns and clusters.

The B.T.-H. Lighting.—A large proportion of the electric lamps used in the *Mauretania* are of the Mazda type, while the many special forms of lighting fixtures were designed by Mr. J. P. McBride, of Messrs. A. McInnes Gardner & Partners, in collaboration with the lighting department of the British Thomson-Houston Co., Ltd.

The rooms included in the B.T.-H. lighting are the cabin-class grand hall and smoking room, and the tourist-class dining saloon, the illumination fittings in which may be seen in Figs. 3, 4, 8 and 20.

For general utility illumination, cornice lighting has been adopted, with laylighting and illuminated panels as architectural features, and specially designed ceiling fittings and wall brackets to meet particular conditions.

The grand hall, from the point of view of illumination, is in three separate sections, the main central portion having a ceiling height equivalent to two 'tween decks, and the port and starboard outboard sections of only one 'tween deck in height. The spacious central area is lighted by means of indirect units, concealed in a specially-designed moulded cornice built into the ceiling, which provide adequate yet well-diffused illumination. The visible light sources, however, are two decorative cornice units running the length of the room, and an extensive laylight over the stage. At the far end, opposite the stage, there is an attractive fireplace, which is lighted indirectly by Mazda lamps concealed in vertical scrolls. The main ceiling illumination is supplemented by four special directional reflectors concealed in spun-metal brackets, one unit being mounted on each of the four main columns. These units are each equipped with a 500-Watt Mazda lamp.

The two outboard sections are each lighted by six three-sided diffusing glass beams, in which Mazda light tubes are used, giving an even spread of illumination over the whole of these areas, while relief from monotony is obtained by illuminated alcoves with *jardinière* fittings, suitably disposed on the outboard bulkheads. Decorative wall brackets are also employed, together with floor standards of tasteful design in the corners of the room and concealed Mazda lamps in metal reflectors over the writing desks.

The smoking room is always a popular rendezvous, and here, again, particular attention has been paid to the lighting requirements. For the illumination of the central section, there are three large circular decorative fittings, together with eight B.T.-H. fittings of similar character, but of smaller diameter, arranged in two rows of four down either side of the ceiling. At one end there is a fireplace lighted by Mazda lamps concealed behind diffusing glass panels, which provide a decorative surround to the central feature of the fireplace and also pick out its main characteristics. Each outboard section is lighted by five fittings, each consisting of three decorative suspended bowls grouped together to give the appearance of a single unit.

On the forward and after ceilings, and at other suitable positions, there are small laylights with standard Mazda lamps, which distribute the light to the corners of the room and on to the walls to provide an even intensity. As a further decorative feature, specially designed B.T.-H. bracket fittings are arranged around the walls. The whole interior is extremely well lighted, there being more than sufficient illumination for comfortable reading, and the other pastimes normally associated with the smoking room.

The central section of the tourist-class dining saloon is illuminated by a large circular B.T.-H. fitting, forward and aft of which are two smaller units of the same design, so arranged that uniform coverage of illumination is obtained. The remainder of the ceiling is treated with recessed panelling, and one of the smaller lighting fittings, to which reference has already been made, is provided at the centre of each ceiling panel.

There are eight columns, each carrying two B.T.-H. brackets using Mazda light tubes, and further columns applied to the outer bulkheads are similarly treated. On the bulkheads there are also a number of windows with the inner glass obscured and lighted from above and behind by concealed Mazda lamps. These features are very pleasing, and add a decorative and interesting effect to the apartment.

In addition to the foregoing interior lighting, the B.T.-H. Co. have been responsible for equipping the *Mauretania* with distinctive external illumination in the form of flood-lighting. Each of her stream-lined funnels is flood-lighted by four B.T.-H. Mazdalux " Three " flood-light projectors equipped with 1,000-Watt Mazda lamps, situated at carefully calculated positions to throw a concentrated and accurately-controlled flood of light on these most spectacular features. Two similar units are also trained on the superstructure of the bridge.

The Osler & Faraday Lighting.—The electric-lighting fittings in the cabin-class entrances and suites, tourist-class entrances and third-class accommodation, together with various other spaces, have been manufactured and supplied by Messrs. Osler & Faraday, Ltd., and are consistent with the usual high standard of workmanship, design and finish always associated with this firm.

A striking example of this is seen in the cabin-class entrance on *B* deck, where, in the central position on the ceiling, is placed a large shallow fitting, which constitutes one of the outstanding features of this fine entrance.

Made in silver-bronze metal with decorative panels of ivory-tinted opal glass, this fitting is designed to create the effect of increased depth necessary to retain the correct proportions, while still maintaining the requisite height essential in such a position. Surrounding this fitting are a series of smaller fittings, all in correct harmony with the main large central feature.

Wall brackets are fitted in the cabin-class library, but the main lighting in the room is indirect from a specially-designed reflector running round the cornice. A very successful result is obtained from this source.

Each fitting has been silenced with various methods of packing which ensure an entire absence of any form of vibration rattle, while all reflectors are made in such a way as to be readily removable for inspection purposes. The glass used throughout is of the type to give equal diffusion of light in every fitting.

Examples of the fittings supplied by Messrs. Osler & Faraday, Ltd., may be seen in the photographs reproduced in Figs. 11, 17 and 30 of this chapter.

Cabin-class Foyer: North Atlantic Wall Map.

PASSENGER AND CREW SERVICES.

CATERING DEPARTMENTS.

IN connection with this important part of the passenger services, the determination of the owners to maintain fully their traditional reputation for a high standard of cuisine is evident from the excellence and completeness of the domestic equipment on board the *Mauretania*. The naval architects responsible for the design of the ship have evidently collaborated closely with the owners' catering superintendent in evolving the efficient and comprehensive services which have been provided ; while the long experience in installations of this type which the contractors supplying the gear have had, has been of invaluable assistance. An indication of this experience is seen in the fact that Messrs. Henry Wilson & Co., Ltd., of Liverpool, who have been responsible for manufacturing the major items of the equipment and for supplying some auxiliary gear on behalf of other sub-contractors, provided the apparatus for the cooking and associated services in the first *Mauretania*. The main differences between the equipment fitted in the famous old Atlantic liner and that supplied for the new vessel are referred to in the following description of the modern installation.

The cabin and tourist-class kitchen and other catering spaces are shown in the plan reproduced herewith, from which it will be seen that they are situated on *B* deck, surrounding the engine-room and after boiler-room casings. This permits the cabin-class services to be arranged mainly at the fore end of the *B*-deck kitchen space in a position adjoining the cabin-class restaurant ; while the after end of the same space is similarly reserved to serve the tourist-class dining saloon, which is immediately abaft the after bulkhead. The third-class kitchens, etc., are also arranged in a position adjoining the accommodation which they serve, the third-class dining saloon being on *C* deck forward of the domestic spaces.

It may be mentioned that the main kitchen and its dependencies on *B* deck, which serve the cabin-class and tourist-class accommodation, occupy an area of over 10,000 sq. ft. When to this is added the areas of the spaces in which the third-class and Kosher kitchens, bakery, deck pantries and bars are arranged, the total extent of the deck space for domestic purposes amounts to about 20,000 sq. ft.

The drawing reproduced herewith indicates the comprehensive nature of the equipment which has been installed in the principal kitchens and associated rooms. Such units as the ranges, roasting, baking and confectioners' ovens, hot-plates, salamanders, fish-fryers, waffle-irons, water-heaters, toasters, etc., are all operated electrically. The British Thomson-Houston Co., Ltd., of Rugby, who have supplied various motors and other electrical fittings to Messrs. Henry Wilson & Co. in connection with the cooking equipment, have also provided the heating elements for use in the various electrical units referred to previously, these being of the Wilson-B.T.H. Torribar type. Other sub-contractors to the makers of the domestic installation have been the Firth-Vickers Stainless Steels, Ltd., of Sheffield, who have supplied the Staybrite stainless steel used extensively in the construction of service tables, dressers, sinks and other parts of the equipment.

Some indication of the completeness of the electrical equipment of the galleys and pantries is given in that the electrical power required to run the installation amounts to almost 800 kW.

Exceptions to the use of electric power are present in that the *bain maries* are steam-heated and that the grills burn charcoal. In connection with the last-mentioned items, it is considered that only by the use of this fuel can a perfectly flavoured grill be obtained. A feature of the passenger services in the *Mauretania* is that she is the first Cunard White Star liner fitted with a grill specially for third-class catering, as it is only a few years since a grill appeared solely on first-class menus.

During the 32 years which have elapsed since the first *Mauretania* was completed and the delivery of the present holder of this famous name, many changes have been made in the design and layout of the different units of the equipment installed for cooking purposes. While the most important change may be said to be the increased use of electric power in the operation of the plant, improvements in many other

directions have also been made. The materials employed are different in most instances from those adopted previously ; the tinned copper hitherto used in the construction of the stockpot has now been replaced by pure nickel or stainless steel ; while the block-tin tops which were fitted on carving tables have now been abandoned in favour of stainless steel. Another difference—this time in the layout of the domestic spaces—is that the kitchens and main pantries are no longer kept separate. A combination room is now adopted as giving a more direct service from the cooking ranges to the restaurant or dining saloon. Such additions as plate-washing machines, improved whisks and other new fittings of a minor nature are also indications of the developments which have taken place in the progressive attempts to provide the best possible services for all classes of passengers.

The combined cabin and tourist-class kitchen of the *Mauretania* contains four electrically-heated island cooking ranges, steam-heated *bainmaries*, fish-fryers, hot presses, charcoal grills, electric salamanders, mixers, etc., the arrangement of which may. be seen from the plan reproduced herewith.

The third-class kitchen equipment is of a similar nature, and includes an island cooking range, charcoal grill, stockpots, fish-fryers, hot press, steam oven, salamander, etc.

The Kosher kitchen on *C* deck is also provided with the necessary range, oven, etc.

The rooms at the sides of the kitchens are allocated to special purposes in association with the catering arrangements, and comprise a fruit room, vegetable room, steam kitchen, sculleries, butchers' shop, larder, *hors-d'œuvres* room, plate scullery, glass and china room, silver room, bakers' shop and confectioners' shop. In these spaces the latest equipment appropriate to the purpose for which the room is used has been installed.

The silver-burnishing machine, dough-divider and ice-breaking machine have been supplied by Messrs. Henry Wilson & Co., Ltd., and are driven by electric motors of from 1 to $2\frac{1}{4}$ H.P. The starters for these motors are of the face-plate type of Messrs. Allen West & Co., Ltd., who have also provided similar starters for the two 4-H.P. motors which drive the two Dawson dish-washing machines.

Six machines in the food-preparing equipment have been supplied by the Peerless Electrical Manufacturing Co., Ltd., of London. A Peerless type-P.M.80 four-speed mixing machine of 3 H.P., and having a capacity of 80 and 40 quarts, has been installed in the cabin and tourist-class combined kitchen and also a similar machine in the bakery. A Q.10-type three-speed mixing machine of $\frac{1}{4}$ H.P., and having a capacity of $12\frac{1}{2}$ quarts, has been fitted in the confectioners' shop and also in the salad room. The remaining two Peerless units are a model-P.C.17 combination sausage and mincing machine of $1\frac{1}{2}$ H.P. installed in the butchers' shop, and a Rotex $2\frac{3}{4}$-H.P. half-sack capacity dough kneader of the stationary-arm type which is provided in the bakery.

Two electric ovens, a mechanical dough mixer and a roll-dividing machine are installed in the bakery, while separate equipment which is provided for confectioners' work includes cold cupboards and a special range for sugar-work, in addition to the mixers to which reference has already been made.

Loud-speakers are fitted in the kitchen spaces, so that instructions can be given from a central position.

About 400 cooking utensils have been supplied by Messrs. Elkington & Co., Ltd., of Birmingham, and these are of pure nickel, copper-coated on the outside to improve their heating characteristics. Pure nickel is also used for fish-frying baskets, baskets of vegetable boilers, liners and covers of stockpots, wire pastry trays, vegetable tureens, etc.

TABLE-WARE, ETC.

Table-ware constitutes an important part of the equipment of a modern passenger liner, and in the case of the *Mauretania* the supplies of glass and china table-ware, plate and cutlery, are most complete and of the same high standard as the remainder of the ship's furnishings.

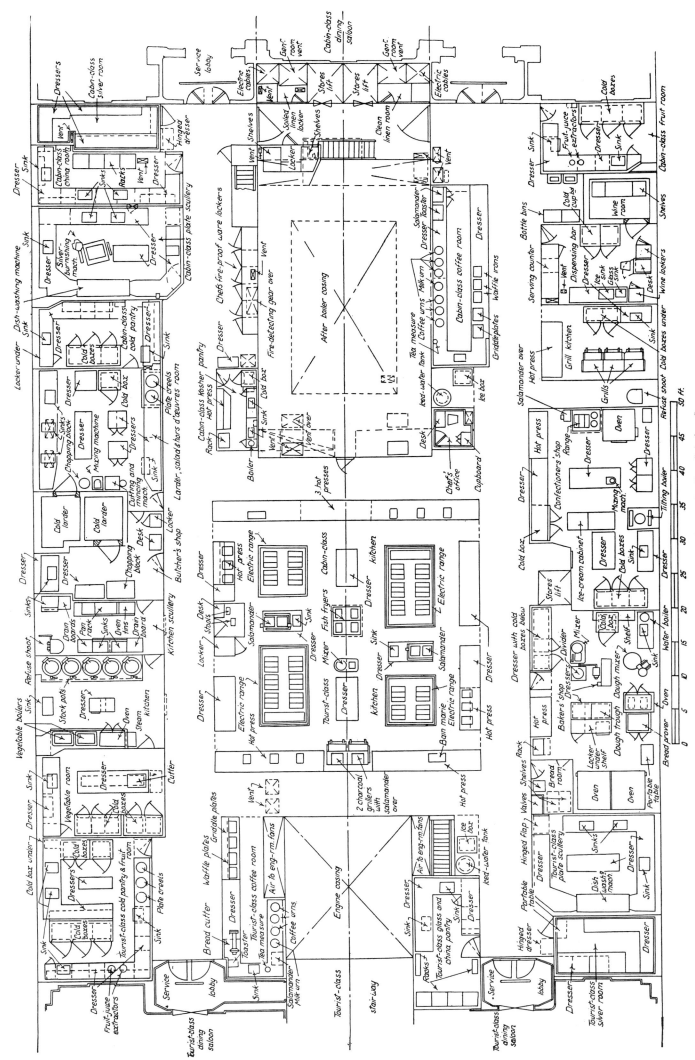

Cabin and Tourist-class Kitchen and other Catering Spaces.

The Embassy-brand table-ware of Messrs. Gladwin, Ltd., of Sheffield, has been supplied to the new vessel.

All the plate, cutlery, etc., are in silver-plated nickel silver, and approximately 14,000 pieces of electro-plated ware and 25,000 pieces of cutlery have been required to equip the ship.

Insulated Storerooms and Cooling Services.

The 17 insulated storerooms are situated in *D* and *E* 'tween decks between Nos. 1 and 2 boiler-rooms, and are divided into separate spaces for butter and milk, bacon and eggs, potatoes, frozen fish, fresh fish, cold meat, frozen meat, fresh meat, ice, ice-cream, lager-beer, minerals, ales and stout, fruit, vegetables, wines, and tobacco. The aggregate net capacity of the insulated spaces (measured inside the insulation) is approximately 16,500 cu. ft. The insulating medium adopted for the refrigerated spaces and the refrigerating machinery which serves these rooms are described in the chapter dealing with the general equipment.

It is interesting to note that included in the foregoing list of insulated rooms is a special chamber for ice-cream, having a capacity of about 600 cu. ft. In order to maintain the low temperature required in this chamber, about 0° F., a separate automatic electrically-driven Sternette Freon machine has been provided by Messrs. L. Sterne & Co., Ltd., of Glasgow.

In connection with the refrigerated spaces, electric thermometers have been fitted in the chambers and connected to a central indicating instrument fitted in the refrigerating-machinery room. These have been supplied by Messrs. Siemens Brothers & Co., Ltd., of London.

In the kitchen spaces, 17 cold cupboards and three drinking-water coolers are installed, these being cooled by means of brine from the main refrigerating plant.

There are, in addition, cold cabinets and water-coolers arranged in the service pantries on the promenade, main, *A* and *B* decks. Eleven cold cabinets, some of which are divided into six compartments, and six drinking-water cooling tanks are cooled by seven independent automatic electrically-driven Sternette Freon plants. Two of these units operate on small brine-coolers, brine being distributed to various cabinets and water-coolers by a small brine pump.

The arrangements for the supply of iced water have been specially designed to meet the requirements of American passengers, so that there may be an ample supply of exceptionally cold drinking water available, even if the ship be cruising in tropical regions. In order that cold water may be instantly available at all draw-off coolers or fountains, special arrangements have been made to ensure that the cold water circulates continuously through the supply pipes.

The hospital is provided with its own self-contained refrigerated cabinet, operated by a super-silent automatic Sternette Freon machine.

Banking and Office Facilities.

In the main entrance halls to the accommodation for each class of passengers, pursers' offices have been arranged in convenient positions, while numerous offices are distributed throughout the vessel for the use of the deck officers and stewards.

A fully equipped printers' shop has been provided forward on *C* deck, which contains all the necessary machinery for dealing with the printing of menus, newspapers and any other notices or publications which may be required for use on board the ship.

Call System.

The entire passenger accommodation is equipped with a complete system of luminous call equipment supplied by Messrs. Gent & Co., Ltd., of Leicester, to enable the passengers to obtain the services of stewards or stewardesses. There are in all some 660 fittings in the system, embodying 1,300 indicator lamps, and ingenuity has been shown in designing the various section indicators so that the calls given to one section may, if so desired, be transferred to some other part of the installation.

In addition to the luminous-call equipment, the same firm have provided 25 ordinary electric-bell indicators of the drop-flag marine type, the total number of indicator signals being in the neighbourhood of 350.

Electric Clocks.

The installation of electric clocks on board the *Mauretania*, which has been supplied by Mr. Thomas Mercer, of St. Albans, is a comprehensive one, and includes 75 secondary clocks, 37 of which have been specially made to the architects' designs, while the remainder are of standard type. The clocks are wired in three lines ; and each line or circuit is subdivided by relays in such a way as to work in batches of 10, while suitable switches provided at the relay boxes enable any particular clock to be isolated from the others. The control unit consists of duplicate chronometer master clocks, each of which gives an impulse every 10 seconds. The impulses are taken through a selector switch and operate each of the three circuits in succession. The necessary means are provided to enable the whole system to be advanced or retarded automatically.

Passenger Elevators and Service Lifts.

As may be seen from studying the general-arrangement plans reproduced on Plates II., III. and IV., adequate facilities have been provided for transit from one level to another, a total of 11 lifts being arranged to deal with the passenger and goods traffic in various parts of the ship. The Express Lift Co., Ltd., of Northampton, have been responsible for the complete installation, which comprises five passenger elevators and six goods lifts.

Three of the passenger elevators are in the cabin-class accommodation, one serves the tourist-class accommodation, and the remaining elevator is reserved for third-class passengers. Each of these elevators is attendant-operated, and is fitted with an auxiliary drive giving automatic and accurate levelling of the lift-car at each deck. In the event of failure in the main electric supply providing power to the elevators, an emergency supply is available, by means of which the passenger-elevator service may be carried on.

The cabin-class passenger elevators have sliding doors fitted both on the car and at the deck entrances, the design of the doors being in keeping with the surrounding decorative schemes. Silver-bronze has been used in the construction of the principal cars and lift entrances, which gives a modern and distinctive appearance to the elevators.

All the passenger elevators are fitted adjacent to, or are embodied in, the main stairways serving each class of passengers, and are all fitted with the latest safety devices.

Of the six service lifts, two have been installed specially for the purpose of handling luggage, and have each a maximum lifting capacity of 30 cwt.

The ship stores are handled by three goods lifts, and the remaining service lift is reserved for the use of the engineers.

The 16 D.C. motors, ranging from 2 to 16 H.P., with a total output nearing 100 H.P., which are provided for operating the elevators and lifts have been supplied by the General Electric Co., Ltd., of London, of which the Express Lift Ltd. are a subsidiary concern ; but apart from these items, together with the sliding shield-plate doors on the goods lifts, the equipment has been constructed throughout at the Northampton works of the lift manufacturers.

Entertainment Facilities.

In perhaps no other branch of the passenger services provided in modern liners has there been such rapid advancement as is represented by the development during the past few years in the methods of sound-reproduction. The rapid strides made in the technique of broadcasting, with the application thereof to relaying music and speech by loud-speakers and amplifiers, the increased quality of reproduction and reliability of sound-film apparatus, and the latest methods of electrically recording music for transmission throughout the ship from gramophones, have all combined to assist in providing several alternative forms of popular entertainment.

The *Mauretania* is fitted with Marconi sound-reproducing equipment which provides transmission from radio, gramophone or microphone sources to all parts of the ship. A specially designed receiver is incorporated to take broadcast programmes, which can be distributed to any of the numerous loud-speakers installed in the public rooms throughout the vessel. Altogether, about 50 loud-speakers are fitted in the lounges, smoking rooms, verandahs, dining saloons and the grand hall. The reason for so many loud-speaking units lies in the fact that modern research has proved the multi-speaker system to give a better distribution of sound and a more even, pleasing tone than are reproduced by one or two large loud-speakers serving the same room. Similarly, research has shown that the presence of persons in a room is responsible for an appreciable absorption of sound. In order to take this factor into consideration, volume controls are fitted in each room to enable the steward in charge to adjust the volume of sound from the loud-speakers as the room becomes filled with, or emptied of, occupants.

In order to harmonise with their surroundings, the loud-speakers are mounted in the panelling or other parts of the structure of the public rooms. In several cases, they are hidden in the ceilings of rooms; while in the grand hall, eight loud-speakers are arranged in the round of the dome.

The main feature of the installation, for which the Marconi International Marine Communication Co., Ltd., of London, have been responsible, is the great flexibility which is provided. While certain rooms can be receiving a broadcast programme, other rooms can be receiving music from gramophone records or from the ship's orchestra by means of microphone relay. These programmes are completely interchangeable, and can be altered at will from a central control panel.

No fewer than three complete cinema theatres are provided in the *Mauretania*, i.e., one for each class of passenger. The theatres are described in the section on the passenger accommodation, but it may be mentioned here that the seating capacity provided—including that of the cabin-class theatre, which accommodates 250 persons—will be sufficient for some 500 passengers.

The motion-picture sound systems in all three theatres have been supplied and installed by the Western Electric Co., Ltd., of London. The equipment in the cabin-class theatre consists of a double-base Western Electric Mirrophonic sound system with super simplex projectors, Peerless low-intensity arcs, and the latest type of Mirrophonic acoustic baffle and multi-cellular loud-speaker system. Westone screens have been fitted. In the tourist and third-class theatres, Western 5T-sound systems have been installed. Western Electric non-synchronous reproducing systems have been fitted in all three theatres, and manager's announcing systems in the cabin and tourist-class theatres.

HAIRDRESSING SALOONS.

Hairdressing saloons are provided for all three classes of passengers, there being two arranged in the cabin-class accommodation on *A* deck amidships—one reserved for the use of ladies and the other for gentlemen. The tourist and third-class hairdressing saloons are arranged on *C* deck aft and forward respectively, in positions adjoining the appropriate entrances. The floors in the hairdressing saloons are covered with ¼-in. Korkoid, laid in panel design of marble colours with special inset motifs.

LAUNDRY PLANT.

A complete laundry plant has been supplied and fitted by Messrs. Thomas Bradford & Co., of Salford, Manchester, and is capable of meeting all possible shipboard requirements.

The installation includes a washing machine of the makers' Rotary type, which will wash the equivalent of 170 shirts in one loading, each loading occupying approximately one hour's working time of the machine. Power is provided by a 1½-H.P. electric motor. One of the first conditions which it is essential that marine laundry plant should meet is the need for economy in water consumption. In view of this requirement, water-saving apparatus has been arranged alongside the washing machine. The procedure adopted is that the water used for the final rinse is pumped into a steel tank over the machine, so as to be available for the first " break-down " of the next batch of clothing.

Other machinery includes an electrically-driven 26-in. self-balancing hydro-extractor, and one Decoudun ironing machine with a roller 72in. long by 24in. diameter. In this latter item, which is used for ironing general and flat work, both the bed and the roller are steam-heated, and the machine is driven by an electric motor fitted on slide rails.

For the purpose of finishing collars, a collar and shirt-ironing machine of the Mirror type is provided, this unit having a roller 18in. long, and being electrically heated and driven.

Another machine which is electrically heated and driven is that used specially for shaping neck-bands.

The remaining part of the comprehensive laundry installation comprises a soap boiler of 40 gallons capacity, a set of wash troughs having steam and water connections, electrically-heated irons, and boards for skirt, sleeve and general-ironing purposes.

The airing room, which is adjacent to the laundry, is heated by a system of steam coils.

HOSPITAL FACILITIES.

In the event of illness, the passengers and crew of the *Mauretania* will have at their disposal the expert advice of a doctor, nurse and qualified sickroom attendants.

The hospitals are arranged in three separate wards. The main hospital, for the use of passengers, is divided into male and female wards; while another ward, provided forward of the main hospital, is reserved for the crew's use. Other facilities include a fully-equipped operating theatre and a dispensary.

SANITARY EQUIPMENT.

The sanitary equipment throughout the vessel has been supplied by Messrs. Shanks & Co., Ltd., of Barrhead, near Glasgow, and the design and details of the fittings are based on those in the *Queen Mary*.

The baths, which are of white porcelain-enamelled cast iron, are fitted with recesses, and are provided with hot and cold-water supplies. In conjunction with the baths, specially designed showers of hinged type have been fitted, the supply of hot and cold fresh water to the showers being controlled by anti-scalding mixing fittings of the duplex type. These mixing valves can be adjusted so as to give the desired temperature of water from the showers.

The washbasins are all made in white-glazed vitreous china and have hot and cold-water taps. The discharges from the basins are fitted with waste traps which are vented throughout, thus completely preventing any blowing-back or leakage of offensive odours.

The w.c.'s are of the Sandra siphonic discharge type, and are made in white-glazed vitreous china.

Among other fittings under the heading of sanitary equipment which Messrs. Shanks have provided are included a complete range of hospital fittings and numerous urinals, slop sinks and similar necessary sanitary appliances.

All the taps and other water fittings are cast in 20 per cent. nickel silver.

SEWAGE DISPOSAL.

The whole of the discharges from the w.c.'s, baths, wash-basins, sinks and other sanitary fittings are taken to six points in the ship, from which they are discharged automatically below the load water-line by specially designed Amphistoma pumps supplied by Adams-Hydraulics, Ltd., of York. The entire system is in duplicate, two pumps, each having its own motor, tank and control gear, being fitted at each of the six sewage compartments. The total sewage flow may be dealt with by six pumps, so that the remaining six are stand-by units in normal circumstances.

When the galvanized-steel sewage tank becomes full, a float-type switch closes and starts up the driving motor of the pump, which discharges the contents of the tank overboard. The switch opens when the tank is empty and stops the motor.

The sewage tanks are cross-connected; so that, in case of emergency, either pump at any of the six positions in the ship is able to empty either tank. In addition, there is a by-pass system which enables water or disinfectant to be circulated through the pumps and tanks for cleaning purposes. Automatic high-level electrically-operated alarm gear is arranged to give warning in the event of the sewage level rising above a pre-determined point.

Eight of the pumps are each driven by an 8-B.H.P. motor; while the remaining four, which operate against an increased head, have each a 10-B.H.P. motor.

An entirely separate tank, with electrically-driven Amphistoma pump and automatic control gear, is fitted to deal with the waste from the butchers' shop.

BAGGAGE ROOMS AND AUTOMOBILE STOWAGE.

An essential feature in modern passenger vessels is that ample space be available for stowing the luggage of passengers;

while it is becoming increasingly desirable that, where possible, garage room be arranged to enable passengers to make ocean crossings and have their own motorcars at their disposal for use at their destination.

These points have been carefully considered in the case of the *Mauretania*, and the first requirement has been met by arranging two large baggage rooms on *E* deck aft. Passengers' luggage not required on the voyage will be stowed in these spaces, transit from *A* deck being by means of two electric lifts, as mentioned elsewhere in this chapter.

Garage space is arranged aft in Nos. 4 and 5 'tween decks between *C* and *D* decks. Access to the spaces for the motorcars is through the cargo hatchways, and a total of about 70 cars may be carried.

MISCELLANEOUS SERVICES.

All three classes of staterooms are fitted with fans, in addition to the ventilating system described in the following chapter.

All the cabin and tourist-class staterooms, as well as many of the third-class rooms, have been provided with socket connections for curling-iron or similar fittings.

Ladies' Hairdressing Saloon.

VENTILATION AND HEATING.

THE task of ensuring that adequate ventilation is provided to all parts of the ship and that the spaces ventilated are maintained at the temperatures suitable to their size and the purpose for which they are used is one which has received particular attention in the *Mauretania*. The latest system of air-conditioning has been applied to five of the principal public rooms, while the remaining 16 public rooms, the passenger staterooms and the officers' and crew's quarters are served by a mechanical system of combined heating and ventilating. In addition to the foregoing arrangements, the ship-side cabin-class rooms are each fitted with an electrical convection heater of a special type. The different installations are detailed separately in the following descriptions.

THE CARRIER AIR-CONDITIONING INSTALLATION.

The air-conditioning plant applied to the principal public rooms in the *Mauretania* includes all the features of the most modern land installations, while the equipment has, in addition,

Fig. 1.—One of the Carrier Air-conditioning Supply Fans which serve the Cabin-class Restaurant.

been specially constructed to meet the heavy requirements of marine service. The installation, which has been provided by the Carrier Engineering Co., Ltd., of London, has been designed to provide comfortable conditions of temperature and humidity in the cabin-class restaurant and grand hall, and in the tourist-class dining saloon, cinema and lounge under all conditions of weather which are likely to be encountered in Atlantic or cruising service.

In hot weather, temperature reductions up to 15 deg. F. will be possible of attainment, while under very warm and humid climatic conditions the relative humidities will be as much as 35 per cent. lower within the rooms served by the equipment than that of the atmosphere outside. A minimum winter temperature of 10 deg. F., or 22 deg. F. below freezing point, has formed the basis of the heating and humidifying capacity of the installation, which, in such weather, will be capable of maintaining internal temperatures at 70 deg. F., with a relative humidity of 45 per cent.

The cabin-class restaurant is served by two plants of equal capacity, one of which is shown in Fig. 1. Each comprises a supply fan, de-humidifier, steam-heating batteries and automatic control dampers. The other four rooms are each served by a single equipment of a similar nature. The plant serving the tourist-class dining saloon may be seen in Fig. 2. By this means it has been possible to have the air-conditioning system in each room under independent control. These plants have a combined capacity of approximately 3,500,000 cu. ft. per hour.

As the separate air-conditioning plants are, of necessity, situated in several positions throughout the ship, automatic controls are required in order that allowance may be made for the hourly variations in the weather conditions and in the occupancy of the rooms with the minimum amount of attention from the engineering staff of the ship. The automatic-control system adopted is pneumatic, and thermostats in the various rooms effect the actual changes in the working of the plant.

Fig. 2.—The Carrier Air-conditioning Plant which serves the Tourist-class Dining Saloon.

The flow of compressed air to the motors, which adjusts the dampers and automatic valves admitting steam to the heating units, is regulated by the thermostats. In this way, the temperature and humidity of the air supplied to the rooms are varied automatically to maintain comfortable internal conditions.

Although the separate air-conditioning plants differ in some respects in the arrangement, each is comprised essentially of a supply fan, Carrier marine-type dehumidifier, preheater and main heater, automatically-operated air dampers and, in the case of the spaces other than the dining saloons, an exhaust fan fitted for the purpose of maintaining balanced conditions of pressure in the rooms.

The dehumidifier is the source of the conditioned air, and may therefore be considered to be the most important component of the plant. It consists of a heavy galvanized sheet-steel casing with a tank beneath it. Arranged in the casing is a series of special spray nozzles, through which water is pumped at a pressure high enough to create an extremely dense bank of mist. The air to be conditioned is drawn through this mist, the temperature of which determines the final condition of the air. In summer, the water sprayed in the dehumidifiers is cooled by means of refrigeration, with the result that air may be both cooled and dehumidified. The refrigeration is supplied from CO_2 machines associated with the ship's main refrigerating machinery. In winter, the dehumidifiers reverse their function and add moisture to, instead of abstracting it from, the air passing through them.

The distributing pump for handling the refrigerated water has been supplied by Messrs. Worthington-Simpson, Ltd., of Newark-on-Trent, and works under the following conditions of service :—Five hundred gallons per minute, 180ft., 1,750 r.p.m.; or, alternatively, 250 gallons per minute, 140ft., at reduced speed. The pump is fitted with an electric motor of 45 H.P. at 1,750/1,450 r.p.m., supplied by Messrs. Laurence, Scott & Electromotors, Ltd. This pump, which is of the makers' Mark 6/7 V1 vertical split-casing centrifugal type, has 6-in. diameter delivery and 7-in. diameter suction branches. The refrigerated-water return pump has been supplied by the same manufacturers, and is of their Mark 4/4 V1 vertical split-casing centrifugal type with 4-in. diameter suction and delivery branches. The conditions of service are as follows :—Two hundred and fifty gallons per minute, 85ft., 1,610 r.p.m. In this case, also, a Laurence-Scott unit is provided, this being of 11 H.P. at 1,610 r.p.m. In both cases, each pump has a gun-metal casing, and a bronze shaft with a renewable sleeve and gun-metal impeller. Two drum-type hand-operated control pillars have been supplied for these pumps by Messrs. Allen West & Co., Ltd.

Among the outstanding features of the application of air-conditioning in the *Mauretania* is the system of air distribution. Uniform draughtless distribution is much more necessary with air-conditioning than with ventilation in the ordinary sense of the word. With the very large quantities of air which must be circulated to maintain favourable conditions in warm and humid weather, care must be taken in the design of the distributing system to ensure that serious draughts are not created with the lower temperatures and humidities which prevail ; while with ordinary ventilation, large quantities of air can be relatively easily introduced without setting up uncomfortable air movement, since both the admission and the room temperatures may be high. It may be said, indeed, that many of the normal systems of ship ventilation must depend upon strong air movement to compensate partly for high temperatures and humidities. At comfortable temperatures and humidities, this same air movement would be regarded as an intolerable draught. In all the rooms in the *Mauretania* which are served by the air-conditioning plants, the necessary distribution of air is effected without draughts, while the means of distribution have been incorporated in the various schemes of decoration without detracting from the appearance of the architectural detail.

All the fans associated with the installation have direct-coupled driving D.C. motors, supplied by the General Electric Co., Ltd., and are generally provided with means of speed control. Special precautions have been taken to ensure that all fans should be silent-running, so that no noise is communicated to the rooms which the plants serve or the structure of the ship in way of the fans. Face-plate type starter regulators have been provided for the nine fan motors, which range from $1\frac{3}{4}$ to $7\frac{1}{4}$ H.P. These starters, which have been supplied by Messrs. Allen West & Co., Ltd., are arranged for key operation, and are fitted with the usual under-voltage and over-current release.

Owing to the great differences in temperatures and humidity between the air surrounding the plants and that supplied by them to the five rooms dealt with, cork insulation has been fitted to the equipment and air-ducting.

THE WINSOR HEATING AND VENTILATING SYSTEM.

This installation, which is most extensive, and covers all the accommodation with the exception of the air-conditioned rooms, has been designed, constructed and erected by the Winsor Engineering Co., Ltd., of Glasgow. The combination of ventilating and heating is obtained by a system of motor-driven fans discharging heated air into the various spaces through trunking. By this means, warmed air, or air at atmospheric temperature, is introduced into the staterooms or officers' and crew's quarters, and, in the case of the cabin-class rooms, provision is made for regulating the temperature of the air in these rooms

by the passengers themselves. It will also be possible for the tourist and third-class passengers to regulate the quantity and direction of flow of the ventilation in their rooms ; while, in the inner staterooms for these two classes of passengers, additional air-tempering valves are provided.

In the 16 public rooms to which the system is applied, and in vestibules and similar spaces, the air is introduced through the Winsor Company's patent type of diffusers, which are specially designed to eliminate any possibility of draught.

Winsor Zephyr-type louvres, made in the latest form of Roanoid material, are fitted throughout the accommodation for the purpose of delivering the air supply ; while in the spaces which are also exhausted by the system, special exhaust grids of the same material have been provided.

In the case of the kitchens and associated domestic spaces, the system provides for very large changes of air, while the supply is by means of a combination of the Zephyr louvres with the patent air diffusers referred to previously. This latter form was adopted to enable the cooking staff to direct the stream of air to any desired point in the kitchens. The principal consideration underlying the design of this part of the equipment was the necessity that no cooking odours should penetrate into the restaurant or dining saloons, while, on the other hand, it was essential that the ventilating system should not be such that large volumes of air would exhaust from the air-conditioned public rooms adjoining the domestic spaces. These requirements have been satisfactorily fulfilled with the specially balanced system which has been provided.

It is important to avoid noise disturbance to passengers from systems such as used for ventilation, as they run continually throughout the working life of the vessel. To ensure that this is fulfilled, the heating units and fans are of the Winsor Company's latest type of welded construction, and are designed to be silent in operation. As an additional precaution, the fan rooms, which are situated in various convenient positions throughout the vessel, are fitted with sound insulation on the bulkheads in way of the passenger accommodation.

In association with the 92 motors, ranging from ·25 to 8·85 H.P., which form the portion of the installation serving the accommodation, starters supplied by Messrs. Allen West and Co., Ltd., have been fitted. For the larger motors, the control pillars are of the drum design ; while for the smaller

Fig. 3.—Inset-type Thermovent Heater in one of the Cabin-class Staterooms.

motors, key-operated starter regulators of the face-plate type have been provided. These latter units are designed to give the required speed by key-operation of the contact arm, and each is fitted with an over-current release with time-lag.

The hold ventilation is by means of Winsor Aerex axial-flow fans of the patented " drop-in " type, in which the rotors run in specially machined races, giving perfect alignment and a high standard of efficiency. These units, which are designed to be silent in operation, are also provided for ventilation to the sewage spaces.

The 10 motors of from ·5 to 1·75 H.P. which serve the hold and sewage-space ventilating system are provided with Allen West starters.

The fans for ventilating the engine-room have also been supplied by the Winsor Engineering Co., as mentioned elsewhere.

The electric motors for this installation have been provided by the General Electric Co., Ltd., to the joint requirements of the shipowners and the ventilation sub-contractors, and are of the makers' super-silent marine type.

THERMOVENT HEATING.

The electrical convection heaters which have been fitted in the ship-side cabin-class staterooms are of the Thermovent type of Messrs. E. K. Cole, Ltd., of Southend-on-Sea, and have been installed by the Sunderland Forge & Engineering Co., Ltd., who were, as already mentioned elsewhere, the sub-

contractors to the shipbuilders for the electrical installation of the *Mauretania*.

The Thermovent heating equipment comprises some 200 heaters of the 500-Watt multi-duct type, the heating units being fitted so as to be flush with the interior bulkheads of the state-rooms, and behind veneered laminated panels which tone with the general decorative schemes and wood panelling of the rooms. The inlet grille is arranged so as to give a luminous effect by means of a series of circular glass rods, which are illuminated by a tube lamp to simulate red-hot bars. This luminous effect is switch-controlled, and there are separate switches for heating and luminous effects. The luminous effect may be seen from the illustration given in Fig. 3.

This patent type of heater was originally developed for the Cunard White Star liner *Queen Mary*, after extensive investigation into marine heating requirements. A feature of the Thermovent heater, which completely overcomes the danger of fires arising from electrical heating units, is that the " vent within a vent " construction used to distribute the convected heat also serves to provide columns of air, acting as a means of insulation between the heating element and the outer surface of the heater. Since the heating element itself operates at only black heat and is, moreover, totally enclosed, a high safety factor is obtained. The Thermovent system of heating has the full approval of the authorities charged with safeguarding the use of such equipment on shipboard.

"Mauretania" in New York's Lower Bay.

SEA TRIALS AND MAIDEN ATLANTIC CROSSINGS.

ALMOST exactly two years after the laying of the keel—in the morning of the 31st May, 1939—the *Mauretania* left the Gladstone Dock and proceeded through the lock into the Mersey. The departure of the vessel from Liverpool was witnessed by enormous crowds on both sides of the river, and her beautiful appearance attracted appreciative comment from the spectators.

On arrival at the Mersey Bar, the compasses were adjusted and the anchor trials completed, after which the vessel proceeded to the Clyde, carrying out preliminary steering and manœuvring trials on the way. A trial of about 12 hours' duration was then commenced, during which time the machinery was gradually worked up to full power.

The *Mauretania* arrived at the Tail of the Bank about 2-30 a.m. on the 1st June, and departed thence at 10-0 a.m., proceeding to the Arran measured mile, where five sets of double

17th June on her maiden voyage to New York. Among the 1,300 passengers on board were the chairman of the Cunard White Star, Ltd. (Sir Percy E. Bates, Bt., G.B.E.), Lady Bates, the managing director of Messrs. Cammell, Laird & Co., Ltd. (Mr. R. S. Johnson), and Mrs. Johnson. The passenger list also included the names of several travellers who had made the maiden voyage in the old *Mauretania* from the same landing stage in 1907.

The first call after leaving Liverpool was at Cobh (Queenstown), where the liner was given an official welcome by civic leaders and officials of local bodies, including a representative of the Lord Mayor of Cork, who presented the captain with a gold medallion inscribed with the arms of the Port of Cork.

After a stay of four hours, the vessel continued her voyage, and arrived in New York on the 24th June, having taken 6 days 19 hours for the crossing from Liverpool. Crowds thronged the

Photograph by]   **The Cunard White Star Liner " Mauretania " on Trial.**   *[George Oulram & Co., Ltd.*

runs were carried out at various speeds. On the conclusion of this progressive trial, official steering and manœuvring tests were undertaken, and the vessel returned to anchor at the Tail of the Bank at about 7-0 p.m. A photograph taken on the occasion of these trials is reproduced herewith.

The following day the vessel left her anchorage at about 4-0 a.m., and proceeded to the Cumbraes, where the direction-finding apparatus was calibrated. At 9-0 a.m., the 24-hour consumption trial was commenced, and the *Mauretania* eventually arrived off the Liverpool Bar at 10-30 a.m. on the 3rd June. She continued right up the river, and entered the Gladstone Dock again at noon.

No official announcement was made regarding the ship's trial-trip results, but it is understood that a speed of 25½ knots was attained, and the performance fully realised the conditions of the contract in every respect. One of the most notable features during the whole of the trials was the complete absence of vibration in any part of the vessel.

Fuel oil for the trials and maiden voyage was supplied by the British Mexican Petroleum Co., Ltd., of London.

Watched by a concourse of nearly 100,000 persons, the *Mauretania* left the Princes Landing Stage, Liverpool, on the

banks of the Hudson River when the *Mauretania* steamed into New York Harbour, the arrival was broadcast, and the sight of the vessel being manœuvred into dock was televised. An elaborate programme of social functions was arranged while the liner was in port, including a reception and dinner given by Sir Percy Bates to those who welcomed the ship.

The *Mauretania* began her return voyage from New York on the 30th June, and is expected at Southampton *via* Cherbourg on the 7th July. Future voyages will commence from the Thames, where the liner will berth in the King George V. Dock.

In command of the *Mauretania* is Captain Arthur Tillotson Brown. Captain Brown served throughout the Great War with the Royal Naval Reserve and wears the ribbon of the 1914-15 Star and other war medals. He was previously in command of the motorship *Britannic*, and was at one time staff captain of the old *Mauretania*. It is of interest to note that Captain Brown was the last captain of the famous old ship, he being in command when she made her final journey from Southampton to the shipbreakers' yard at Rosyth in July, 1935.

The chief engineer of the new *Mauretania* is Mr. H. H. Cuttle.

Plate VII—Maiden Voyage Arrival of "Mauretania" in New York, 24th June, 1939.

Plate VIII—Cabin-class Lounge.

Plate IX—Cabin-class Lounge.

Plate X—Cabin-class Restaurant.

Plate XI—Cabin-class Restaurant.

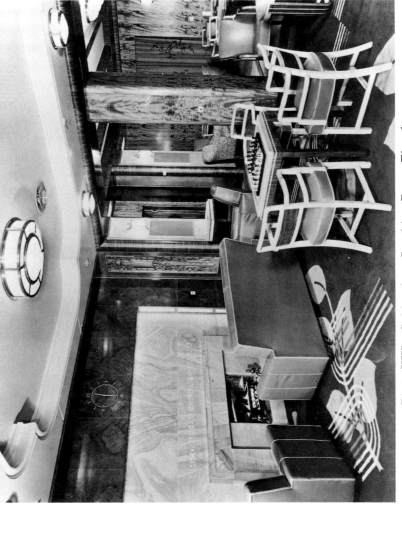

Plate XII—Cabin-class Observation Lounge and Cocktail Bar.

Plate XIII—Cabin-class Smoking Room Fireplace.

Plate XIV—Cabin-class Children's Playroom.

Plate XV—Cabin-class Verandah Bar.

Plate XVII—Cabin-class Special Suite Bedroom.

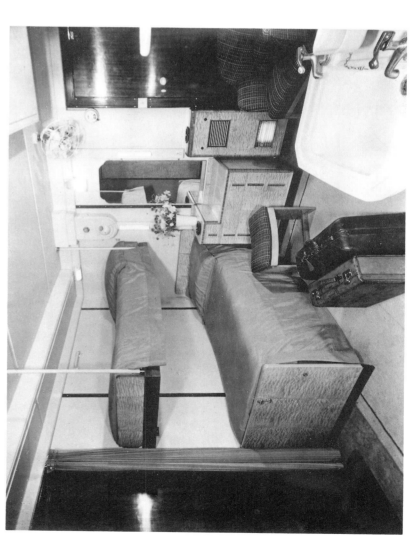

Plate XIX—Third-class 4-Berth Stateroom.

Plate XVI—Cabin-class Special Suite Bedroom.

Plate XIII—Tourist-class 2-Berth Stateroom.

Plate XXI—Tourist-class Dining Saloon.

Plate XXIII—Tourist-class Smoking Room.

Plate XX—Tourist-class Dining Saloon.

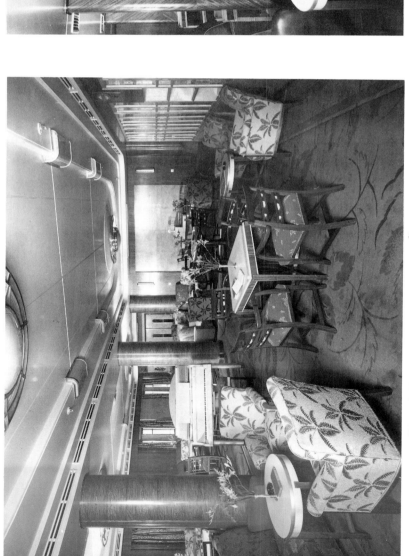

Plate XXII—Tourist-class Lounge.

Plate XXIV—Third-class Lounge.

Plate XXV—Third-class Smoking Room.

Plate XXVI—Third-class Dining Saloon.

Plate XXVII—Gentlemen's Hairdressing Saloon.

Plate XXVIII—Cabin-class Smoking Room.

Plate XXIX—Cabin-class Lounge.

Plate XXX—Tourist-class Smoking Room.

Plate XXXI—Cabin-class Gift Shop Windows.

Plate XXXII—"Mauretania" Docked at Pier 90 in New York.

Plate XXXIII—"Mauretania" Docked at Pier 90 in New York.

Bon Voyage!

R M S
MAURETANIA

Over 225 miles of Henley Cables were used for
the electrical installation of this new Cunarder.
We wish her Bon Voyage, and as great a
success and popularity in her day as the old
" Mauretania " achieved in hers.

You may, or may not, remember that the old
" Mauretania "—the dear old " Mauretania "—
was equipped throughout with Henley Cables.

225
Miles of HENLEY CABLES

Complete wiring installation by
**Sunderland Forge & Engineering
Co. Ltd. Sunderland**
Built by
**Cammell, Laird & Co. Ltd.,
Birkenhead**

W. T. Henley's Telegraph Works Co. Ltd. Holborn Viaduct, London, E.C.1